Student/Instructor Solution Supplement
to Accompany
Pine/Hendrickson/Cram/Hammond:

# ORGANIC CHEMISTRY

## FOURTH EDITION

•

### STANLEY H. PINE
Professor of Chemistry
California State University
Los Angeles

**McGraw-Hill Book Company**
New York  St. Louis  San Francisco  Auckland  Bogotá  Hamburg
Johannesburg  London  Madrid  Mexico  Montreal  New Delhi  Panama
Paris  São Paulo  Singapore  Sydney  Tokyo  Toronto

Student/Instructor Solution Supplement
to Accompany Pine/Hendrickson/Cram/Hammond:
ORGANIC CHEMISTRY Fourth Edition
Copyright © 1980 by McGraw-Hill, Inc. All rights reserved.
Printed in the United States of America. The contents, or
parts thereof, may be reproduced for use with
ORGANIC CHEMISTRY
Fourth Edition
by Pine, Hendrickson,
Cram and Hammond
provided such reproductions bear copyright notice, but may not
be reproduced in any form for any other purpose without
permission of the publisher.

0-07-050116-5

4567890 WHWH 898765432

TO THE STUDENT:

Your textbook, "Organic Chemistry", fourth edition, develops concepts of organic chemistry from basic principles of the electronic and structural characteristics of atoms and molecules. As the logic of organic chemistry is developing, you can test your comprehension of material by working problems related to the particular topics under consideration. Problems within the chapters are designed to test your understanding and to guide you through the relevant thought processes. They will often suggest the need for further study. The end-of-chapter supplementary problems provide a broader basis for reinforcing concepts and they offer the intellectual challenge that makes learning exciting.

You will derive the greatest benefits from the problems if each one is attempted as it is encountered in the text. Use a paper and pencil to work through a problem. Consider the experimental facts that are presented and try to see how they can fit into the broader picture of the subject. Aides such as molecular models may also be helpful for visualizing the spatial characteristics of particular molecules. Be sure that your answer "makes sense" for the course in organic chemistry is not meant to be tricky nor mysterious.

The "Student Solutions supplement is a tool to be used in the learning process. The Supplement should be consulted only after you have made a conscientious effort at solving the problem. After working through a problem, you can check your answer against an acceptable solution. You will find that many of the problems may have more than one answer. Only one answer is commonly given in the Supplement but you should not hesitate to discuss alternate ideas with your instructor.

Stanley H. Pine

# 1 WHAT IS ORGANIC CHEMISTRY?

**1-1**

Weight of C in sample from $CO_2$ recovered = $\dfrac{12.011}{44.011}$ x 8.80 = 2.402 mg.

Weight of H in sample from $H_2O$ recovered = $\dfrac{2.016}{18.016}$ x 3.60 = 0.403 mg.

%C = $\dfrac{2.402}{6.00}$ x 100 = 40.03

mg/atms C = $\dfrac{40.03}{12.011}$ = 3.33

%H = $\dfrac{0.403}{6.00}$ x 100 = 6.72

mg/atms H = $\dfrac{6.72}{1.008}$ = 6.7

%O (by difference) = 53.25

mg/atms O = $\dfrac{53.25}{16.00}$ = 3.33

The atom ratio is 3.33:6.7:3.33 = 1:2:1.

$\therefore$ Empirical formula = $CH_2O$

**1-2**

Weight of C in sample from $CO_2$ recovered = $\dfrac{12.011}{44.011}$ x 10.35 mg = 2.824 mg

Weight of H in sample from $H_2O$ recovered = $\dfrac{2.016}{18.016}$ x 3.42 mg = 0.383 mg

%C = $\dfrac{2.824}{4.337}$ x 100 = 65.11

mg/atms C = $\dfrac{65.11}{12.011}$ = 5.421

%H = $\dfrac{0.383}{4.337}$ x 100 = 8.83

mg/atms H = $\dfrac{8.83}{1.008}$ = 8.76

%O (by difference) = 26.06

mg/atms O = $\dfrac{26.06}{16.00}$ = 1.629

The atom ratio is 5.42:8.76:1.629 = 10:16:3

$\therefore$ Empirical formula = $C_{10}H_{16}O_3$

1-3

a) H·· :Cl:

b) H·· :S:· ·H

c) H·· :O:· ·H

d) :N·· ·H with H above and H below

e) H·· :C: ·N·· ·H with H above and H below

f) H·· :O:· ·Cl:

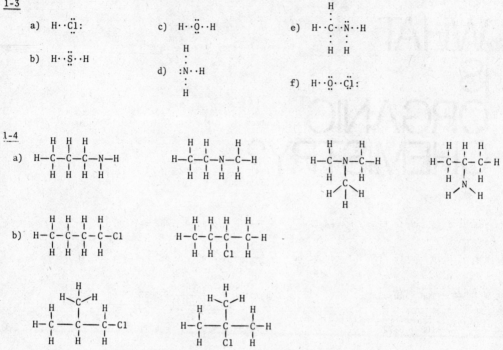

1-4

a)

b)

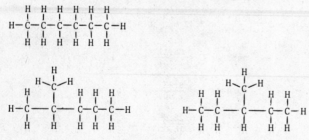

c) As the number of isomers increases it is best to use some systematic approach to be sure that none are missed. In the problem below we begin with a linear array of all six carbon atoms. Then one is removed from the straight chain and placed as a branch along a five-carbon chain. Only two such formulas are obtained since the other possibilities repeat a branched or the original six carbon linear formula. The sequence continues by using a four-carbon chain to which the additional two carbon atoms can be connected on the same or two different nonterminal carbon atoms. Placing a carbon at the end of the four carbon sequence leads to one of the five carbon structures already drawn. An attempt to place three carbons on a three carbon chain leads to the four, five, or six carbon chains already formulated. The formulas are completed by adding hydrogen atoms.

1-4 Contd...

c) Contd...

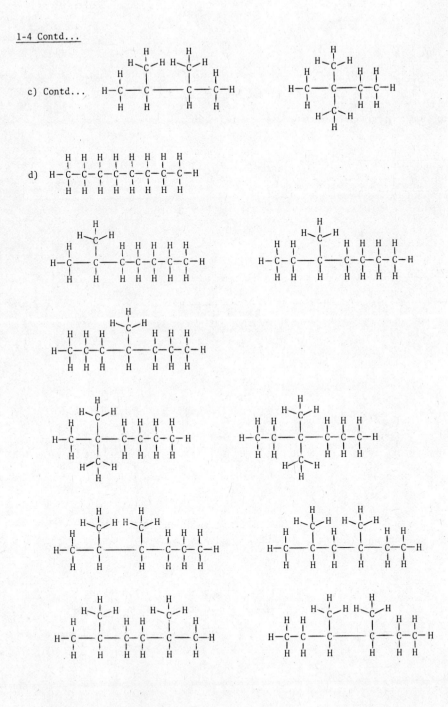

d)

1-4 Contd...

d) Contd...

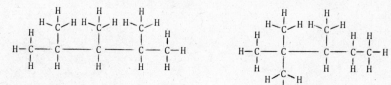

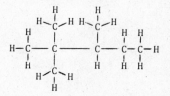

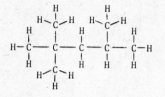

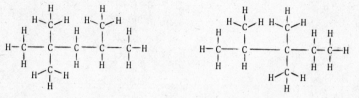

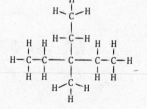

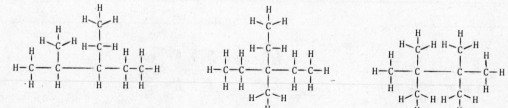

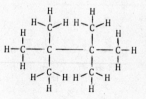

1-5

a) 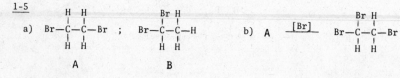     b) A

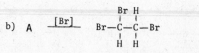

A    B

<u>1-6</u>

a)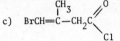

b)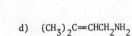

c)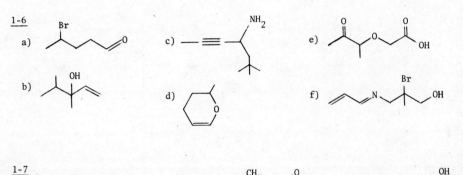

d)

e)

f)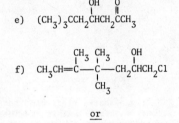

<u>1-7</u>

a)  $(CH_3)_2CHCH_2CH_2OH$

b)  $\underset{\displaystyle CH_3CH-CHCH(CH_3)_2}{\overset{\displaystyle Cl\quad OH}{}}$

c)  $\underset{\displaystyle BrCH=C-CH_2C}{\overset{\displaystyle CH_3}{}} \overset{O}{\underset{Cl}{}}$

d)  $(CH_3)_2C=CHCH_2NH_2$

e)  $(CH_3)_3CCH_2\overset{OH}{C}HCH_2\overset{O}{C}CH_3$

f)  $CH_3CH=\overset{CH_3}{C}-\overset{CH_3}{\underset{CH_3}{C}}-CH_2\overset{OH}{C}HCH_2Cl$

or

$CH_3CH=C(CH_3)C(CH_3)_2CH_2CH(OH)CH_2Cl$

<u>1-8</u>

a)  $C_5H_{10}$  *IHD = 1*

One ring or one double bond.

b)  $C_{10}H_{18}$  *IHD = 2*

Two double bonds; one triple bond;
two rings; one ring and one double bond.

c)  $C_7H_{16}$  *IHD = 0*

Saturated noncyclic hydrocarbon.

d)  $C_8H_{12}$  *IHD = 3*

Three double bonds; three rings; one
double bond and two rings; two double
bonds and one ring; one triple bond and
one ring; one triple bond and one
double bond.

<u>1-9</u>

a) The nuclear charge increases as one moves across the periodic table, thus affinity for electrons increases.

b) As one moves down in the periodic table the outer (valence) electrons move further from the nuclear charge. Electron affinity decreases.

<u>1-10</u>  a)  $CH_3-Br$   b)  $(CH_3)_2C=O$   c)  $CH_3CH_2-NH_2$   d)  $CH_3-CCl_3$

1-11

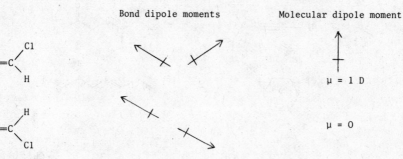

Bond dipole moments        Molecular dipole moment

$\mu = 1$ D

$\mu = 0$

1-12

a) 

Nitrogen shares eight electrons, thus is assigned
four of them. That is one less than the five
associated with the free atom so that nitrogen is
assigned +1. The singly bonded oxygen possesses
six nonbonding electrons plus one from the shared
pair. The total of seven is one more than is
expected for oxygen giving it a -1 charge.

b) 

Nitrogen possesses four of the
shared electrons resulting in a
+1 charge. Oxygen possesses six
nonbonding plus one shared
electron and has one negative
charge.

1-13

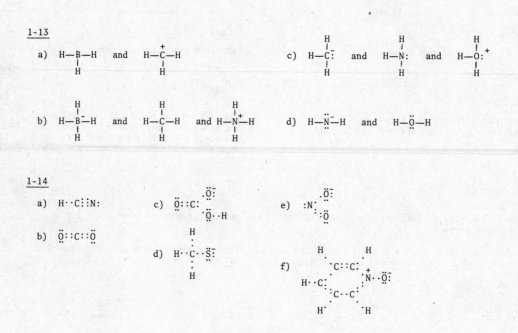

1-15  a)  Substitution     c)  Substitution     e)  Elimination

 b)  Elimination     d)  Addition     f)  Elimination

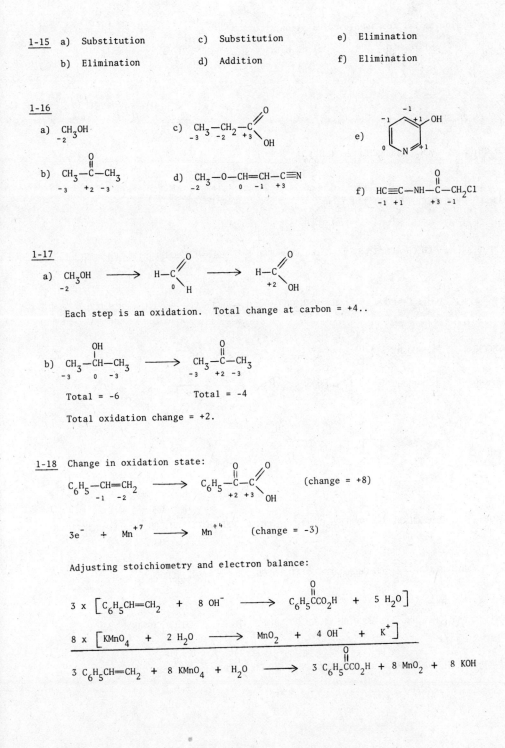

1-16

a)  $CH_3OH$
 $-2$

b)  $CH_3-\overset{O}{\overset{\|}{C}}-CH_3$
 $-3$  $+2$  $-3$

c)  $CH_3-CH_2-C\overset{O}{\diagdown}_{OH}$
 $-3$  $-2$  $+3$

d)  $CH_3-O-CH=CH-C\equiv N$
 $-2$  $0$  $-1$  $+3$

e)

f)  $HC\equiv C-NH-\overset{O}{\overset{\|}{C}}-CH_2Cl$
 $-1$  $+1$  $+3$  $-1$

1-17

a)  $CH_3OH \longrightarrow H-C\overset{O}{\diagdown}_{H} \longrightarrow H-C\overset{O}{\diagdown}_{OH}$
 $-2$  $0$  $+2$

Each step is an oxidation.  Total change at carbon = +4..

b)  $CH_3-\overset{OH}{\overset{|}{CH}}-CH_3 \longrightarrow CH_3-\overset{O}{\overset{\|}{C}}-CH_3$
 $-3$  $0$  $-3$     $-3$  $+2$  $-3$

Total = -6          Total = -4

Total oxidation change = +2.

1-18  Change in oxidation state:

$C_6H_5-CH=CH_2 \longrightarrow C_6H_5-\overset{O}{\overset{\|}{C}}-C\overset{O}{\diagdown}_{OH}$     (change = +8)
 $-1$  $-2$     $+2$  $+3$

$3e^- + Mn^{+7} \longrightarrow Mn^{+4}$     (change = -3)

Adjusting stoichiometry and electron balance:

$3 \times \left[ C_6H_5CH=CH_2 + 8\ OH^- \longrightarrow C_6H_5\overset{O}{\overset{\|}{C}}CO_2H + 5\ H_2O \right]$

$8 \times \left[ KMnO_4 + 2\ H_2O \longrightarrow MnO_2 + 4\ OH^- + K^+ \right]$

$3\ C_6H_5CH=CH_2 + 8\ KMnO_4 + H_2O \longrightarrow 3\ C_6H_5\overset{O}{\overset{\|}{C}}CO_2H + 8\ MnO_2 + 8\ KOH$

1-19 See answer to problem 1-1 for sample calculation.

a) $C_8H_8O_5$      b) $C_4H_5O$      c) $C_5H_9Br$      d) $C_4H_5NO$

1-20

a) $CH_3SCH_3$ ; $CH_3CH_2SH$

b) $CH_3CH_2CH_2CH_2CH_3$ ; $(CH_3)_2CHCH_2CH_3$ ; $(CH_3)_4C$

c)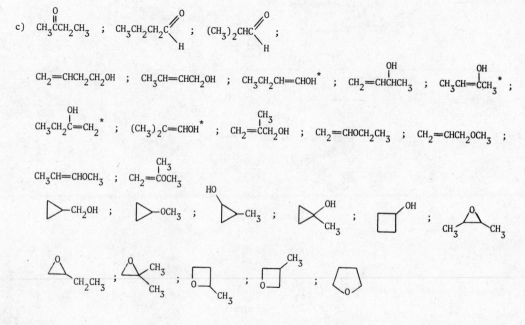

d) $CH_3CH_2CH(OH)_2$ ; $CH_3\overset{OH}{\underset{|}{C}}HCH_2OH$ ; $HOCH_2CH_2CH_2OH$ ; $CH_3CH_2OCH_2OH$ ; $CH_3\overset{OH}{\underset{\underset{OH}{|}}{\overset{|}{C}}}CH_3$ ; $CH_3OCH_2CH_2OH$

$CH_3\overset{OH}{\underset{|}{O}}CHCH_3$ ; $CH_3OCH_2OCH_3$ ; $CH_3OOCH_2CH_3$ ; $CH_3CH_2CH_2OOH$ ; $(CH_3)_2CHOOH$

e) $CH_3CH_2\overset{OH}{\underset{|}{C}}HNH_2$ ; $CH_3\overset{OH}{\underset{|}{C}}HCH_2NH_2$ ; $HOCH_2CH_2CH_2NH_2$ ; $HOCH_2\overset{CH_3}{\underset{|}{C}}HNH_2$ ; $CH_3CH_2CH_2NHOH$ ;

$(CH_3)_2CHNHOH$ ; $CH_3CH_2OCH_2NH_2$ ; $CH_3OCH_2CH_2NH_2$ ; $CH_3\overset{CH_3}{\underset{|}{O}}CHNH_2$ ; $CH_3\overset{OH}{\underset{|}{C}}HNHCH_3$ ; $CH_3CH_2\overset{OH}{\underset{|}{N}}CH_3$ ;

1-20 Contd...

e) Contd..

$HOCH_2CH_2NHCH_3$ ; $CH_3CH_2NHCH_2OH$ ; $CH_3OCH_2NHCH_3$ ; $CH_3CH_2NHOCH_3$ ; $(CH_3)_2NCH_2OH$ ;

$(CH_3)_2NOCH_3$ ; $CH_3\overset{OH}{\underset{NH_2}{\underset{|}{\overset{|}{C}}}}CH_3$ ; $CH_3CH_2CH_2ONH_2$ ; $CH_3CH_2ONHCH_3$ ; $(CH_3)_2CHONH_2$

f) $CH_3CH_2C\overset{O}{\underset{H}{\diagup}}$ ; $CH_3\overset{O}{\overset{||}{C}}CH_3$ ; $CH_2{=}CHOCH_3$ ; $CH_2{=}\overset{OH}{\overset{|}{C}}CH_3{}^*$ ; $CH_2{=}CHCH_2OH$ ; $CH_3CH{=}CHOH{}^*$ ;

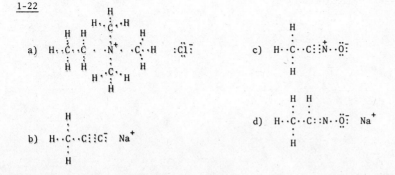

$^*$These compounds actually exist as more stable tautomers (sec. 6-3C).

1-21

a) The formula requires one more or one less H-atom (or other single bonded atom) to accomodate the tetracoordinate carbon. The formula requires an even number of H's.

b) Amines require one more H-atom than the parent hydrocarbon; i.e., an odd number of H's.

c) The formula requires one more or one less H-atom; i.e., an even number of H's.

d) The formula has one too many H-atoms and violates the tetracoordinate nature of a carbon atom or the dicoordinate nature of a sulfur atom.

e) The total number of H plus Cl atoms must be even and not exceed 6 ($2n + 2$).

f) The total number of H plus Cl atoms must be odd and not exceed $2n + 3$.

1-22

a) (Lewis structure diagram)

b) (Lewis structure diagram)

c) (Lewis structure diagram)

d) (Lewis structure diagram)

1-23

a) Substitution      e) Addition        i) Addition

b) Addition          f) Elimination     j) Addition

c) Addition          g) Addition        k) Elimination

d) Addition          h) Substitution


1-24                                                    Change

a) $\underset{-4}{CH_4}$ + $Cl_2$ $\longrightarrow$ $\underset{-2}{CH_3Cl}$ + $HCl$        +2

b) $\underset{-3\ -2\ -1\ -2}{CH_3CH_2CH{=}CH_2}$ + $HCl$ $\longrightarrow$ $\underset{-3\ -2\ \ 0\ -3}{CH_3CH_2CHClCH_3}$        0

   (Total = -8)                    (Total = -8)

c) 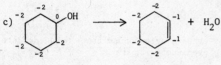 $\longrightarrow$ 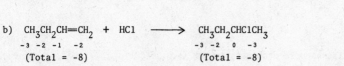 + $H_2O$        0

   (Total = -10)          (Total = -10)

d) $\underset{-3\ -2\ +3}{CH_3CH_2\overset{O}{C}}\underset{OH}{}$ + $\underset{-2}{CH_3OH}$ $\longrightarrow$ $\underset{-3\ -2\ +3}{CH_3CH_2\overset{O}{C}}\underset{\underset{-2}{OCH_3}}{}$ + $H_2O$        0

   (Total = -2)                (Total = -4)

e) 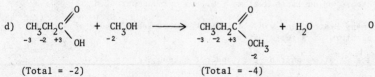 + $O_3$ $\xrightarrow{H_2O}$ 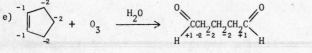        +4

   (Total = -8)                (Total = -4)

# 2 CLASSES AND NOMENCLATURE OF ORGANIC COMPOUNDS— FUNCTIONAL GROUPS

2-1 The following responses make use of several commonly used representations for condensed structural formulas.

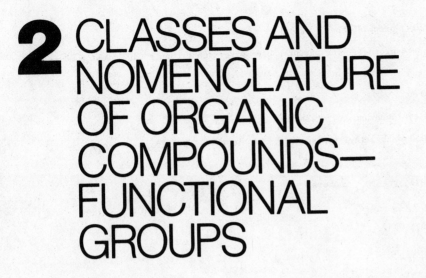

a) $CH_3CH(CH_3)CH(CH_3)CH(CH_3)CH_2CH_3$

b)

c) $CH_3CH_2C(CH_3)_2CH_2\overset{\underset{\displaystyle CH_2CH_3}{|}}{C}HCH_2CH_3$

d)

e) $CH_3(CH_2)_8\overset{\underset{\displaystyle CH_3CH(CH_2)_3CH_3}{|}}{C}H(CH_2)_9CH_3$

f)

g) $CH_3$ — $C_2H_5$

h)

i) $CH_3\overset{\underset{\displaystyle}{}}{\overset{CH_3}{|}}CHCH_2CH_2CH_2CH_2\overset{CH_3}{\underset{\underset{\displaystyle CH_3}{|}}{\overset{|}{C}H}}CHCH_2CH_3$

j) $CH_3CH_2CH(CH_3)C(CH_3)_2CH(CH_3)CH_2CH_3$

k) $CH_3\overset{\underset{\displaystyle CH_3}{\overset{CH_3}{|}}}{C}H\overset{\overset{CH_2CH_2CH_3}{|}}{C}HCHCH\overset{\underset{\displaystyle CH_3}{|}}{C}HCH_2CH_3$

l) $CH_3CH_2CH\overset{\overset{\triangle}{}}{C}H_2\overset{\overset{CH_2CH_2CH_3}{|}}{C}HCH_2CH_2CH_2CH_3$

2-2

a) 3,4-Dimethylheptane

b) 5-(1-Methylpropyl)nonane  or  5-*sec*-Butylnonane

c) 1-(1-Methylethyl)-3-methylcyclohexane  <u>or</u>  1-Isopropyl-3-methylcyclohexane

<u>2-2 Contd...</u>

d)  4-Ethyl-3,3-dimethyl-4-propyldecane

(Two decane chains are presnet.  The parent chosen gives substituents the lowest numbers.)

e)  2,3-Dimethylpentane

f)  2,3,5-Trimethylhexane

g)  (1,1-Dimethylethyl)cyclopentane <u>or</u> *tert*-Butylcyclopentane

h)  2,4-Dimethyl-3,3-di(1-methylethyl)pentane <u>or</u>  2,4-Dimethyl-3,3-diisopropylpentane


<u>2-3</u>  A, C, D, E, and H  all are $C_6H_{14}$ isomers.


<u>2-4</u>  a) $C_nH_{2n}$        b) $C_nH_{2n-2}$;  *IHD* = 2


<u>2-5</u>  a)  Ethenyl        b)  3-Propenyl        c)  1-Methylethenyl


<u>2-6</u>

a)  $CH_3\overset{\underset{\textstyle CH_3}{|}}{C}=CHC(CH_3)_3$

b)  $CH_2{=}CHCH_2CH_2CH{=}CH_2$

c)  $CH_2{=}CHCH\overset{\underset{\textstyle CH_2CH_3}{|}}{}CH_2CH_2CH_3$

d)  $CH_2{=}C(CH_3)CH_2CH_3$

e)

f)  $CH_2{=}\overset{\underset{\textstyle C_2H_5}{|}}{C}CH_2\overset{\underset{}{|}}{C}CH_2CH_2CH_3$


<u>2-7</u>

a)  1-Ethyl-3,4-dimethylcyclohexene

b)  1,3-Dicyclobutylpropene

c)  4-Cyclopentyl-3-methyl-1,3-pentadiene

d)  2,2,5,5-Tetramethyl-3-hexene

e)  2-Isopropyl-3-(3,3-dimethylbutyl)-1,4-pentadiene <u>or</u>

    2-(1-Methylethyl)-3-(3,3-dimethylbutyl)-1,4-pentadiene

f)  4-Vinyl-2,4-heptadiene <u>or</u>  4-Ethenyl-2,4-heptadiene

g)  Butylbenzene        h)  1-Ethyl-3-methylbenzene <u>or</u> *m*-Ethyltoluene

2-8

a) 1,3-Hexadiene-5-yne          c) 2,4,6-Octatriyne

b) 4-Methyl-2-pentyne           d) Ethynylbenzene


2-9

a) 3-Methyl-1-butanol                    d) 2-Cyclohexenol

b) 2-Ethyl-5,5-dimethyl-1-heptanol       e) 1,3-Propanediol

c) 3-Methyl-5-hexyn-2-ol                 f) 1-Phenylethanol


2-10  The three hydroxy groups account for a significant degree of hydrogen bonding which increases intermolecular attractions and decreases volatility.


2-11  In higher molecular weight alcohols the functional group accounts for only a small part of the molecule and its associated physical properties.


2-12

a) 2-Isopropyl-5-methylcyclohexanol  or  2-(1-Methylethyl)-5-methylcyclohexanol

b) 3,7-Dimethyl-2,6-octadien-1-ol


2-13  Hydrogen bonding is not very important in thiols compared to alcohols because the electrons on the larger sulfur atom are more diffuse, thus the atom is less basic than oxygen.


2-14

a) 3-Methyl-1-butanethiol      b) 2-Propene-1-thiol      c) 1-Propanethiol


2-15

a) Dimethyl ether; Methoxymethane;  2-Oxapropane

b) *tert*-Butyl isopropyl ether;  2-*tert*-Butoxypropane;  2-Isopropoxy-2-methylpropane;

2,2,4-Trimethyl-3-oxapentane

c) Cyclohexyl methyl ether;  Methoxycyclohexane

d) Methyl vinyl ether;  Methyl ethenyl ether;  Methoxyethene;  2-Oxa-3-butene (Ether takes priority over alkene)

<u>2-16</u>   Hydrogen bonding between ether molecules is not possible because no hydroxy hydrogen atoms are present. Ether molecules are thus not strongly associated with each other and their boiling points are low. However, water is moderately soluble in ethers (and alcohols) because the ether oxygen atom can form hydrogen bonds to the water hydrogen atoms.

<u>2-17</u>

<u>2-18</u>

a)   *tert*-Butylamine;  2-Methyl-2-propylamine;   2-Methyl-2-propanamine

b)   *N*-Ethyl-*N*-methyl-1-propylamine;   *N*-Ethyl-*N*-methyl-1-propanamine

c)   3-Butenylamine;  3-Butenamine

d)   *N*,*N*-Diethylaniline;   *N*,*N*-Diethylbenzenamine

<u>2-19</u>   The tertiary amine does not have a hydrogen atom on the nitrogen so that intermolecular hydrogen bonding is not possible.

<u>2-20</u>

a)  2-Bromo-2-methylpropane

b)  1,1,2-Trichloroethene

c)  3-Fluorocyclopentene

d)  1,3-Dichloro-5-methylbenzene;   3,5-Dichlorotoluene

e)  1,4-Diiodobutane

f)  Tetrachloromethane

<u>2-21</u>

a)  1-Phenylethanone;  Methyl phenyl ketone

b)  2-Chloro-3-pentanone;  1-Chloroethyl ethyl ketone

c)  1-Cyclohexyl-1-propanone;  Cyclohexyl ethyl ketone

d)  5-Methyl-4-hexen-3-one;  Ethyl 2-methyl-1-propenyl ketone

e)  3-Chloro-4-hydroxycyclohexanone.

2-22

a) 2-Methyl-2-butenal

b) 3-Chloro-2-methylpentanal

c) Ethanedial

d) Cyclobutanecarbaldehyde

e) 6-Bromo-2-oxocyclohexanecarbaldehyde
   (Ketone has priority over bromine)


2-23

a) 2-Methyl-3-phenylpentanoic acid

b) 2-Chlorobutanedioic acid

c) Cyclopentanecarboxylic acid

d) 2-Cyclopropylethanoic acid

e) 3-Cyclohexene-1,2-dicarboxylic acid


2-24

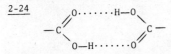

Hydrogen bonding between two molecules is particularly favorable.


2-25

a) 2,2-Dimethylpropanoyl chloride

b) Methyl 3-chloro-3-methylbutanoate

c) 3-Cyclohexyl-2-methylpropanenitrile

d) *N*-Phenylmethanamide;  *N*-Phenylformamide

e) Propanoic anhydride

f) Ethyl cyclobutanecarboxylate

g) *N*-Methylbenzamide;
   *N*-Methylphenylcarboxamide

h) 3-Phenylpentanenitrile


2-26

a) $Cl-\!\!\!\bigcirc\!\!\!-CO_2H$

b)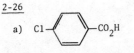

c) $(CH_3)_2CHCH_2CH_2CO_2CHCH_2CH_3$ with $CH_3$

d) 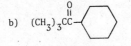$-CO_2C_2H_5$

e) $CH_3OCH_2CH{=}CHCO_2H$

f) $CH_3C$ with $O$ and $NC_6H_5$, $CH_3$

g) $CH_3CH_2CH_2CHCH_2CHCH_2CHC{\equiv}N$ with Cl Cl Cl

h) $(CH_3)_3CCO_2H$

2-26 Contd...

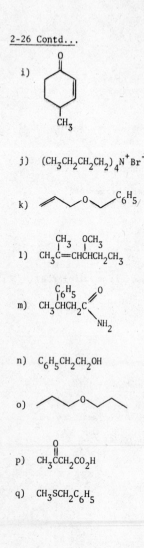

i)

j)  $(CH_3CH_2CH_2CH_2)_4N^+Br^-$

k)

l)

m)

n)  $C_6H_5CH_2CH_2OH$

o)

p)  $CH_3CCH_2CO_2H$

q)  $CH_3SCH_2C_6H_5$

r)

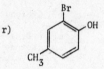

s)  $[(CH_3)_2CH]_3N$

t)

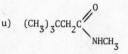

u)

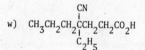

v)  $CH_2=CHCH=CHCH=C(CH_3)_2$

w)  $CH_3CH_2CH_2CCH_2CH_2CO_2H$
    with $CN$ above and $C_2H_5$ below

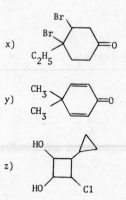

x)

y)

z)

2-27

a)  2,5-Dimethyl-3-chloro-4-heptanone

b)  3-Amino-5-ethyl-1-hydroxybenzene

c)  2-Amino-4,4-dimethylpentanoic acid

d)  3-(1-Hydroxyethyl)-5-methylheptanal

e)  3-Bromo-5-ethylcyclopentanone

f)  2-Methyl-5-amino-2-cyclohexenone

g)  2-Ethyl-2-methyl-4-(*N*-ethylamino)butanal

h)  4-Hydroxy-5-methyl-2-hepten-6-ynoyl chloride

2-27 Contd...

i)   3-Ethyl-3,5-dihydroxypentanamide

j)   3-Chloro-$N$-ethyl-3-methylpentanamide

k)   3-Hydroxy-4-methyl-4-pentenal

l)   3,6,9-Trimethyl-2,4,6,8-decatetraenoic acid

m)   3-Methyl-2-butanone

n)   4-Methyl-2-hexyne

o)   5-Methyl-3-phenyl-2-hexanol

p)   Benzyl ethyl ether

q)   5-Oxopentanoic acid

r)   $N$,3,3-Trimethylbutanamine   or
     5,5-Dimethyl-2-azahexane

s)   Chloromethylcyclopropane

t)   1-Chloro-4-methylbenzene

u)   4-Chloro-1-vinylbenzene   or
     4-Chloro-1-ethenylbenzene

v)   2-Isobutylcyclopentanone   or
     2-(2-Methylpropyl)cyclopentanone

w)   1,4-Cyclooctadiene

x)   Cyclobutylethanoic acid

y)   3-Chloro-5-methyl-4-hexenoic acid

z)   Methyl 3-chlorobutanoate

2-28

a)   CH$_3$CCH$_2$CH$_3$   (with O double bonded above the second C)

     2-Butanone

b)   CH$_3$CH$_2$CH$_2$C (=O, H)       (CH$_3$)$_2$CHC (=O, H)

     Butanal                      2-Methylpropanal

c)   CH$_3$CH$_2$C (=O, OCH$_3$)        CH$_3$C (=O, OCH$_2$CH$_3$)

     Methyl propanoate            Ethyl acetate
                                  Ethyl ethanoate

d)   CH$_3$CH$_2$CH$_2$CH$_2$OH      CH$_3$CH$_2$CHCH$_3$ (OH)      (CH$_3$)$_2$CHCH$_2$OH      (CH$_3$)$_3$COH

     1-Butanol            2-Butanol            2-Methyl-1-propanol       2-Methyl-2-propanol
                                                                         $tert$-Butyl alcohol

e)   CH$_3$OCH$_2$CH$_2$CH$_3$      CH$_3$CH$_2$OCH$_2$CH$_3$      (CH$_3$)$_2$CHOCH$_3$

     Methyl propyl ether   Diethyl ether        Isopropyl methyl ether

2-29  a)  $CH_3OCH_3$  and  $CH_3CH_2OH$

Dimethyl ether    Ethanol

b) Ethanol    c) Ethanol

2-30

a)  $\underset{\underset{OH}{|}}{CH_3CHC}(CH_3)_2CH_2\underset{\underset{CH_3CHCH_2CH_3}{|}}{CHCHCH_2CH_3}$ $\underset{C_2H_5}{\overset{C_2H_5}{}}$

b)  $C_6H_5CH_2CH_2CO_2\underset{\underset{CH_3}{|}}{CHCH_2CH_3}$

c)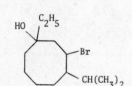

d)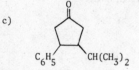

e)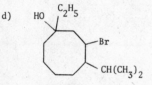

f)  $(C_2H_5)_3\overset{+}{NH}$  $OH^-$

g)  $(CH_3)_2NCH_2CH_2\underset{\underset{OH}{|}}{CHCH_3}$

h)  $(CH_3)_2CHSCH(CH_3)_2$

i)  $HOCH_2CH_2\underset{\underset{C_2H_5}{|}}{\overset{\overset{OH}{|}}{C}CH_2CH_2CH_3}$

j)  $(CH_3)_2\overset{\overset{OH}{|}}{C}(CH_2)_5CH_3$

k)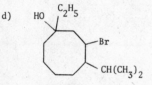

l)  $CH_3\underset{\underset{Cl}{|}}{CH}CH_2\overset{\overset{O}{||}}{C}(CH_3)_2CH{=}CHCH_2CH_3$

m)  $\underset{\underset{OH}{|}}{HOCH_2CH_2}\overset{\overset{ClCH_2CH_2CH_2CH_2}{|}}{CHCHCH_3}$

n)

o)  $Br{-}$ $-CH_2CH_2CH_2CO_2H$

2-31

a) 5-Bromo-7-methyl-2,4,6-octatrienal

b) 3-Phenyl-2-butanone

c) 2,5-Dimethyl-4-hexen-3-one

d) 1,5-Diamino-2-pentanol

e) 5-*tert*-Butyl-3,5-nonanediol

f) 1-Ethoxy-2-propanol

g) 3-Bromo-2-ethyl-6-methylcyclohexanone

h) 3-(3-Bromopropyl)-1-ethyl-4-methylcyclohexene

i) 4-Chloro-3-(2-methylpropyl)-2-heptanone

j) Methyl 2-methoxy-6-methyl-3-cyclohexenecarboxylate

k) 3-(4-Chlorophenyl)-1,2-diphenylpropenone

l) 4-Bromo-5-hydroxy-2-pentanone

m) 3-Phenylpentanenitrile

n) 3-*tert*-Butyl-2,2,4,4-tetramethylpentane

o) 3-Methyl-2-oxa-4-phenylpentane

p) 4-*tert*-Butyl-1-methoxybenzene

q) 4-Chloro-2-methylpentanenitrile

r) 2-Methyl-4-nitro-2-pentanol

s) 2,4-Dimethyl-5-heptene-2,4-diol

t) 3-Amino-2-*sec*-butyl-5-cyclohexenol

u) Methyl 3-bromo-2-hydroxy-2-methylbutanoate

v) 4-Bromo-*N*,3-dimethyl-2-hydroxy-4-hepten-6-ynamide

w) 2-Bromo-2-methyl-3-cyclopentenone

x) 2-Chloro-4-cyano-6-propylcyclohexanone

y) 2-Butyl-4-chloro-5-methyl-2,4-hexadienoyl chloride

z) 1-Cyclopropyl-4-hydroxy-1-butanone

# 3 BONDING IN ORGANIC MOLECULES

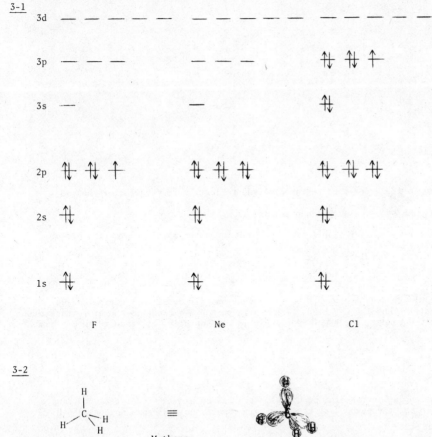

3-1

|  | F | Ne | Cl |
|---|---|---|---|

3-2

Methane

3-2

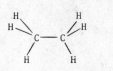   $\equiv$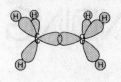

Ethane

3-3

a)   $>C=O$   $\equiv$    O

$-C\equiv N$   $\equiv$    N

3-4

$sp^3$ = 25% $s$ + 75% $p$

$sp^2$ = 33% $s$ + 67% $p$

$sp$ = 50% $s$ + 50% $p$

3-5   The 112° C-C-C angle is larger than tetrahedral and reflects more $s$-character than $sp^3$, therefore is assigned $sp^{3-}$ (calculation predicts $sp^{2.7}$).

The 106° H-C-H angle is smaller than tetrahedral and indicates more $p$-character than $sp^3$, i.e., $sp^{3+}$ (Calculation predicts $sp^{3.3}$).

3-6   Fluorine is more electronegative than H so that electron-pair density is attracted away from the carbon atom along the C-F bond. VSEPR between the C-F bonds is therefore less than that between the C-H bonds. The F-C-F bond angle is consequently less than the H-C-H bond angle.

3-7

a)   The ammonium cation has tetrahedral bond angles typical of a symmetrical tetracoordinate central atom. In $NH_3$ the nonbonding electron pair repels the N-H bonds more than N-H bonds repel each other.

b)   $H_2S$ possesses two nonbonding electron pairs which repel the electrons of the S-H bonds.

3-7 Contd..

c) The central atoms, S and P. are third row and thus larger than an N atom. The bonding electron pairs are further from each other so that their repulsions are less. The nonbonding pairs which are closer to the nucleus have a greater repulsive effect.

3-8 As the atoms attached to the trigonal carbon atom become more electronegative the angles betweeen them become smaller because of decreasing repulsion close to the central carbon atom.

3-9

a) Electron repulsions decrease as the more electronegative atoms attract electron density away from the central atom.

b) The nonbonding electron pairs on the carbonyl oxygen atom increase repulsions relative to the carbon-carbon double bond.

c) The molecule containing chlorine has intermediate angles even though chlorine is the largest atom. The size of the atoms (nonbonded repulsions) is not the major factor in this case.

3-10

a) i) VSPER predicts a linear (180°) geometry because repulsions involve two identical sets of bonds connected to the central carbon atom.

   ii) An orbital picture connects an $sp$ hybrid at the center carbon atom to $sp^2$ orbitals of the two terminal carbons. Overlap of the two sets of $p$-orbitals produces pi-orbitals in perpendicular planes.

b) Both hybrid orbital ($sp^3$) and VSEPR arguments predict a near tetrahedral geometry. VSEPR theory predicts greater repulsion by the electron pair resulting in H-C-H angles smaller than 109.5°. Hybrid orbital theory predicts more $s$ character associated with the nonbonding electrons since they are closer to the nucleus as is an $s$ orbital. Greater $p$ character is thus expected in the C-H bonds and bond angles are less than tetrahedral.

3-11 They are identical since diatomic molecules have only one bond.

3-12 The electronegative fluorine atoms attract electron density closer to each carbon atom. The carbon-carbon distance consequently decreases.

3-13

a)

| Bonds broken | kcal/mol | kJ/mol |
|---|---|---|
| C—C | 83 | 347 |
| C—O | 86 | 359 |
| O—H | 111 | 464 |
| | 280 kcal/mol | 1170 kJ/mol |

| Bonds formed | | |
|---|---|---|
| C—H | 99 | 414 |
| C=O | 192 | 803 |
| | 291 kcal/mol | 1217 kJ/mol |

$\therefore \Delta H° = 280 - 291 = -11$ kcal/mol
$(= 1170 - 1217 = -47$ kJ/mol$)$

$\therefore$ Reaction is exothermic

b)

| Bonds broken | kcal/mol | kJ/mol |
|---|---|---|
| 2 C—N | 146 | 610 |
| N=N | 100 | 418 |
| | 246 kcal/mol | 1028 kJ/mol |

| Bonds formed | | |
|---|---|---|
| C—C | 83 | 347 |
| N≡N | 226 | 945 |
| | 309 kcal/mol | 1292 kJ/mol |

$\therefore \Delta H° = 246 - 309 = -63$ kcal/mol
$(= 1028 - 1292 = -264$ kJ/mol$)$

$\therefore$ Reaction is exothermic

c)

| Bonds broken | kcal/mol | kJ/mol |
|---|---|---|
| C—C | 83 | 347 |
| C—H | 99 | 414 |
| C—O | 86 | 359 |
| | 268 kcal/mol | 1120 kJ/mol |

3-13 Contd...

c) Contd...

| Bonds formed | kcal/mol | kJ/mol |
|---|---|---|
| C=C | 146 | 610 |
| O—H | 111 | 464 |
| | 257 kcal/mol | 1074 kJ/mol |

∴ ΔH° = 268 - 257 = 11 kcal/mol
   (= 1120 - 1074 = 46 kJ/mol)

∴ Reaction is endothermic

d)

| Bonds broken | kcal/mol | kJ/mol |
|---|---|---|
| C—H | 99 | 414 |
| C—N | 73 | 305 |
| N=O | 145 | 606 |
| | 317 kcal/mol | 1325 kJ/mol |

| Bonds formed | kcal/mol | kJ/mol |
|---|---|---|
| O—H | 111 | 464 |
| C=N | 147 | 615 |
| N—O | 53 | 221 |
| | 311 kcal/mol | 1300 kJ/mol |

∴ ΔH° = 317 - 311 = 6 kcal/mol
   (= 1325 - 1300 = 25 kJ/mol)

∴ Reaction is endothermic

3-14

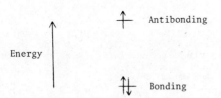

Energy

Antibonding

Bonding

The Pauli exclusion principle requires that the third electron occupy the antibonding molecular orbital. That is a high energy configuration.

3-15  The VSEPR theory would suggest that the electronegative chlorine atoms attract electron density away from the carbon atoms and the Cl-C-Cl bond angles decrease from a trigonal

3-15 Contd...
geometry as repulsions near the carbons decrease.
In the hybrid orbital picture the decrease in electron density at carbon increases the
$p$-character at that atom.  A carbon hybrid orbital with greater $p$-character than that of an
$sp^2$ orbital will have bond angles smaller than 120°.

3-16

a) $sp^3$          c) $sp$          e) $sp^2$

b) $sp^3$          d) $sp^3$          f) $sp^2$

3-17

a) The angle is much less than the 109.5° predicted for $sp^3$ hybrid orbitals, thus is expected
to be high in $p$ character.  The orbital is predicted to be between $sp^4$ and $sp^5$ in hybrid
character.

b) Since the C-C-C component of the molecular orbitals is high in $p$ character, the H-C-H part
must be high in $s$ character and thus possess an angle greater than 109.5°.  This angle is
actually found to be about 115°.

3-18

i) If four $sp^3$ hybrid orbitals from the oxygen atom were used to accommodate the two hydrogen
atoms and the two electron pairs, a tetrahedral angle of 109.5° would be the basis for
prediction.  Since the nonbonding electrons are closer to the nucleus, the orbital which they
occupy would have more $s$ character.  The orbitals of the O-H bonds would thus have a higher
$p$ character and an angle smaller than 109.5°.

ii) The VSEPR argument assumes that the nonbonding pairs are closer to the nucleus and repel each
other more than do the bonding electrons.  The bonding orbitals thus move closer together
than 109.5°.

3-19 The C-Cl bond length decreases as the atoms substituted on carbon increase in
electronegativity.  Electron attraction is relayed to the carbon atom and subsequently
results in attraction of the C-Cl bonding electrons and shortening of that bond.  A related
rationale is that the related electronegativity difference generates a dipolar structure
$$\delta+ \quad \delta-$$
in which the oppositely charged atoms attract each other (C——Cl).

3-20 Because the central sulfur atom is larger than an oxygen atom the electrons of the S-H bonds
are farther apart than those of the O-H bonds in water.  Repulsion is less and the bond
angle is thus smaller.

# 4 THE SHAPES OF MOLECULES— STEREOCHEMISTRY

4-1  The bond dipole moments of the two methyl to carbon bonds cancel in the trans isomer.  In the cis isomer the vector components of each bond dipole add together to give a resultant molecular dipole.

4-2

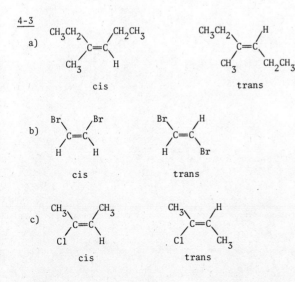

cis-cis-2,4-Hexadiene      trans-trans-2,4-Hexadiene      cis-trans-2,4-Hexadiene

Because of identical substitution at each end of the diene system, *cis-trans* and *trans-cis* are identical.

4-3

a)

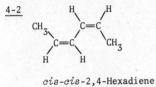

cis                    trans

b)

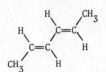

cis                    trans

c)

cis                    trans

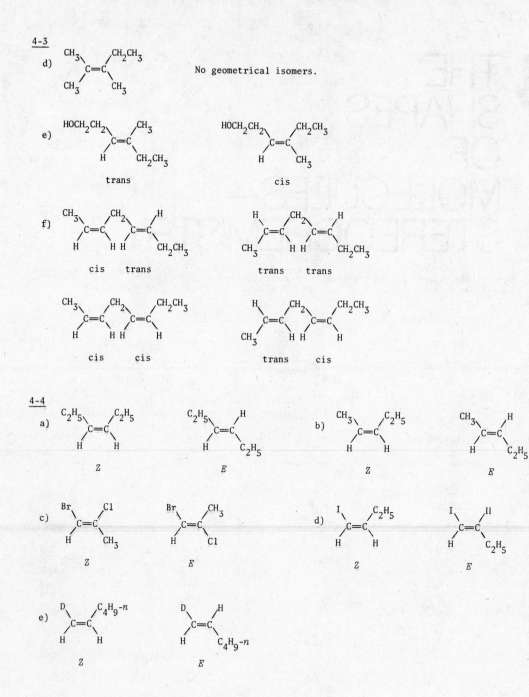

4-3

d)                                No geometrical isomers.

e)

        trans                          cis

f)

     cis    trans                 trans    trans

     cis    cis                   trans    cis

4-4

a)              Z              E              b)              Z              E

c)              Z              E              d)              Z              E

e)              Z              E

4-5

a)  Z-3-Chloro-4-methyl-3-hexene

(Chloro takes precedence over methyl in numbering.)

b)  E-1-Bromo-2-chloromethyl-4,4,4-trideuterio-3-methyl-2-butene

(The choice of parent name in this case is based on the longest carbon chain with the higher priority groups.)

c)  Z-1-Ethyl-2-methylcyclooctene

(Numbering priority goes to the more complex group or by alphabetical order.)

d)  Z-2-Ethyl-4-methyl-2-penten-1-ol

4-6  Because the terminal double bond has two identical substituents (H's) attached to one end and does not give rise to geometrical isomers.

4-7

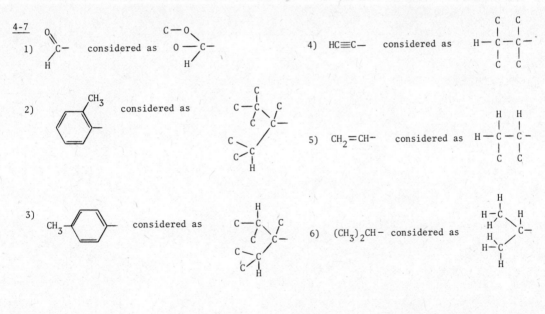

4-8

a)  Z-3-Phenyl-3-hexene

b)  Z-3-Hydroxymethyl-3-penten-2-one

c)  Z-3-Cyclobutyl-4-(1-methylethyl)-3-heptene

   or  Z-3-Cyclobutyl-4-isopropyl-3-heptene

4-8 Contd..

d) *E*-2-(4-Methylphenyl)-2-butenoic acid

  or *E*-2-*p*-Tolyl-2-butenoic acid

4-9  The following three formulas represent one of the many possible spatial arrangements of 2,3-dichlorobutane.

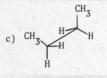 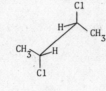 

4-10

a)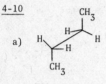

b)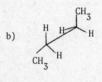

c)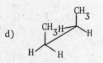

d)

4-11

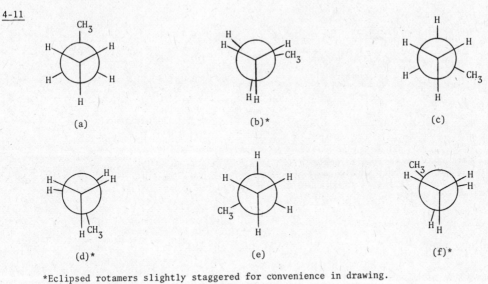

(a)    (b)*    (c)

(d)*    (e)    (f)*

*Eclipsed rotamers slightly staggered for convenience in drawing.

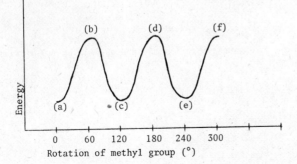

4-12  Chair cyclohexane is expected to have greater nonbonded repulsions than ethane because there are gauche interactions between the methylene ($CH_2$) groups (see fig. 4-9b).  The gauche butane is probably a good model for one-half of the cyclohexane ring.

4-13

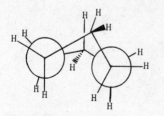

4-14  A planar structure introduces angle strain at all carbon atoms whereas the proposed ring flip via the twist boat involves only minor angle strain as one side of the ring flips into the twist boat. Eclipsing strain would also be considerable because all twelve hydrogen atoms are eclipsed.

4-15

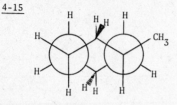    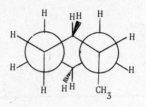

Equatorial                              Axial

The axial conformation has unfavorable gauche methyl-methylene as well as 1,3-diaxial interactions.

4-16

| | $\Delta G°$ (relative) | |
|---|---|---|
| trans eq.-eq. | 0 | (no axial $CH_3$ groups) |
| cis { eq.-ax. or ax.-eq. | 1.7 kcal/mol (7.3 kJ/mol) | (one axial $CH_3$ group) |
| trans. ax.-ax. | 3.4 kcal/mol (14.6 kJ/mol) | (two axial $CH_3$ groups) |

4-17

a)
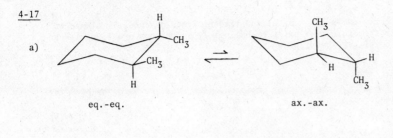

eq.-eq.                    ax.-ax.

b)
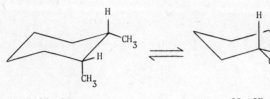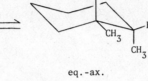

ax.-eq.                    eq.-ax.

c)
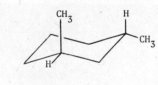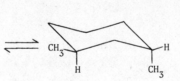

ax.-eq.                    eq.-ax.

d)
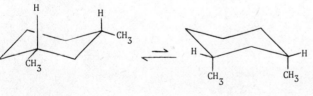

eq.-eq.                    ax.-ax.

4-18
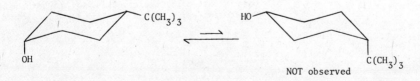

NOT observed

4-18 Contd...
    *tert*-Butyl is sterically unfavorable as an axial substituent, thus essentially always is equatorial. The cis isomer therefore must exist predominately in the conformation with an axial hydroxy and an equatorial *tert*-butyl group.

4-19  A planar molecule would have all hydrogen atoms eclipsed. The envelope shape enables the hydrogen atoms to be somewhat staggered.

4-20

Cl

The two bonds to one ring will lie in a plane perpendicular to the plane containing the two bonds to the second ring.

4-21

a)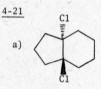

c)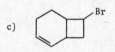

b)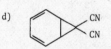

d)

4-22

Bicyclo[2.2.1]heptane      1,7,7-Trimethylbicyclo[2.2.1]-2-heptanone

4-23

*cis*-Decalin

The trans isomer is lower in energy because the cis isomer possesses additional nonbonded H-H repulsions. Also, the trans isomer has both bonds equatorial while one is axial in the cis isomer.

4-24

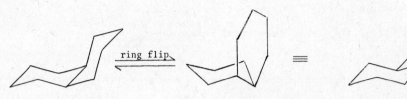

(The structure on the right has been rotated 60° to show that both rings are chair conformations.)

4-25

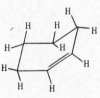

4-26  In all cases the single bonds on each end of the double bond must be highly strained for they lie in planes which are essentially perpendicular to each other.

4-27

The Cl and one H atom must be in one plane

Both Cl atoms or both H atoms must be in one plane

The H and one Cl atom must be in one plane

$CH_2Cl_2$ has an axis of symmetry through the carbon, $CH_3Cl$ has an axis of symmetry along the C-Cl bond, and $CHCl_3$ has an axis of symmetry along the C-H bond.

4-28

a)  Compare molecular models.

4-28 Contd...

b)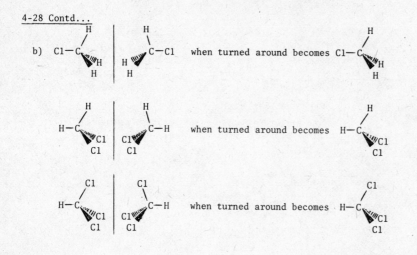

4-29

a) Achiral

b) Chiral at carbon atom 3

c) Achiral

d) Chiral at both carbon atoms 2 and 3

e) Achiral - possesses a plane of symmetry perpendicular to the molecular plane and passing through the Cl and Br atoms.

f) Chiral at carbon atom 4

g) Chiral at carbon atom 1 of the ethanol

h) Achiral - the molecule has plane of symmetry

4-30

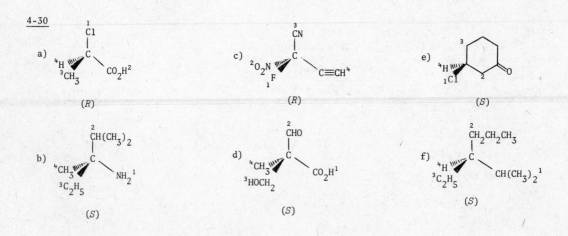

4-31

a)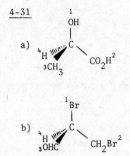

b)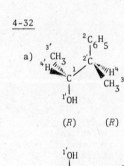

c)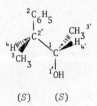

d)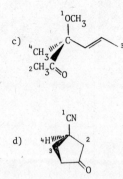

e)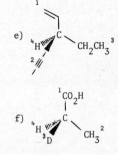

f) 

4-32

a)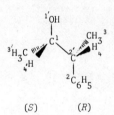

(R)          (R)

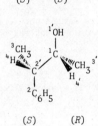

(S)          (S)

(S)          (R)

(S)          (R)

b)   NO

4-33

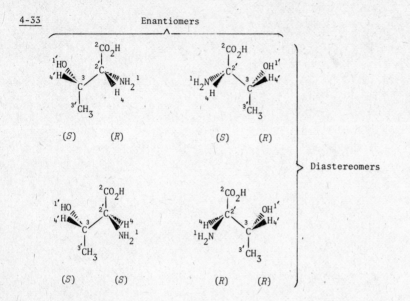

4-34  The configurations are $(R,R)$ for $(+)$-tartaric acid and $(S,S)$ for $(-)$-tartaric acid; that is, configuration is identical at each carbon atom. For the *meso*-tartaric acid the configurations are $(R,S)$ or $(S,R)$. In the meso isomer the groups around both chiral atoms are identical. The chiral centers have a mirror image relationship so that the molecule has an internal plane of symmetry.

4-35  If we envision a planar structure along the ring flip pathway, that is the symmetrical intermediate.

4-36

a) *trans*-1,3-Dimethylcyclohexane is resolvable into enantiomers.  Note that either pair of ring-flip conformers are actually identical.

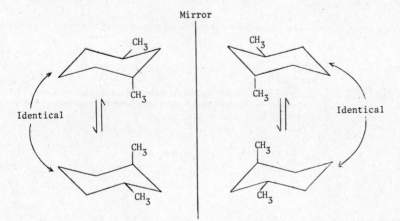

b) *cis*-1,3-Dimethylcyclohexanes (a,a and e,e) has a plane of symmetry, thus is achiral.

c) *cis*-3-Methylcyclohexanol is resolvable into enantiomers.

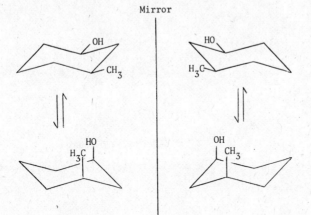

d) and  e)  1,4-Disubstituted cyclohexanes have a plane of symmetry, thus are not resolvable.

4-37

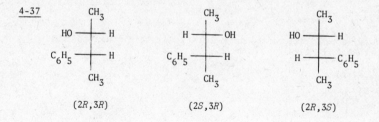

(2R,3R)          (2S,3R)          (2R,3S)

4-38  Follow the conventions for what a Fischer projection formula means in relation to a
3-dimensional molecule.  The 3-D drawings can be moved out of the plane of the paper for
comparison.

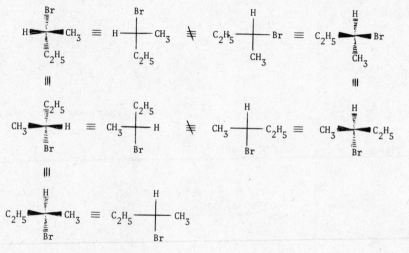

4-39

a)  3-Methyl-1-hexene

b)  Z-1-Methylcyclohexene

c)  E-3-Fluoro-3-iodo-2-methyl-2-propen-1-ol

d)  Z-2-Ethyl-2-butenal

e)  E-3-Hydroxymethyl-4-phenyl-3-hexen-1-ol

4-40

a)

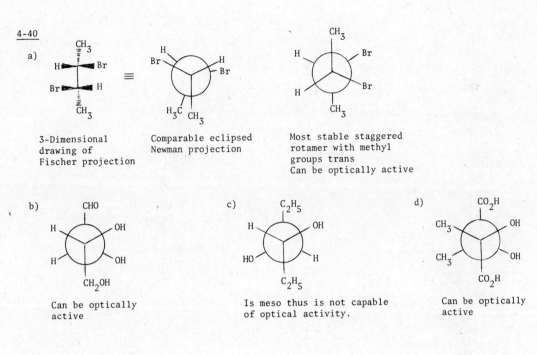

3-Dimensional
drawing of
Fischer projection

Comparable eclipsed
Newman projection

Most stable staggered
rotamer with methyl
groups trans
Can be optically active

b)

CHO
H
OH
H
OH
CH₂OH

Can be optically
active

c)

C₂H₅
H
OH
HO
H
C₂H₅

Is meso thus is not capable
of optical activity.

d)

CO₂H
CH₃
OH
CH₃
OH
CO₂H

Can be optically
active

4-41

a) *R*      c) *R*      e) *S*

b) *S*      d) *S*      f) *R*

4-42

a)  Three asymmetric carbon atoms       b)  4 pairs of enantiomers

∴ $2^3$ = 8 stereoisomers

c)  The most stable conformation has as many substituents equatorial as is possible.

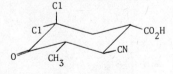

4-43  A chair conformation would require that one *tert*-butyl group be axial; a very unfavorable
position for that large group.  The twist-boat conformation illustrated below allows both
*tert*-butyl groups to minimize nonbonded interactions.

4-43 Contd..

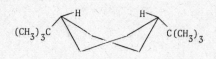

4-44

a)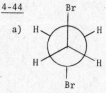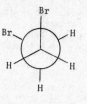

b)   Anti              Gauche              Gauche

c)

Anti ... Gauche ... Gauche ... Anti

180  120  60  0  60  120  180

Br-Br Dihedral angle (°)

4-45

a)  2

b)  Although four stereoisomers ($2^2 = 4$) might have been predicted only three actually exist; a pair of *dl* isomers and a meso form.

c) and d)

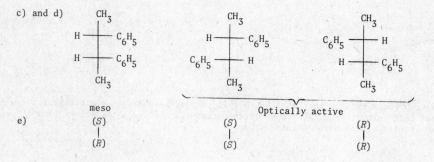

meso                    Optically active
e)  $(S)$               $(S)$               $(R)$
    |                   |                   |
    $(R)$               $(S)$               $(R)$

4-46

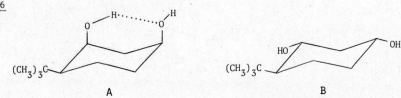

A                              B

The *tert*-butyl group determines ring conformation by remaining equatorial.   In A both
hydroxy groups are axial and located in a 1,3-relationship favorable for interaction.

4-47

a)

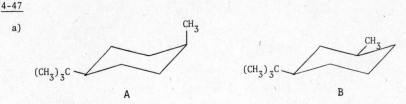

A                              B

b)   Ring flip of A would give the conformer with a less favorable axial *tert*-butyl group
(>4 kcal/mol) but more favorable equatorial methyl group (1.7 kcal/mol).   The process is
endergonic by >2.3 kcal/mol.
Ring flip of B puts both groups in an axial position and is endergonic by >5.7 kcal/mol.

4-48   The more stable conformer is indicated.   In some cases isomers are predicted to have
identical conformational energies.

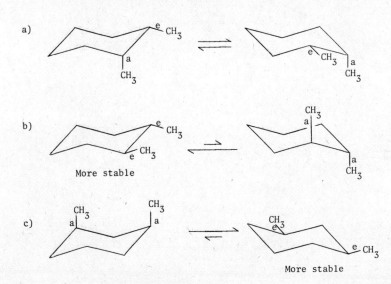

a)

b)          More stable

c)          More stable

4-48 Contd...

d)

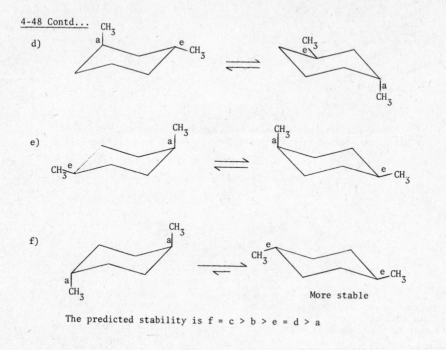

e)

f)

More stable

The predicted stability is f = c > b > e = d > a

4-49

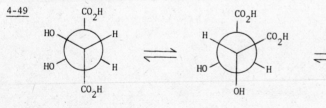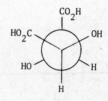

Most stable rotamer

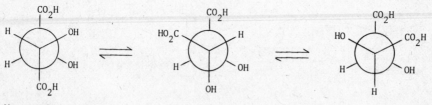

Most stable rotamer

This is a mirror image of the sequence above

4-49 Contd...

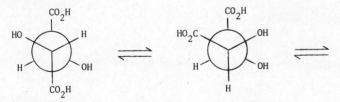

Most stable of the
  meso rotamers.

The relative stabilities indicated for the three isomers are based on group sizes. Intramolecular hydrogen bonding between hydroxy, carboxy, and hydroxy-carboxy could alter those predictions.

4-50

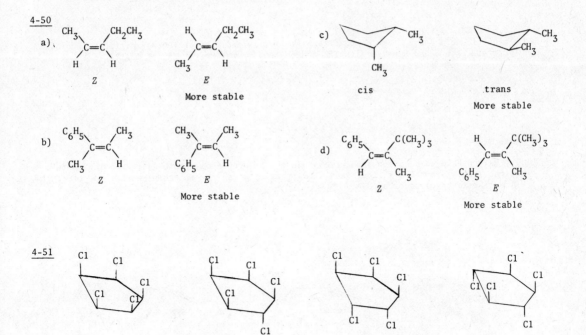

4-51

None are optically active because they all have a plane of symmetry,

4-52

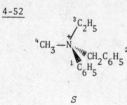
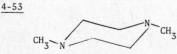

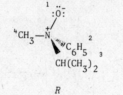

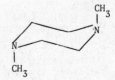

$S$                                    $R$

4-53

$\mu = 0$                    $\mu = 1.55$ D          $\mu = 0$
                        (calculated)

4-54  Ricinoleic acid has a $Z$ and $E$ geometrical isomer in addition to the asymmetric carbon atom. There are both $Z$ and $E$ pairs with ($R$) and ($S$) configurations at the asymmetric carbon.

4-55

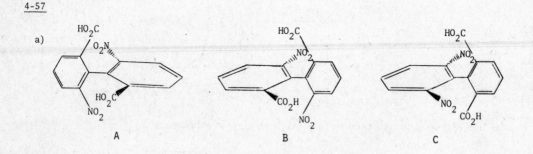

$$\xrightarrow[\text{Catalyst}]{\text{H}_2}$$

4-56  The carbon-halogen bond lengths increase as the halogen atom becomes larger.  The centers of the larger atoms are further away from other atoms in the molecule so that the effect of size is effectively decreased.

4-57

a)

A              B              C

4-57 Contd...

b)

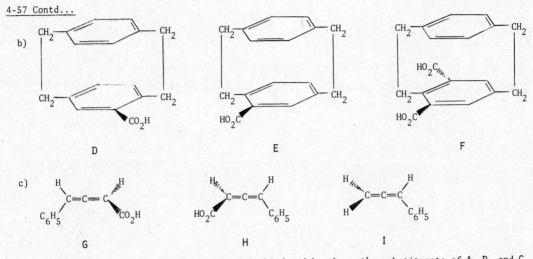

D

E

F

c)

G

H

I

Free rotation about the aryl-aryl bond is hindered by the *ortho* substituents of A, B, and C.

Compounds A and B are enantiomers. Compound C is achiral because identical ortho substituents lead to a plane of symmetry.

Compounds D, E, and F (known as paracyclophanes) are not free to rotate because the carbon bridges connecting the aromatic rings are too short. Compounds D and E are enantiomers while F is achiral because it possesses a plane of symmetry.

Allenes G and H are chiral because of the perpendicular orientation of the two cumulative double bonds. Allene I is also rigid but has a plane of symmetry.

# 5 SPECTROSCOPY

## 5-1

a) Empirical formula = molecular formula = $C_8H_8O_5$

b) Empirical formula ≠ molecular formula = $C_8H_{10}O_2$

c) Empirical formula = molecular formula = $C_5H_9Br$

d) Empirical formula ≠ molecular formula = $C_8H_{10}N_2O_2$

## 5-2

i)  $2.1 = \dfrac{\nu_A - \nu_{TMS}}{60 \times 10^6 \text{ Hz}} \times 10^6$

$\nu_A - \nu_{TMS} = 126$ Hz

ii)  $2.1 = \dfrac{\nu_A - \nu_{TMS}}{100 \times 10^6 \text{ Hz}} \times 10^6$

$\nu_A - \nu_{TMS} = 210$ Hz

## 5-3

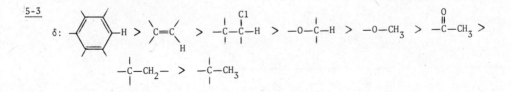

## 5-4 The chemical shift data listed below are experimental values.

a) $CH_3OCH_3$ ; δ = 3.2 ppm

b) $ClCH_2C\equiv CH$ ; δ = 2.4 ppm (b); 4.1 ppm (a)
   (a)   (b)

c) $(CH_3)_3N$ ; δ = 2.1 ppm

d) $(CH_3)_4C$ ; δ = 0.9 ppm

e)  ; δ = 1.5 ppm

f) $(CH_3)_3COH$ ; δ = 1.2 ppm (a); OH proton
   (a)   (b)                          variable

g) $CH_3C\overset{O}{\diagup}$  ;  δ = 2.0 ppm (a); 3.6 ppm (b)
   (a)  $OCH_3$
        (b)

h) $CH_3C\equiv CCH_3$ ; δ = 1.8 ppm

5-5

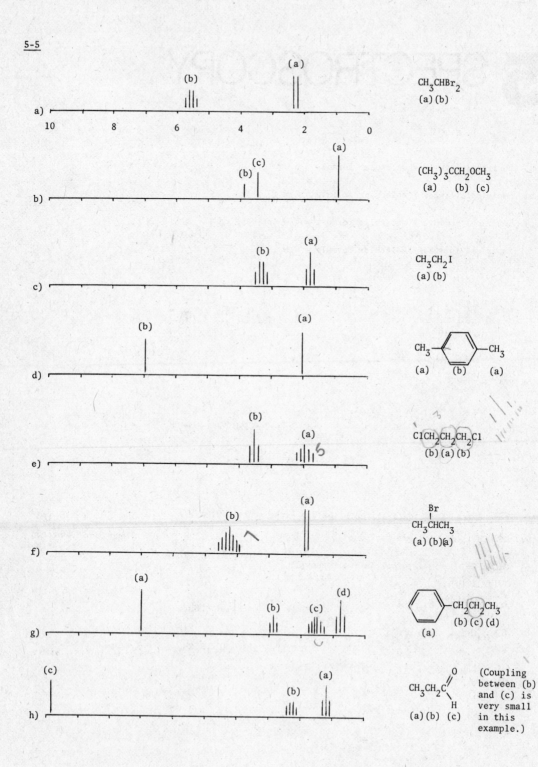

*(handwritten margin notes: H—C≡C—Br    H—C≡C—CH₂—Br    IHD = 2)*

**5-6**

i) The $CH_3$ resonance is a triplet due to splitting by the adjacent $CH_2$ group.

ii) The $CH_2$ resonance shows splitting into a quartet by the adjacent $CH_3$ group plus additional splitting of each part of the quartet into a doublet by the hydroxy H.

iii) The OH resonance is a triplet because of splitting by the adjacent $CH_2$ group.

**5-7**

a) $Cl_2CHCH_2Cl$ - *IHD* = 0; doublet and triplet indicate one and two adjacent protons.

b) $CH_3C\overset{O}{\underset{H}{\diagup\diagdown}}$ - *IHD* = 1; resonance deshielded to 9.8 ppm is typical of an aldehyde. Note that there is some coupling between the methyl protons and the aldehydic proton.

c) $CH_3C\overset{O}{\underset{OH}{\diagup\diagdown}}$ - *IHD* = 1; differs from (b) in having two oxygen atoms and no splitting since protons are not on adjacent atoms.

d) *(aromatic ring structure: benzene ring with H's and $CH_3$)* - *IHD* = 4; peak at 7.2 ppm is typical of aromatic compounds; the peak area ratio of 5:3 indicates monosubstitution; a singlet of area = 3 is typical of a methyl group.

**5-8** The aromatic protons of benzene are chemically and magnetically equivalent, thus no spin-spin splitting occurs. The aromatic resonance of many aromatic compounds is a broadened singlet because of very small couplings between nonequivalent protons on the aromatic ring.

**5-9** Integral areas would show zero, one and two, alkene protons respectively.

**5-10**

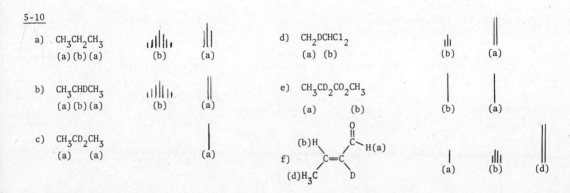

a) $CH_3CH_2CH_3$
   (a)(b)(a)        (b)        (a)

b) $CH_3CHDCH_3$
   (a)(b)(a)        (b)        (a)

c) $CH_3CD_2CH_3$
   (a)    (a)                  (a)

d) $CH_2DCHCl_2$
   (a)  (b)            (b)      (a)

e) $CH_3CD_2CO_2CH_3$
   (a)      (b)        (b)      (a)

f) $(b)H$ and $(d)H_3C$ on $C=C$ with $C\overset{O}{\diagup\diagdown}H(a)$ and $D$
   (a)      (b)      (d)

5-11

a) $ClCH_2CH_2CH_2Cl$     - $IHD$ = 0; chemical shifts, peak area ratios relative to the molecular formula and the pentet splitting pattern lead to the structure.

b) $CH_3CO_2C_2H_5$     - $IHD$ = 1; a triplet-quartet pattern is typical of an ethyl group with the $CH_2$ deshielded by the ester oxygen atom; note the typical position of the resonance peak for an unsplit methyl group adjacent to C=O.

c)     - $IHD$ = 4 and a peak at 6.8 ppm suggests an aromatic group; the area ratio of 1:3 is actually 3:9 as per the molecular formula; the single aromatic peak is consistent with a symmetrical structure; the singlet of 9 protons is characteristic of three equivalent methyl groups.

d) $CH_3CH_2\overset{O}{\overset{\|}{C}}CH_3$     - $IHD$ = 1; note that the $CH_2$ group of ethyl adjacent to C=O is at 2.3 ppm in contrast to the $CH_2$ connected to an oxygen atom in (b).

e) $CH_3\overset{O}{\overset{\|}{C}}{\small OCH_2C_6H_5}$     - $IHD$ = 5; the chemical shifts and absence of splitting lead to the structure. Note that the $CH_2$ is deshielded to 5.1 ppm by a combination of the O atom and $C_6H_5$ group.

5-12

a) Hydroxy; the spectrum is that of *m*-methylphenol.

b) Carbonyl; the spectrum is that of 1-phenylpropanone.

$C_6H_5CCH_2CH_3$

d) Hydroxy and carbon-carbon double bond; the spectrum is that of 2-propenol.

$CH_2=CHCH_2OH$

d) Carbonyl; the spectrum is that of propyl propanoate.

$CH_3CH_2CO_2CH_2CH_2CH_3$

e. Primary amine; the spectrum is that of 1,2-diaminobenzene.

f) Carboxylic acid; the spectrum is that of butanoic acid.

$CH_3CH_2CH_2CO_2H$

5-13

a) [benzene ring]—Cl

- *IHD* = 4 only fits an aromtic compound in this case; a weak C-H absorption is typical as are peaks at 1400-1600 cm$^{-1}$; the pattern at 600-800 cm$^{-1}$ is typical of a monosubstituted aromatic with an additional peak at 680 cm$^{-1}$ due to the C-Cl stretching absorption.

b) CH$_3$CCH$_2$CH$_3$
   (with O double bonded above the second C)

- *IHD* = 1; the presence of O and a strong peak at 1710 cm$^{-1}$ is typical of a ketone C=O; there is no indication of an aldehydic C-H stretching absorption; only one ketone has this molecular formula.

c) CH$_3$CO$_2$H

- *IHD* = 1; the broad peak at ≈ 3000 cm$^{-1}$ with a strong absorption at 1710 cm$^{-1}$ is typical of a carboxylic acid. Only one carboxylic acid has this molecular formula.

d) 1-Octene

- *IHD* = 1 for this hydrocarbon and a "relatively intense" peak at 1650 cm$^{-1}$ is typical of an unsymmetrical alkene; the C-H stretching frequency of a terminal alkene is at 3100 cm$^{-1}$. Final analysis would depend on a match with the spectra of known compounds.

e) Z-2,5-Dimethyl-3-hexene

- *IHD* = 1 for this hydrocarbon fits an alkene (or carbocycle); the peak at 750 cm$^{-1}$ is typical of a cis (Z) alkene and the very small peak at 1650 cm$^{-1}$ suggests a relatively symmetrical alkene. Final analysis would depend on a match with the spectra of known compounds.

f) C$_6$H$_5$CH$_2$C≡N

- Presence of N and a peak at 2250 cm$^{-1}$ indicates —C≡N; *IHD* = 6 (2 for the nitrile) suggests an aromatic compound in this case and the pattern at 1400-1600 cm$^{-1}$ confirms this; the pattern at 700-800 cm$^{-1}$ shows monosubstituted aromatic.

g) C$_6$H$_5$C
   (with O double bonded above and H below)

- The strong absorption at 1710 cm$^{-1}$ is typical of C=O while two peaks at 2700-2800 cm$^{-1}$ suggest —C (with O double bonded above and H below) ; *IHD* = 5 (one for —C=O) and weak C-H stretching at 3050 cm$^{-1}$ suggest an aromatic compound; a conjugated aldehyde accounts for the shift of the aldehyde carbonyl absorption.

5-14

a) [benzene ring]—C≡CH

- The nmr spectrum suggest a monosubstituted aromatic (C$_6$H$_5$—) which accounts for a molecular weight contribution of 77. The presence of only one additional H in the spectrum suggests that C$_2$H remains to be accounted for to fit the molecular weight. A IR peak at 3310 cm$^{-1}$ and the position of the single H in the nmr spectrum suggest a terminal alkyne.

5-14 Contd..

b)  $CH_3\overset{\overset{\displaystyle OH}{|}}{CH}CH_3$

- The IR suggest a hydroxy group. Eight protons in the nmr spectrum require at least three carbon atoms ($C_nH_{2n+2}$) while the low molecular weight and nmr splitting patterns fit only one alcohol.

c)  $CH_3CH_2I$

- The typical nmr pattern for an ethyl group plus the low boiling point provide the structure.

d)  $(CH_3)_3CCH{=}CH_2$

- The IR absorption at 1640 cm$^{-1}$ suggests a nonsymmetrical alkene. The 12 hydrogen atoms in the nmr spectrum require at least six carbon atoms ($C_nH_{2n}$) and the low bp confirms that more are unlikely. A single nmr peak of nine H's at 1.0 ppm is typical of the *tert*-butyl group. The remaining nmr peaks fit a terminal alkene.

e)  $(CH_3)_3CCH_2NH_2$

- A fishy smelling liquid containing nitrogen is typical of amines and the the IR double peak at 3300 cm$^{-1}$ suggests a primary amine. From the elemental analysis we calculate:
$$\frac{68.93}{12.01} = 5.74; \qquad \frac{15.04}{1.008} = 14.92; \qquad \frac{16.08}{14.005} = 1.15$$
∴ the empirical formula is $C_5H_{13}N$. A *tert*-butyl and two unsplit groups of protons are evident from the nmr spectrum. (Remember that hydrogen atoms on N and O usually don't split adjacent protons.)

f)

- *IHD* = 2. The molecular formula shows that the nmr peak areas correspond to 4:4:2 with the two H's at a chemical shift typical of alkenes. The four H's at 2.0 ppm are the allylic methylene groups.

g)  $C_6H_5CH_2\overset{\overset{\displaystyle O}{\|}}{C}CH_2\overset{\underset{\displaystyle CH_3}{|}}{CH}CO_2H$

- A broad IR absorption at 2900-3300 cm$^{-1}$ along with a C=O absorption and the nmr peak at 11.2 ppm suggest —$CO_2H$. The second carbonyl absorption cannot be an aldehyde because no aldehydeic H is present in the nmr spectrum, thus is presumed to be a ketone. The nmr also shows a monosubstituted benzene ring. These units (—$CO_2H$, C=O, and $C_6H_5$—)

or

$C_6H_5CH_2\overset{\overset{\displaystyle O}{\|}}{C}\overset{\underset{\displaystyle CH_3}{|}}{CH}CH_2CO_2H$

account for 150 MW units. The eight remaining H's require at least four carbon atoms and $C_4H_8$ fits the required MW. The singlet at 2.6 ppm is a deshielded and unsplit methylene. Chemical shifts and splitting patterns lead to two possible structures.

h)  $N{\equiv}CCH_2CH_2CO_2CH_3$

- The IR peak at 2240 cm$^{-1}$ in a nitrogen containing compound suggests a nitrile. The C=O peak at 1730 cm$^{-1}$ is consistent with an ester and the nmr singlet at 3.8 ppm fits a methyl ester. The singlet at 2.7 ppm can only fit two magnetically equivalent $CH_2$ groups. In this compound, the nitrile and ester affect the $CH_2$'s identically.

5-15

The aromatic resonance peak of four protons and the triplet-pentet multiplets, when related to the molecular formula, provide the structure.

5-16  A - Fig. 5-53 - The Ir shows and 0-H stretching absorption but no peaks for the additional
                      functional groups of the other alcohols, B and F.

      B - Fig. 5-56 - A typical isopropyl doublet and heptet in the nmr spectrum could fit
                      compounds A and B.  The rest of the nmr spectrum is not consistent with A.
                      In particular note that the H atom on the carbon connected to OH (the
                      carbinol carbon atom) is deshielded to 4.1 ppm and split by the adjacent H
                      and long range by the terminal C-H.  The terminal acetylenic H at 2.4 ppm
                      also clearly shows this long range splitting.

      C - Fig. 5-54 - The nmr spectrum shows only saturated hydrocarbon peaks, thus can fit none
                      of the other compounds.

      D - Fig. 5-57 - The only characteristic IR absorption is a weak peak at 2260 cm$^{-1}$.  Though
                      this could fit B or D, the 0-H absorption characteristic of B is not present.

      E - Fig. 5-55 - This is the only compound with an aromatic group (multiplet at 7.1 ppm).

                      The singlet at 2.3 ppm is characteristic of $CH_3-\overset{\overset{O}{\|}}{C}-$.

      F - Fig. 5-58 - The nmr spectrum clearly shows alkene protons between 5-6 ppm.  The two
                      broad peaks between 0.8-1.7 ppm is typical of straight chain alkanes, in
                      this case $-CH_2CH_2CH_3$.  The hydroxy H is an unsplit singlet (2.1 ppm) and
                      carbinol H is at 4.0 ppm.

5-17

$Cl-\!\!\!\bigcirc\!\!\!-\overset{\overset{O}{\|}}{C}CH_3$

The dual molecular ion peaks are characteristic of a chlorine atom.
The IR absorption and nmr singlet suggests a methyl ketone while the
symmetrical aromatic multiplet with an area ratio of four is typical
of para disubstitution.

5-18

$\qquad \overset{OH}{\underset{|}{}}$
A - $C_6H_5CHCH_3$

B - $C_6H_5CH_2CH_2OH$

An *IHD* = 4 is consistent with the presence of an aromatic ring as are
the nmr spectra.  The aromatic peak areas indicate monosubstitution.
The IR spectra indicate a hydroxy group but both spectra are quite
similar.  These two groups account for $C_6H_6O$.  The nmr splitting
patterns and chemical shifts provide the information for the
arrangements of the remaining $C_2H_4$ and for final structural
assignments.

5-19

$N\equiv CCH_2CO_2CH_2CH_3$

*IHD* = 3 which can be accounted for by a triple bond and a carbonyl
group as are indicated by the IR spectrum.  The nmr spectrum shows
an ethyl group with the $CH_2$ deshielded as is typical for an ethyl

ester.  Since there is no single H resonance peak in the nmr spectrum
the triple bond cannot be due to a terminal acetylene in this case
and the compound must be a nitrile.

5-20

$$C_6H_5CH_2\overset{\overset{O}{\|}}{C}CH_3$$

$IHD = 5$. The nmr shows a monosubstituted aromatic and the IR shows a carbonyl. These groups account for the $IHD$ and $C_7H_5O$ of the molecular formula. The nmr shows that the remaining $C_2H_5$ must be due to deshielded methyl and methylene groups that do not split each other.

5-21

$$CH_3CH{=}CHCO_2C_2H_5$$

The IR spectrum suggests a carbonyl group and possibly a nonsymmetrical alkene. Those two groups account for the $IHD$ of 2. The second oxygen is consistent with an ester group and the triplet-quartet with the deshielded quartet suggests an ethyl ester. The nmr multiplets at 5.9 and 7.0 are indicative of alkene protons. The doublet at 1.9 ppm is probably a methyl group adjacent to a C-H and further split by long range coupling with a proton.

5-22 In each of the following $^{13}C$ nmr spectra the chemical shift of each carbon atom is indicated. Resonance peaks move further downfield (to higher chemical shift values) when electronegative atoms or groups are near the atom.

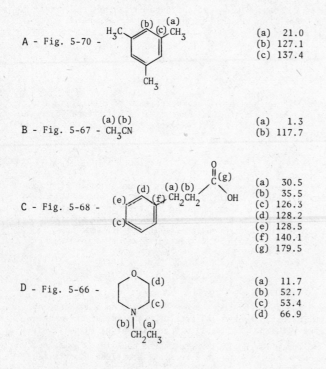

A - Fig. 5-70 -

(a)  21.0
(b)  127.1
(c)  137.4

B - Fig. 5-67 - $CH_3CN$  (a)(b)

(a)   1.3
(b)  117.7

C - Fig. 5-68 -

(a)  30.5
(b)  35.5
(c)  126.3
(d)  128.2
(e)  128.5
(f)  140.1
(g)  179.5

D - Fig. 5-66 -

(a)  11.7
(b)  52.7
(c)  53.4
(d)  66.9

5-22 Contd...

E - Fig. 5-69 -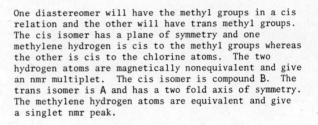

(a)  50.1
(b)  70.4

F - Fig. 5-65 -

(a)  11.4
(b)  18.8
(c)  29.3
(d)  36.4

5-23

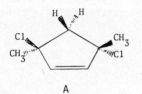

A

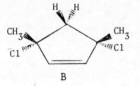

B

One diastereomer will have the methyl groups in a cis relation and the other will have trans methyl groups. The cis isomer has a plane of symmetry and one methylene hydrogen is cis to the methyl groups whereas the other is cis to the chlorine atoms. The two hydrogen atoms are magnetically nonequivalent and give an nmr multiplet. The cis isomer is compound B. The trans isomer is A and has a two fold axis of symmetry. The methylene hydrogen atoms are equivalent and give a singlet nmr peak.

# 6 STRUCTURE, REACTIVITY, AND ORGANIC TRANSFORMATIONS

6-1

$$CH_3\ddot{O}H + B:^- \rightleftharpoons CH_3\ddot{O}:^- + BH \qquad \text{Methanol as an acid}$$

$$CH_3\ddot{O}H + HX \rightleftharpoons CH_3\overset{+}{O}H_2 + X:^- \qquad \text{Methanol as a base}$$

6-2  A proton is a Lewis acid for it is an electron pair acceptor.  It is not a proton donor.

6-3

a)  $CH_3CO_2H + H_2O \overset{K}{\rightleftharpoons} CH_3CO_2^- + H_3O^+$

$$K_a = \frac{[CH_3CO_2^-][H_3O^+]}{[CH_3CO_2H]} = 1.76 \times 10^{-5}$$

$$pK_a = -\log 1.76 \times 10^{-5} = (0.25 - 5) = 4.75$$

The concentration of $H_3O^+$ is determined by assuming that $[CH_3CO_2H] \approx 1$ for a 1N solution since the percent dissociation is small.  Since $[H_3O^+] = [CH_3CO_2^-]$ in this case, $[H_3O^+]^2 = 1.76 \times 10^{-5}$ and $[H_3O^+] = 4.2 \times 10^{-3}$.

$$\therefore pH = -\log 4.2 \times 10^{-3} = 2.4$$

b)  $\dfrac{4.2 \times 10^{-3}}{1} \times 100 = 0.4 \%$

6-4

a) For the monoprotic acid HA, in aqueous media:

$$HA + H_2O \xrightleftharpoons{K_a} H_3O^+ + A^-$$

$$K_a = \frac{[H_3O^+][A^-]}{[HA]}$$

$$-\log K_a = -\log[H_3O^+] - \log\frac{[A^-]}{[HA]}$$

$$= -\log[H_3O^+] + \log\frac{[HA]}{[A^-]}$$

$$\therefore pK_a = pH + \log\frac{[HA]}{[A^-]}$$

b) For a monoprotic acid at one-half neutralization $[HA] = [A^-]$

$$K_a = [H_3O^+] \text{ and } \log K_a = \log[H_3O^+].$$

Since $pK_a = -\log K_a$ and $pH = -\log[H_3O^+]$, then $pK_a = pH$

6-5

a)   $\Delta G°$  $\uparrow$   [HCl + $H_2O$]

                                      $\Delta G° < 0$

           [$H_3O^+$ + $Cl^-$]

b) $\Delta G°$ $\uparrow$   [$CF_3CO_2H$ + $H_2O$]    [$CF_3CO_2^-$ + $H_3O^+$]       $\Delta G° \approx 0$

6-5 Contd...

c)

$$[C_6H_5O^- + H_3O^+]$$

$\Delta G°$                               $\Delta G° > 0$

$$[C_6H_5OH + H_2O]$$

6-6

| Base | Conjugate acid | $pK_a$ |
|------|----------------|--------|
| NaH | H-H | - |
| $t$-BuLi | $(CH_3)_3CH$ | >50 |
| $n$-BuLi | $CH_3(CH_2)_2CH_3$ | ≈50 |
| LiNEt$_2$ | $Et_2NH$ | ≈37 |
| NaNH$_2$ | $NH_3$ | 36 |
| $(C_6H_5)_3CNa$ | $(C_6H_5)_3CH$ | 32 |
| $KOC(CH_3)_3$ | $(CH_3)_3COH$ | 18 |
| $NaOC_2H_5$ | $C_2H_5OH$ | 16 |
| NaOH | HOH | 15.7 |
| $Et_3N$ | $Et_3\overset{+}{N}H$ | ≈10 |
| pyridine | pyridinium | 5.2 |
| $CH_3CO_2Na$ | $CH_3CO_2H$ | 4.8 |

6-7

a) For the two reactants, consider dissociation of the acid and the conjugate acid of the base.

$$CH_3CO_2H \xrightleftharpoons{K_a} CH_3CO_2^- + H^+ \qquad K_a = \frac{[CH_3CO_2^-][H^+]}{[CH_3CO_2H]} = 10^{-4.8}$$

$$C_2H_5\overset{+}{N}H_3 \xrightleftharpoons{K'_a} C_2H_5NH_2 + H^+ \qquad K'_a = \frac{[C_2H_5NH_2][H^+]}{[C_2H_5\overset{+}{N}H_3]} = 10^{-10}$$

6-7 Contd...

a) Contd...

For the total reaction

$$CH_3CO_2H + C_2H_5NH_2 \; \underset{}{\overset{K}{\rightleftharpoons}} \; CH_3CO_2^- + C_2H_5\overset{+}{N}H_3$$

$$K = \frac{[CH_3CO_2^-][C_2H_5\overset{+}{N}H_3]}{[CH_3CO_2H][C_2H_5NH_2]} = \frac{K_a}{K_a'} = \frac{10^{-4.8}}{10^{-10}} = 10^{5.2}$$

The reaction is considered complete since $K > 10^2$. Note that the value of the equilibrium constant for these acid-base reactions is calculated from the ratio of the $K_a$ value of the acid to the $K_a$ value of the conjugate acid of the base.

b) $CH_3O^- + CH_3COCH_2CO_2CH_3 \; \rightleftharpoons \; CH_3OH + CH_3CO\overset{..}{C}HCO_2CH_3$

$$K = \frac{10^{-11}}{10^{-15}} = 10^4 \quad \therefore \text{complete}$$

c) $CO_3^{2-} + HCN \; \rightleftharpoons \; HCO_3^- + CN^-$

$$K = \frac{10^{-9.1}}{10^{-10.2}} = 10^{1.1} \quad \therefore \text{only about 70\% complete}$$

d) $CH_3NO_2 + \langle \rangle :^- \; \rightleftharpoons \; \overset{..}{:}CH_2NO_2 + \langle \rangle$

$$K = \frac{10^{-10.2}}{10^{-16}} = 10^{5.8} \quad \therefore \text{complete}$$

e) $HC{\equiv}CH + NH_2^- \; \rightleftharpoons \; HC{\equiv}C\overset{..}{:}^- + NH_3$

$$K = \frac{10^{-25}}{10^{-36}} = 10^{11} \quad \therefore \text{complete}$$

f) $HCO_3^- + HCO_2H \; \rightleftharpoons \; H_2CO_3 + HCO_2^-$

$$K = \frac{10^{-3.7}}{10^{-6.4}} = 10^{2.7} \quad \therefore \text{complete}$$

6-7 Contd...

g) $Cl_2CHCO_2H$ + $C_6H_5NH_2$ $\rightleftharpoons$ $Cl_2CHCO_2^-$ + $C_6H_5\overset{+}{N}H_3$

$K = \dfrac{10^{-1.3}}{10^{-4.6}} = 10^{3.3}$ ∴complete

h) $C_6H_5OH$ + 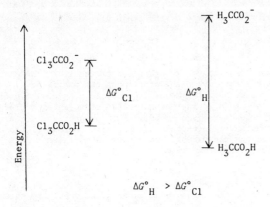 $\rightleftharpoons$ $C_6H_5O^-$ +

$K = \dfrac{10^{-10}}{10^{-5.2}} = 10^{-4.8}$ ∴equilibrium lies far to the left

6-8 The effects of bond dipole interactions and of solvation are expected to be greater in the carboxylate anions than in the acids. Thus relative differences in energies of the two systems are greater for the conjugate bases. Nevertheless, even small differences in relative energies of the acids can influence the overall acidities.

6-9 The inductive effect of the halogen atoms is related to their electronegativities. The most electronegative atom, fluorine, has the greatest acidifying influence.

6-10 The trifluoromethyl group stabilizes the anion of the conjugate base relative to the alcohol by inductive electron withdrawal.

6-10 Contd...

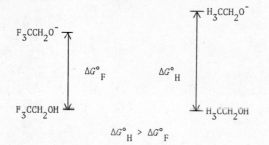

$\Delta G^{\circ}_{H} > \Delta G^{\circ}_{F}$

(Alcohols arbitrarily set as equal in energy)

6-11   The greater "s" character of an unsaturated carbon atom suggests that the electrons are
attracted more closely to the nucleus.  To the degree that this effect is transferred to
adjacent groups, the unsaturated substituent will be electron withdrawing.

6-12   Each successive negative charge decreases the stability of the conjugate base by electrostatic
repulsions and therefore decreases acidity.

6-13   The two carboxy groups of maleic acid are closer together than those of fumaric.  The
electron withdrawing inductive effect of one carboxy on the other enhances the first
ionization of maleic acid to a greater degree.  But the monoanion of maleic acid is closer
to the undissociated carboxy group and tends to hold the second acidic hydrogen atom close
to the molecule (see also intramolecular H-bonding - sec. 6-2B).  Furthermore, the second
ionization of maleic acid is particularly unfavorable because the negative charges of the
dianion repel each other.  In fumaric acid the two carboxy groups are on opposite sides of
the molecule.  Their effect on each other is less than in maleic acid.

6-14   The carboxylic acid group provides a proton to the amine in an internal acid-base reaction.

$$H_2NCH_2CO_2H \rightleftharpoons H_3\overset{+}{N}CH_2CO_2^{-}$$

6-15

a)  Oxalic   $\equiv$  Ethanedioic acid          d)  Glutaric  $\equiv$  Pentanedioic acid

b)  Malonic  $\equiv$  Propanedioic acid          e)  Maleic    $\equiv$  $Z$-Butenedioic acid

c)  Succinic $\equiv$  Butanedioic acid           f)  Fumaric   $\equiv$  $E$-Butenedioic acid

6-16  Solvation stabilization of the conjugate base from *tert*-butyl alcohol is hindered due to crowding by the three methyl groups.  Dissociation is therefore relatively less favorable for *tert*-butyl alcohol than for methanol.  In the gas phase solvation is not a factor.  The gas phase data indicate that *tert*-butyl alcohol is intrinsically more acidic than methanol, that is, $-CH_3$ is more electron donating than $-C(CH_3)_3$.

6-17  The order reflects steric interactions between the alkyl groups of the acid and base.  As more alkyl groups are brought close to each other the equilibrium constant for the acid-base reaction decreases.

6-18  The hydrogen bonding which favors dissociation of the ortho carboxylic acid inhibits further ionization of the phenolic proton.  That kind of intramolecular association cannot take place with the para isomer.

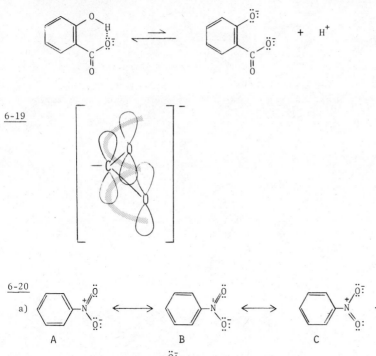

6-19

6-20

a)

Structures A and B differ in the arrangement of bonds in the aromatic ring (i.e., they represent the two Kekulé forms) while C differs in the nitro group.  Structure D is one of the many forms in which positive charge is delocalized into the aromatic ring.

6-20 Contd...

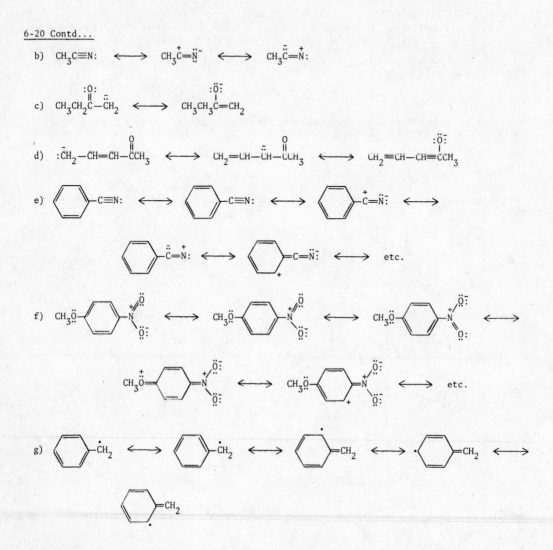

6-21  They are structural isomers.  Carbon atoms move and the sequence of covalently bonded atoms is different.

6-22

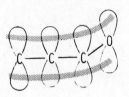

6-23

a)   $H_2\ddot{N}-C\equiv N:$   ⟷   $H_2\overset{+}{N}=C=\bar{\ddot{N}}:$        The noncharged structure is favored.

Most important

b)   $H_2C=\overset{+}{N}H_2$   ⟷   $H_2\overset{+}{C}-\ddot{N}H_2$        The structure in which the carbon atom has an electron octet is favored even though the more electronegative atom (nitrogen) has a positive charge.

Most important

c)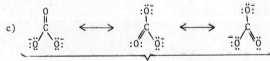

All are equally important

d)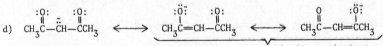

Most important - energetically equivalent

e)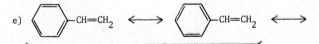

Most important - energetically equivalent

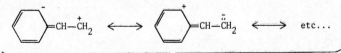

These plus related ring-delocalized charged structures are not very important

6-23 Contd...

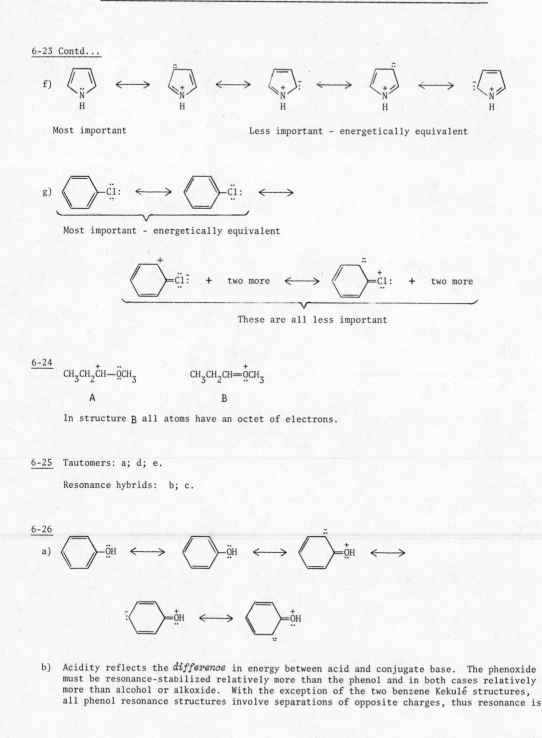

f)

Most important        Less important - energetically equivalent

g)

Most important - energetically equivalent

+ two more ⟷ + two more

These are all less important

6-24

$CH_3CH_2\overset{+}{C}H-\overset{..}{\overset{..}{O}}CH_3$     $CH_3CH_2CH=\overset{+}{\overset{..}{O}}CH_3$

A              B

In structure B all atoms have an octet of electrons.

6-25  Tautomers: a; d; e.

Resonance hybrids:  b; c.

6-26

a)

b)  Acidity reflects the *difference* in energy between acid and conjugate base.  The phenoxide
    must be resonance-stabilized relatively more than the phenol and in both cases relatively
    more than alcohol or alkoxide.  With the exception of the two benzene Kekulé structures,
    all phenol resonance structures involve separations of opposite charges, thus resonance is

6-26 Contd...

b) Contd... not very important for the phenol.

c)

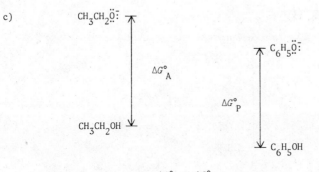

$$\Delta G^\circ_A > \Delta G^\circ_P$$

(Absolute energy levels are arbitrary)

6-27

a)

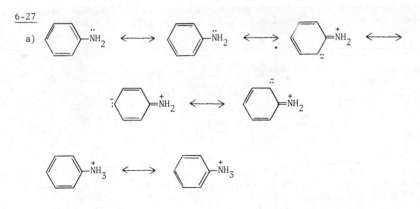

b)  In this case, it is the base (aniline) which is stabilized by resonance.  Conjugation between the N and aromatic ring would require five bonds to nitrogen.

6-27 Contd...

  b) Contd...

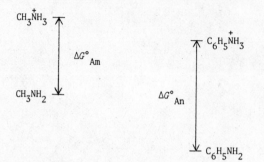

$\Delta G°_{An} > \Delta G°_{Am}$

(Absolute energy levels are arbitrary)

6-28  Resonance between the meta nitro group and the electrons on oxygen is not possible.  Only an inductive influence can operate and thus the acid strengthening effect of nitro is relatively small in this case.

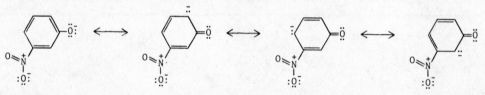

6-29  The carbonyl group in this hydroxy ketone is three atoms away from the acidic hydroxy. Inductive  interactions are expected to be very small.  However conjugation between the carbonyl and oxygen anion can stabilize the conjugate acid in a manner similar to that of a carboxylic acid.  The p$K_a$ value is thus similar to that of a carboxylic acid.

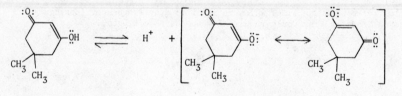

6-30  The smaller difference in dipole moments between the aromatic system ($\Delta\mu = 2.0$) compared to the aliphatic system ($\Delta\mu = 4.8$) can be attributed to contributions from delocalized structures which oppose the $\overset{+}{N}\!-\!\overset{-}{O}$ dipole.

6-30 Contd...

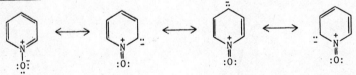

6-31

$\Delta K = 10^{11}$

$\Delta\Delta G° = -2.3 \ RT \log K = -2.3 \times 1.99 \times 10^{-3}$ kcal/mol-$K$ x 298 x 11 = 15.0 kcal/mol

$(= -2.3 \times 8.31 \times 10^{-3}$ kJ/mol-$K$ x 298 x 11 = 62.7 kJ/mol)

6-32

a)  $CH_2=CH-CH=CH_2 \longleftrightarrow \overset{+}{C}H_2-CH=CH-\overset{..}{C}H_2 \longleftrightarrow \overset{..}{C}H_2-CH=CH-\overset{+}{C}H_2$

To the extent that charge separated structures contribute to the resonance hybrid that is 1,3-butadiene, the 2-3 bond has some double bond character thus is shortened whereas the 1-2 and 3-4 bonds have single bond character and are lengthened.

b)  The single bond connects carbon atoms that possess $sp^2$ hybrid orbitals. Since those orbitals have more $s$ character than do $sp^3$ orbitals, electrons are held closer to the nucleus and bond lengths are expected to be shorter.

6-33

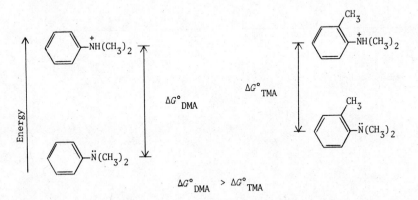

(Conjugate acids arbitrarily set as equal in energy.)

6-34  Resonance stabilization of the phenoxide requires coplanarity of orbitals of the nitro group, the benzene ring, and the phenoxide oxygen atom. A methyl group ortho to the nitro group sterically inhibits planarity. The nitro group must twist about the C-N bond and thereby the resonance stabilization of the phenoxide is reduced.

6-35

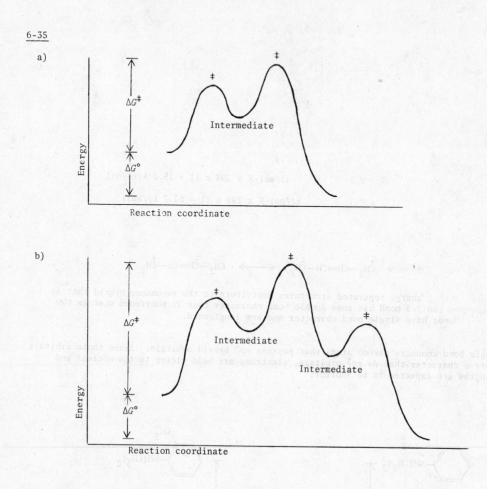

a)

b)

6-36  This elimination is believed to be a one step process (sec. 6-5B).

$$\begin{array}{ccc} & \delta- & & \delta- \\ HO---- & H----CH & ----CH_2----Cl \\ & & | & \\ & & Cl & \end{array}$$

6-37

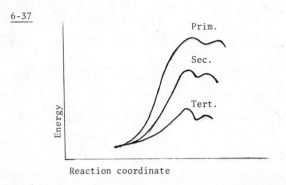

6-38

a) Alkyl groups are electron donating, thus destabilize a carbanion. Three alkyl groups of a tertiary carbanion will have a greater destabilizing effect than those of a secondary carbanion, etc...

b) The benzene ring can delocalize the electrons of the carbanion and stabilize the species.

6-39 To remove >50% of one proton the conjugate acid of the base must have a $pK_a$ value equal to or greater (be less acidic) than the substrate. The conjugate acids of the bases are:

$CH_3CO_2H$        $pK_a = 4.8$        $C_2H_5OH$        $pK_a = 16$        $(C_6H_5)_3CH$        $pK_a = 32$

$(C_2H_5)_3\overset{+}{N}H$        $pK_a = 10$        $(CH_3)_3COH$        $pK_a = 18$

a) $C_6H_5\underline{N}H_2$ ;        $pK_a = 27$        $\therefore (C_6H_5)_3C^-Na^+$

b) $CH_3CH=CHC\underline{H}_3$ ;        $pK_a = 35$        $\therefore$ None

c) $C_2H_5COC\underline{H}_3$ ;        $pK_a = 20$        $\therefore (C_6H_5)_3C^-Na^+$

d) $(NC)_2C\underline{H}_2$ ;        $pK_a = 11.2$        $\therefore (C_6H_5)_3C^-Na^+$, $(CH_3)_3CO^-Na^+$, $C_2H_5O^-Na^+$

e) $CH_3-$⟨benzene ring⟩$-O\underline{H}$ ; $pK_a \approx > 10$        $\therefore$ same as (d)

6-39 Contd...

f)   $O_2N$—⟨benzene ring⟩—$NH_2$ ;  $pK_a = 18$    $\therefore (C_6H_5)_3C^-Na^+$;  $(CH_3)_3CO^-Na^+$

6-40  A statistical factor is involved.  The two "independent" carboxylic acid groups lead to two
times the probability for donation of a proton.

6-41

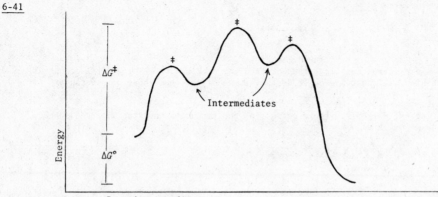

6-42

a)  BH because $\Delta G_B$ has the smallest value

b)  CH

c)  AH

6-43  In each case the charge of the conjugate base can be stabilized through conjugation with the
carbonyl group.  However the relative electronegativities O > N > C leads to better
stabilization of charge on the carboxylic acid, etc...

6-44  Propylene is thermodynamically more stable.  Both isomers give the same amounts of $CO_2$ and
$H_2O$ but combustion of propylene is less exergonic, thus propylene is energetically closer
to the stable products.

6-45

a)  R⁻ + H⁺

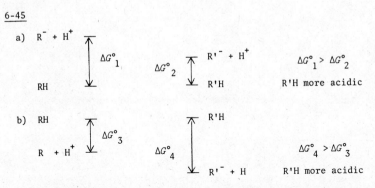

$\Delta G^{\circ}_1$          $\Delta G^{\circ}_2$          R'⁻ + H⁺          $\Delta G^{\circ}_1 > \Delta G^{\circ}_2$

RH          R'H          R'H more acidic

b)  RH          R'H

$\Delta G^{\circ}_3$          $\Delta G^{\circ}_4$

R + H⁺          $\Delta G^{\circ}_4 > \Delta G^{\circ}_3$

R'⁻ + H          R'H more acidic

Note that in both cases above the conjugate base of R'H has become relatively more favorable thermodynamically than the conjugate base of RH.

6-46

a)  $p$-Cyanophenol; because of resonance stabilization of the conjugate base.

b)  $CH_3CH{=}CHOH$; because of resonance stabilization of the conjugate base.

c)  $NCCH_2CN$; because two groups stabilize the conjugate base.

d)  ; because the $t$-butyl group remains equatorial, the $-CO_2^-$ and $-CO_2H$ groups are trans-diaxial in this chair conformation.  In the other isomer intramolecular H-bonding between the diequatorial groups decreases acidity.

e)  $CH_3CF_2OH$; because the inductive electron-withdrawing effect by F falls off with distance.

f)  ; because the charge of the conjugate base is delocalized over larger system.

g)  ; because of charge delocalization of the conjugate base by the carbonyl group.

6-47  Sulfuric acid is a relatively stronger acid than acetic.  Acid-base relationships are *relative*.

6-48

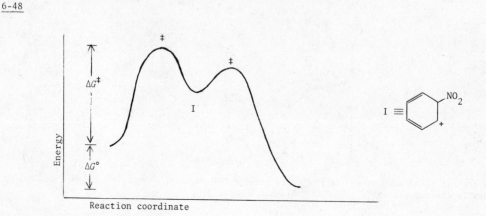

6-49  The conjugate acid of guanidine has three energetically equivalent resonance structures and the equilibrium lies far to the right.

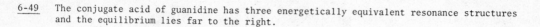

6-50

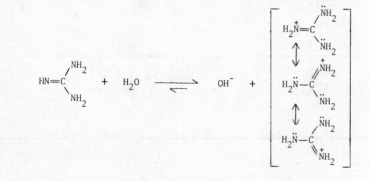

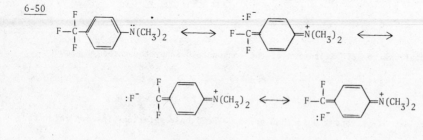

6-51  The nitrogen atom of simple amides such as A is not basic because the electrons are delocalized by the carbonyl group.  In B, such conjugation would require that a double bond form at the bicyclic bridgehead.  This would be very unfavorable energetically (Bredt's rule).

<u>6-51</u> Contd...  The position of the carbonyl IR absorption indicates greater strain in the bicyclic
molecule.

<u>6-52</u>  $RT = 1.99 \times 10^{-3} \times 298 = 0.6$ kcal/mol (2.5 kJ/mol)

<u>6-53</u>  In each comparison, resonance structures can account for the differences in dipole moments.

a)  $CH_2{=}CH{-}\ddot{C}l\!:$  $\longleftrightarrow$  $\bar{\ddot{C}}H{-}CH{=}\overset{+}{\ddot{C}}l\!:$

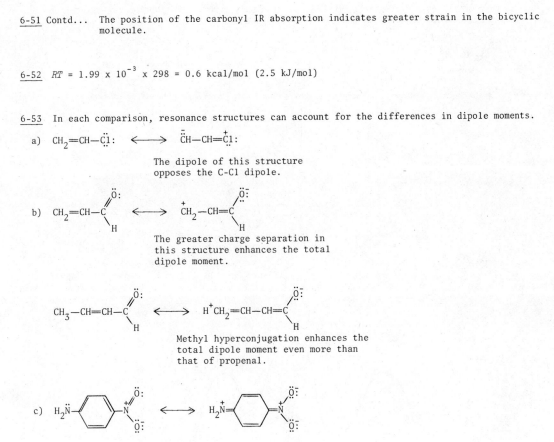

               The dipole of this structure
               opposes the C-Cl dipole.

b)  $CH_2{=}CH{-}C$  $\longleftrightarrow$  $\overset{+}{C}H_2{-}CH{=}C$

               The greater charge separation in
               this structure enhances the total
               dipole moment.

$CH_3{-}CH{=}CH{-}C$  $\longleftrightarrow$  $H^+CH_2{=}CH{-}CH{=}C$

               Methyl hyperconjugation enhances the
               total dipole moment even more than
               that of propenal.

c)  $H_2\ddot{N}$  $\longleftrightarrow$  $H_2\overset{+}{N}{=}$

Interaction between two groups on the aromatic ring increases the total charge separation
more than occurs in each monosubstituted molecule.

<u>6-54</u>  The $p$-orbitals of the two double bonds are perpendicular to each other, thus do not interact
as is required for conjugation.

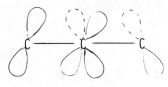

6-55  The base abstracts a proton to form a cyclopentadienyl anion. Protonation can take place at any carbon atom of the resonance stabilized system.

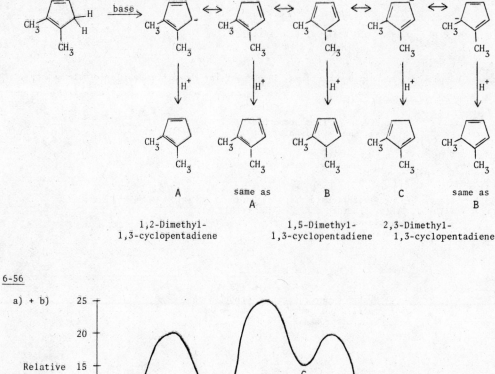

| A | same as A | B | C | same as B |

1,2-Dimethyl-
1,3-cyclopentadiene

1,5-Dimethyl-
1,3-cyclopentadiene

2,3-Dimethyl-
1,3-cyclopentadiene

6-56

a) + b)

Relative Energy (kcal/mol)

Reaction coordinate

c) B ⟶ C

d) $\Delta G° = 5$ kcal/mol (21 kJ/mol)

$\Delta G^{\ddagger} = 25$ kcal/mol (104 kJ/mol)

6-57  Acidity properties suggest that A is a carboxylic acid and B is a phenol. The nmr spectra
suggest that both are *p*-disubstituted aromatic compounds with deshielded, but unsplit methyl
groups.  The compounds are

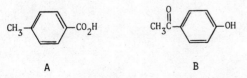

A                         B

Note that the methyl groups are deshielded similarly by the carbonyl group or the aromatic
ring.

# 7 NUCLEOPHILIC ADDITIONS TO THE CARBONYL GROUP— ALDEHYDES AND KETONES

7-1

a)

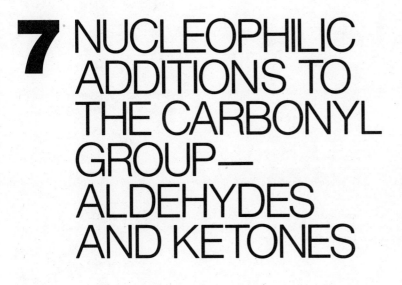

A          B          C

b)  Using vector addition of the carbonyl group dipoles gives:

A  $\mu \approx 3.0$ D        B  $\mu \approx 5$ D        C  $\mu \approx 0$ D

7-2  No, for the carbonyl carbon atom would then possess ten electrons.

7-3  The aromatic aldehyde is stabilized more than the aliphatic aldehyde because of resonance with the benzene ring.

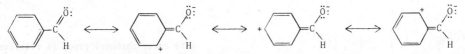

At the transition state leading to product, the unsaturated carbonyl group is gone.  The extra resonance stabilization is lost.  The result is that the activation energy for reaction of the aromatic compound is relatively greater because the aliphatic compound never had a significant resonance energy to lose.

7-4  The major difference between the two resonance hybrids is that the charge separated resonance structure of the ketone involves a secondary carbocation ion and that of the aldehyde a primary carbocation ion.  Secondary carbocations are the more stable.

7-4 Contd...

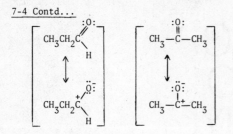

7-5

a) The addition of cyanide to the carbonyl group is rate controlling.

b) The addition of H$^+$ does not enter into the rate controlling step.  The proton is provided by the weak acid HCN after cyanide has added to the carbonyl group.  HCN is too weak of an acid to appreciably protonate the carbonyl oxygen atom.

7-6

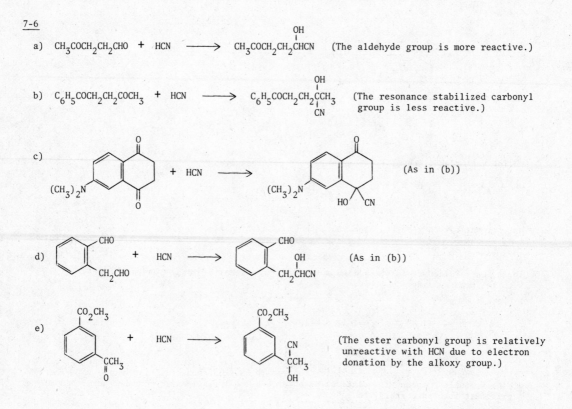

a) $CH_3COCH_2CH_2CHO$ + HCN $\longrightarrow$ $CH_3COCH_2CH_2\overset{OH}{\underset{}{C}}HCN$   (The aldehyde group is more reactive.)

b) $C_6H_5COCH_2CH_2COCH_3$ + HCN $\longrightarrow$ $C_6H_5COCH_2CH_2\overset{OH}{\underset{CN}{C}}CH_3$   (The resonance stabilized carbonyl group is less reactive.)

c) + HCN $\longrightarrow$   (As in (b))

d) + HCN $\longrightarrow$   (As in (b))

e) + HCN $\longrightarrow$   (The ester carbonyl group is relatively unreactive with HCN due to electron donation by the alkoxy group.)

7-6 Contd...

f) 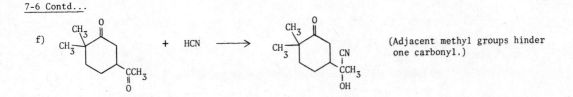          (Adjacent methyl groups hinder
                                  one carbonyl.)

7-7  Conjugation between the benzene ring and the carbonyl group stabilizes acetophenone relative
     to acetone.

That interaction is not important in either of the cyanohydrin products.  Acetophenone is
stabilized sufficiently relative to its cyanohydrin that the addition reaction is slightly
endergonic (K < 1).  Resonance is not significant in acetone or its cyanohydrin so that this
reaction is exergonic.

7-8  There is little difference between the stabilities of cyclopentanone and cyclohexanone.
     However the cyanohydrins differ in their nonbonded interactions.  More eclipsing strain is
     present in the cyclopentanone cyanohydrin than in the completely staggered cyclohexanone
     cyanohydrin.  Conversion of cyclohexanone to its cyanohydrin is therefore more exergonic.

          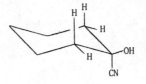

7-9  For the reaction

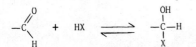

the difference between X = Cl and X = CN will reflect formation of the new C-X bond and the
breaking of the original H-CN vs H-Cl bonds.

| | Bonds broken | | Bonds formed | | $\Delta H°$ |
|---|---|---|---|---|---|
| For HCN | H—CN | 130 kcal/mol<br>(544 kJ/mol) | C—CN | -122 kcal/mol<br>(-511 kJ/mol) | 8 kcal/mol<br>(33 kJ/mol) |
| For HCl | H—Cl | 103 kcal/mol<br>(431 kJ/mol) | C—Cl | -84 kcal/mol<br>(-352 kJ/mol) | 19 kcal/mol<br>(79 kJ/mol) |

The addition of HCl is more endothermic.

7-10  In acid:

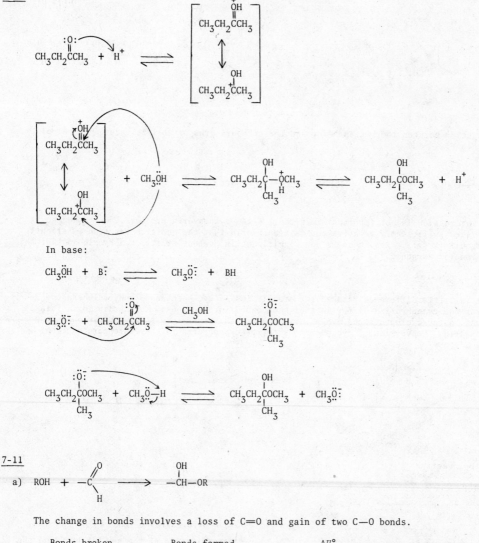

In base:

$CH_3\ddot{O}H + B\bar{:} \rightleftarrows CH_3\ddot{O}\bar{:} + BH$

7-11

a)  $ROH + -\overset{O}{\underset{H}{\overset{\|}{C}}} \longrightarrow -\overset{OH}{\underset{}{CH}}-OR$

The change in bonds involves a loss of C=O and gain of two C—O bonds.

| Bonds broken | Bonds formed | $\Delta H°$ |
|---|---|---|
| C=O  176 kcal/mol | 2 x C—O  -172 kcal/mol | 4 kcal/mol |
| (736 kJ/mol) | (-718 kJ/mol) | (18 kJ/mol) |

b)  Since $\Delta G° = \Delta H° - T\Delta S°$, a more favorable entropy (more positive $\Delta S°$) makes the value of $\Delta G°$ more negative and energetically favorable.  A less favorable (more negative) entropy leads to a relatively more positive value of $\Delta G°$.

7-12

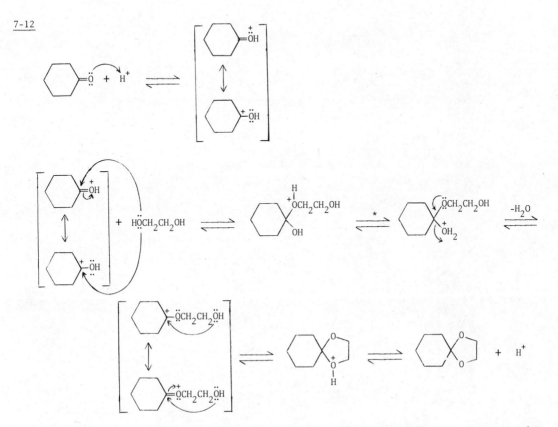

*We will often use an abbreviated notation that shows a proton moving from one atom to another in a single molecule.  In solution the departing proton normally goes to solvent, then some other proton is donated back to the substrate by the solvent molecules.

7-13   The ester group functions as an electron-withdrawing substituent on the ketone carbonyl. The positive character of the carbonyl carbon atom is enhanced so the initial attack by the nucleophilic oxygen atom is favored.

7-14

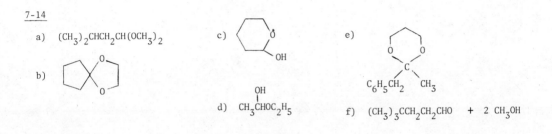

a)   $(CH_3)_2CHCH_2CH(OCH_3)_2$

b)

c)

d)   $CH_3\overset{OH}{\underset{|}{C}}HOC_2H_5$

e)

f)   $(CH_3)_3CCH_2CH_2CHO$   +   $2 CH_3OH$

7-15

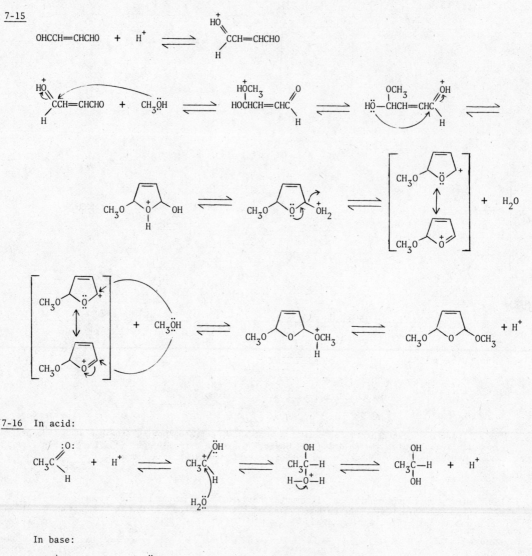

7-16 In acid:

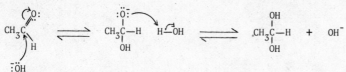

In base:

7-17  The *t*-butyl group is large and results in significant crowding when the addition of $H_2O$ converts the trigonal carbonyl group to a tetrahedral configuration. The value of the equilibrium constant for that substrate is less than 1, while the less crowded acetaldehyde has an equilibrium constant slightly greater than 1.

7-18
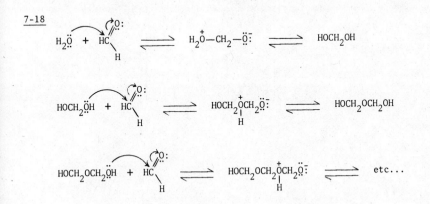

7-19

a)  Cyclopropanone is a relatively strained compound. Addition to the carbonyl group converts the $sp^2$ hybridized carbon atom to $sp^3$ with an associated decrease in angle strain.

b) + c)  The electron withdrawing groups ($CF_3$ or C=O) on either side of the central carbonyl destabilize the compound relative to the hydrate because of dipole repulsions. Conversion to the hydrate reduces those interactions. Another explanation is that the reverse reaction, loss of $H_2O$ with the C—O bonding electrons is inhibited by the adjacent electron withdrawing groups.

7-20
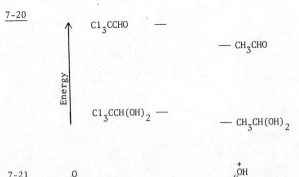

7-21
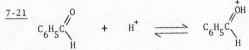

7-21 Contd...

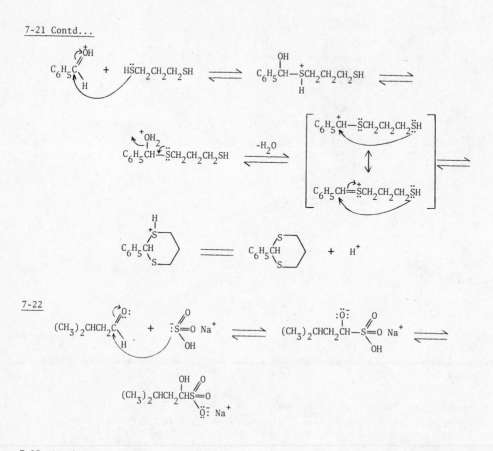

7-22

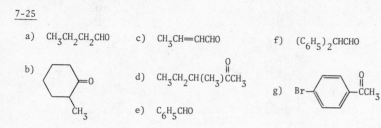

7-23 Alcohols are almost as acidic as water. The hydroxy proton, like that from water, readily reacts with LiAlH$_4$.

7-24 Base minimizes the availability of protons which would slowly react with the hydride from NaBH$_4$.

7-25

a) $CH_3CH_2CH_2CHO$

b) 

c) $CH_3CH=CHCHO$

d) $CH_3CH_2CH(CH_3)CCH_3$

e) $C_6H_5CHO$

f) $(C_6H_5)_2CHCHO$

g) Br—⟨⟩—CCH$_3$

7-25 Contd...

h)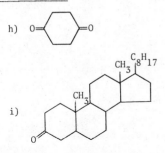

i)

7-26

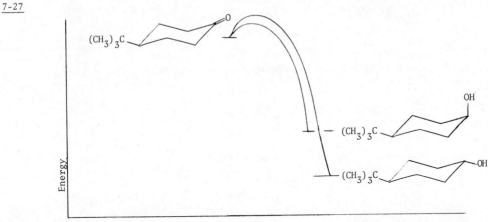

7-27

Energy

Reaction coordinate

7-28

a) The alcohol products each possess a plane of symmetry passing through the -OH, the -C(CH$_3$)$_3$, and the 1 and 4 ring carbon atoms.

b) The hydride adds to both sides of the ketone molecule to produce a racemic product mixture. Symmetrical reactants always lead to racemic mixtures unless the reagent or medium is asymmetric.

7-29

a)

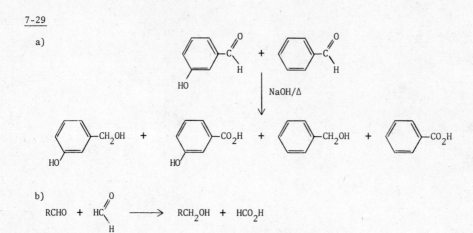

b)

RCHO + HC(=O)(H) $\longrightarrow$ RCH$_2$OH + HCO$_2$H

Formaldehyde is inexpensive and the formic acid produced is usually easily removed from the reaction mixture as the water-soluble salt, sodium formate.

7-30 The hydride transfer is rate controlling and requires a significant energy of activation ($\Delta G^{\ddagger}$).

7-31

a) Reaction of base with the initially formed anion can produce the dianion.

$$\overset{:\ddot{O}:^-}{\underset{OH}{-\overset{|}{\underset{|}{C}}-H}} \;+\; :\ddot{O}H^- \;\rightleftharpoons\; \overset{:\ddot{O}:^-}{\underset{:\ddot{O}:}{-\overset{|}{\underset{|}{C}}-H}} \;+\; H_2O$$

b) Loss of the hydride anion reduces the high negative charge present in the dianion molecule.

7-32

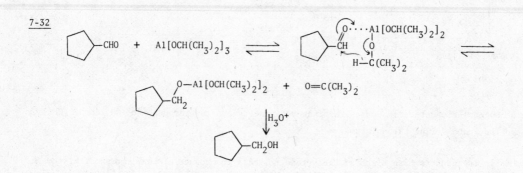

7-33

a)  The first step in the Oppenauer oxidation is an alcohol exchange in which the cyclohexanol replaces one molecule of isopropyl alcohol.

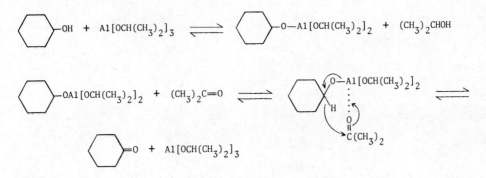

b)  Formation of the product is favored by:

i) Use of a large excess of acetone, often as the solvent;

ii) Use of a ketone solvent with a higher bp than the product so that product can be distilled from the reaction mixture as it is formed.

7-34

a)  $(CH_3)_2CHCH_2Br$ + Mg $\longrightarrow$ $(CH_3)_2CHCH_2MgBr$    d) $C_6H_5I$ + Mg $\longrightarrow$ $C_6H_5MgI$

b)  $C_6H_5CH_2X$ + Li $\longrightarrow$ $C_6H_5CH_2Li$    e) $CH_3CH_2X$ + Li $\longrightarrow$ $CH_3CH_2Li$

c)  2 $CH_3MgX$ + $CdX_2$ $\longrightarrow$ $(CH_3)_2Cd$

X = halide, usually Cl or Br

7-35

a)  $(CH_3)_2CHCH_2CH_2OH$

   3-Methyl-1-butanol
   (Isoamyl alcohol)

b)  $C_6H_5CHCH_2CH_3$
          |
          OH

   1-Phenyl-1-propanol

c)  $(CH_3)_2\overset{\overset{\displaystyle OH}{|}}{C}C{\equiv}CCH_3$

   2-Methyl-3-pentyn-2-ol

d)  
   1-Methylcyclohexanol

7-36

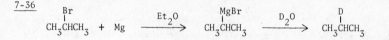

$$\underset{\substack{| \\ CH_3CHCH_3}}{\overset{Br}{}} + Mg \xrightarrow{Et_2O} \underset{\substack{| \\ CH_3CHCH_3}}{\overset{MgBr}{}} \xrightarrow{D_2O} \underset{\substack{| \\ CH_3CHCH_3}}{\overset{D}{}}$$

7-37 Both involve a 6-atom cyclic complex. The hydride comes from the atom beta to the metal.

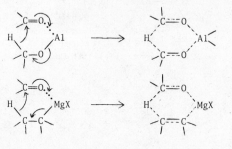

7-38 The first step in devising a synthetic sequence is the recognition of possible components (*synthons*) from which the product molecule (*the target*) can be constructed. In the Grignard reactions below, the carbinol carbon atom (the carbon atom bonded to hydroxy) must have originally been part of a carbonyl group so that some carbonyl compound is readily identified as one potential reactant. The second reactant, the Grignard reagent, must form a bond to this carbonyl carbon atom by addition of the nucleophilic carbon atom. Thus the original organohalogen compound is defined. As syntheses become more complex and multiple steps are involved, it is often useful to devise a sequence by working backwards, from product to reactants.

In each of the following examples, the Grignard reagent is prepared from the appropriate organohalogen compound and magnesium metal in diethyl ether or tetrahydrofuran (THF). THF is a higher boiling ether solvent commonly used when reaction is not favorable in diethyl ether.

a) $C_6H_5MgBr + (CH_3)_2C=O$

       or     $\overset{O}{\overset{\|}{}}$

    $CH_3MgI + C_6H_5CCH_3$
$\xrightarrow[\text{2)}H_2O/NH_4Cl]{\text{1)}Et_2O}$ $C_6H_5\overset{\substack{OH \\ |}}{C}(CH_3)_2$

b) $(CH_3)_2CHCH_2MgBr + HCHO$ $\xrightarrow[\text{2)}H_3O^+]{\text{1)}Et_2O}$ $(CH_3)_2CHCH_2CH_2OH$

c) $CH_3CH_2MgI + (CH_3)_2C=O$

       or     $\overset{O}{\overset{\|}{}}$

    $CH_3MgI + CH_3CCH_2CH_3$
$\xrightarrow[\text{2)}H_2O/NH_4Cl]{\text{1)}Et_2O}$ $(CH_3)_2\overset{\substack{OH \\ |}}{C}CH_2CH_3$

d) $C_6H_5CH_2MgCl + HCHO$ $\xrightarrow[\text{2)}H_3O^+]{\text{1)}Et_2O}$ $C_6H_5CH_2CH_2OH$

7-38 Contd...

e)  $C_6H_5MgBr$  +  $C_6H_5\overset{\overset{O}{\|}}{C}C_6H_5$  $\xrightarrow[2)H_3O^+]{1)Et_2O}$  $(C_6H_5)_3COH$

f)  $CH_3MgI$  +  $CH_3CH_2\overset{\overset{O}{\|}}{C}CH_2CH_2CH_3$

<u>or</u>

$CH_3CH_2MgI$  +  $CH_3\overset{\overset{O}{\|}}{C}CH_2CH_2CH_3$  $\xrightarrow[2)H_2O/NH_4Cl]{1)Et_2O}$  $CH_3CH_2\overset{\overset{CH_3}{|}}{\underset{\underset{OH}{|}}{C}}CH_2CH_2CH_3$

<u>or</u>

$CH_3CH_2CH_2MgI$  +  $CH_3\overset{\overset{O}{\|}}{C}CH_2CH_3$

7-39

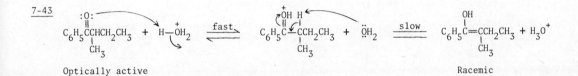

Intramolecular H-bonding in a six-membered cyclic structure.

7-40  Such an intramolecular proton shift is not consistent with the catalytic role of added acid or base.

7-41  The structure with the charge on oxygen is expected to make the greater contribution to the resonance hybrid since oxygen is more electronegative and can accommodate the negative charge better than carbon can.

$CH_3\overset{\overset{:\ddot{O}:}{\|}}{C}-\ddot{\underset{..}{C}}H_2$  $\longleftrightarrow$  $CH_3\overset{\overset{:\ddot{O}:^-}{|}}{C}=CH_2$

7-42  Those data confirm that formation of the carbon-halogen bond is not rate controlling.  No information is provided about the actual rate of the halogenation step in each of the reactions.

7-43

$C_6H_5\overset{\overset{:O:}{\|}}{\underset{\underset{CH_3}{|}}{C}}CHCH_2CH_3$  +  $H-\overset{+}{O}H_2$  $\xrightarrow{fast}$  $C_6H_5\overset{\overset{+}{O}H}{\underset{\underset{CH_3}{|}}{C}}CCH_2CH_3$  +  $\ddot{O}H_2$  $\xrightarrow{slow}$  $C_6H_5\overset{\overset{OH}{|}}{C}=CCH_2CH_3$  +  $H_3O^+$

Optically active                                                                                    Racemic

7-43 Contd...

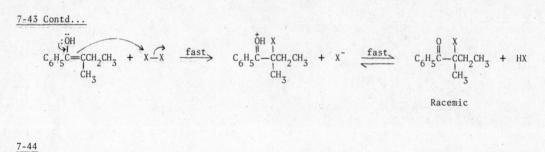

Racemic

7-44

$$CH_3CH_2CHO \ + \ CH_3CH_2CH_2CHO \ \xrightarrow{\text{base}}$$

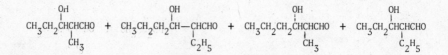

7-45

a)  The branched aldehyde is much more sterically hindered toward carbanion addition than is formaldehyde.

b)

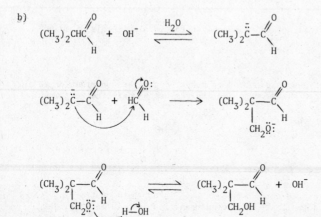

7-46  To obtain an α,β-unsaturated carbonyl product the compound acting as the nucleophile in the aldol reaction must have two hydrogen atoms alpha to the carbonyl group. One is lost during formation of the enolate anion and the second is lost in the dehydration step. In this example, the product of self condensation, 2-methylpropanal, does not have that second proton.

7-46 Contd...

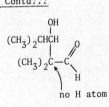

no H atom

7-47 Two enolate anions can form from the unsymmetrical ketone,

$:\overset{-}{C}H_2\overset{O}{\overset{\|}{C}}CH_2CH_3$    and    $CH_3\overset{O}{\overset{\|}{C}}\overset{\cdot\cdot}{C}HCH_3$.

The aldol products are--

and

7-48

a)   $C_6H_5CHO$  +  $CH_3CHO$  $\xrightarrow{\text{NaOH/H}_2\text{O}}$  $C_6H_5CH=CHCHO$

b)   2 $C_6H_5\overset{O}{\overset{\|}{C}}CH_3$  $\xrightarrow{\text{NaOMe/MeOH}}$  $C_6H_5\overset{O}{\overset{\|}{C}}CH=\underset{CH_3}{C}C_6H_5$

c)   $(CH_3)_3CCHO$  +  $CH_3CHO$  $\xrightarrow{\text{NaOH/H}_2\text{O}}$  $(CH_3)_3\overset{OH}{\underset{}{C}}CHCH_2CHO$

d)   $CH_3CH_2CHO$  +  $CH_3\overset{O}{\overset{\|}{C}}CH_3$  $\xrightarrow{\text{NaOH/H}_2\text{O}}$  $CH_3CH_2\overset{OH}{\underset{}{C}}HCH_2\overset{O}{\overset{\|}{C}}CH_3$

e)   $OHC(CH_2)_5CHO$  $\xrightarrow{\text{NaOMe/MeOH}}$

f)   $C_6H_5\underset{CH_3}{\overset{}{C}}HCH_2CHO$  +  $CH_3CH_2CHO$  $\xrightarrow{\text{NaOMe/MeOH}}$  $C_6H_5\underset{CH_3}{\overset{}{C}}HCH_2\underset{CH_3}{\overset{OH}{C}}HCHCHO$

7-48 Contd...

g)   $2 \, C_6H_5CHO \; + \; CH_3COCH_3 \; \xrightarrow{\text{NaOH/H}_2O} \; C_6H_5CH{=}CHCOCH{=}CHC_6H_5$

h)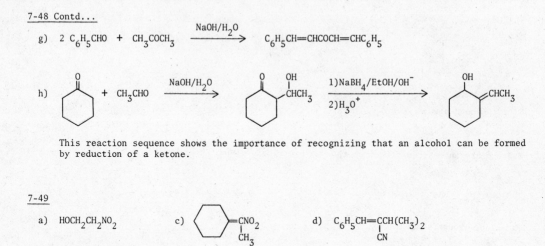

This reaction sequence shows the importance of recognizing that an alcohol can be formed by reduction of a ketone.

7-49

a)   $HOCH_2CH_2NO_2$

b)   $(HOCH_2)_3CNO_2$

c)   (cyclohexane)$=CNO_2$ with $CH_3$

d)   $C_6H_5CH{=}CCH(CH_3)_2$ with $CN$

7-50   Nitrogen, a second row element, cannot normally accommodate more than eight electrons in its outer shell.

7-51

a)   $(C_6H_5)_3\overset{+}{P}{-}\overset{-}{C}HC_6H_5 \; + \; HCHO \; \longrightarrow \; C_6H_5CH{=}CH_2 \; + \; (C_6H_5)_3P{=}O$

b)   $(C_6H_5)_3\overset{+}{P}{-}\overset{-}{C}HC_6H_5 \; + \;$ (cyclopentane)$=O \; \longrightarrow \; C_6H_5CH{=}$(cyclopentane) $\; + \; (C_6H_5)_3P{=}O$

c)   $(C_6H_5)_3\overset{+}{P}{-}\overset{-}{C}HC_6H_5 \; + \; C_6H_5CHO \; \longrightarrow \; C_6H_5CH{=}CHC_6H_5 \; + \; (C_6H_5)_3P{=}O$

$Z$ and $E$

7-52

a)   The imine double bond is part of a highly conjugated system.

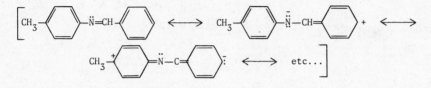

7-52 Contd...

b)  $p\text{-}CH_3C_6H_4\overset{\cdot\cdot}{N}H_2$  +  $C_6H_5C\underset{H}{\overset{\cdot\cdot}{\underset{\parallel}{C}}}\overset{\cdot\cdot}{O}\!:$  $\rightleftharpoons$  $p\text{-}CH_3C_6H_4\overset{+}{N}H_2\overset{\cdot\cdot}{\underset{\cdot\cdot}{C}}HC_6H_5$  $\rightleftharpoons$  $p\text{-}CH_3C_6H_4\overset{OH}{\underset{\cdot\cdot}{N}HCHC_6H_5}$

$p\text{-}CH_3C_6H_4\overset{\cdot\cdot}{N}H\overset{OH}{\underset{\parallel}{\overset{\cdot\cdot}{C}}}HC_6H_5$  $\xrightarrow{H^+}$  $\xrightarrow{H_3O^+}$  $p\text{-}CH_3C_6H_4\overset{+}{N}H\!=\!CHC_6H_5$  +  $H_2O$  $\rightleftharpoons$

$p\text{-}CH_3C_6H_4\overset{\cdot\cdot}{N}\!=\!CHC_6H_5$  +  $H_3O^+$

7-53

a)  Enamine formation is reversible.  Removal of water helps to drive the reaction toward completion.

b)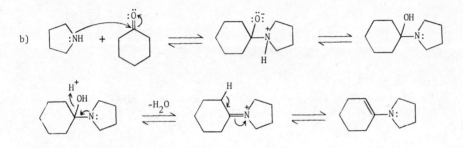

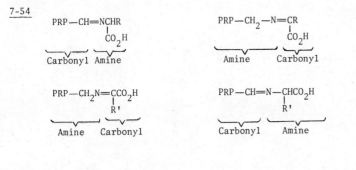

7-54

PRP—CH=NCHR
          |
          CO$_2$H
$\underbrace{\hspace{1.5cm}}_{\text{Carbonyl}}$ $\underbrace{\hspace{1.5cm}}_{\text{Amine}}$

PRP—CH$_2$—N=CR
              |
              CO$_2$H
$\underbrace{\hspace{1.5cm}}_{\text{Amine}}$ $\underbrace{\hspace{1.5cm}}_{\text{Carbonyl}}$

PRP—CH$_2$N=CCO$_2$H
              |
              R'
$\underbrace{\hspace{1.5cm}}_{\text{Amine}}$ $\underbrace{\hspace{1.5cm}}_{\text{Carbonyl}}$

PRP—CH=N—CHCO$_2$H
              |
              R'
$\underbrace{\hspace{1.5cm}}_{\text{Carbonyl}}$ $\underbrace{\hspace{1.5cm}}_{\text{Amine}}$

7-55

a)  i)  $p\text{-}CH_3OC_6H_4CHO$  +  $NH_2OH$  $\longrightarrow$  $p\text{-}CH_3OC_6H_4CH\!=\!NOH$

7-55 Contd...

ii) $p\text{-}CH_3OC_6H_4CHO$ + $O_2N$⬡$NHNH_2$ ($NO_2$) $\longrightarrow$ $p\text{-}CH_3OC_6H_4CH{=}NNH$⬡($NO_2$)($NO_2$)

iii) $p\text{-}CH_3OC_6H_4CHO$ + $H_2NNHCONH_2$ $\longrightarrow$ $p\text{-}CH_3OC_6H_4CH{=}NNHCONH_2$

(The amide nitrogen atom is *not* the nucleophile because of delocalization of its electron pair by the carbonyl group.)

iv) $p\text{-}CH_3C_6H_4CHO$ + $C_6H_5NHNH_2$ $\longrightarrow$ $p\text{-}CH_3OC_6H_4CH{=}NNHC_6H_5$

b) $p\text{-}CH_3OC_6H_4C\overset{\ddot{O}:}{\underset{H}{}}$ + $\ddot{N}H_2OH$ $\rightleftharpoons$ $p\text{-}CH_3OC_6H_4CH{-}\overset{+}{N}H_2OH$ $\rightleftharpoons$

$p\text{-}CH_3OC_6H_4C\overset{OH\ H}{\underset{}{}}{-}NOH$ $\rightleftharpoons$ $p\text{-}CH_3OC_6H_4CH{=}NOH$ + $H_3O^+$

7-56  The nitrile-Grignard adduct forms a ketone only after the addition of water. Any unreacted Grignard reagent is also destroyed in the hydrolysis step.

7-57

i) Formation of an iminium ion:

⬡$=O$ + $(CH_3)_2NH$ $\rightleftharpoons$ ⬡$={\overset{+}{N}}(CH_3)_2$ + $H_2O$

ii) Reduction:

⬡$={\overset{+}{N}}(CH_3)_2$ + $NaBH_3CN$ $\longrightarrow$ ⬡$-N(CH_3)_2$

7-58

$HO_2CCH_2CH_2\overset{O}{\overset{\|}{C}}CO_2H$ + $H^+$ $\rightleftharpoons$ $HO_2CCH_2CH_2\overset{\overset{+}{O}H}{\overset{\|}{C}}CO_2H$

7-58 Contd...

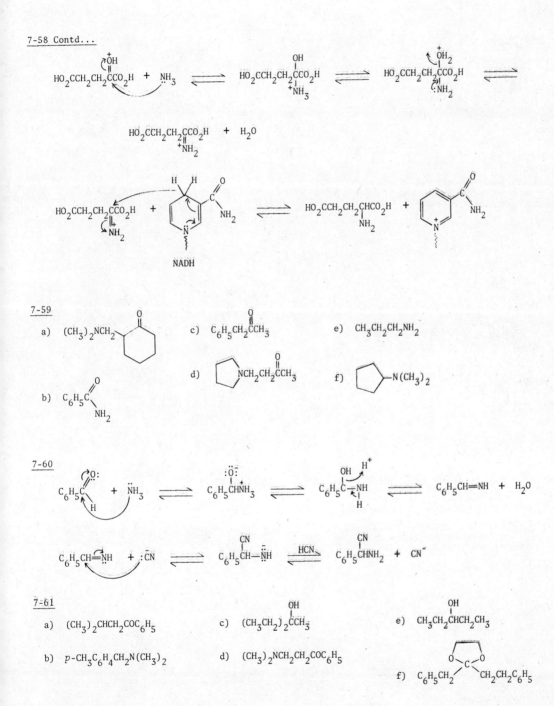

7-59

a) $(CH_3)_2NCH_2$ [cyclohexanone with substituent]

b) $C_6H_5C$ (=O) $NH_2$

c) $C_6H_5CH_2CCH_3$ (=O)

d) [pyrrolidine]$NCH_2CH_2CCH_3$ (=O)

e) $CH_3CH_2CH_2NH_2$

f) [cyclopentane]$N(CH_3)_2$

7-60

[reaction scheme]

7-61

a) $(CH_3)_2CHCH_2COC_6H_5$

b) $p$-$CH_3C_6H_4CH_2N(CH_3)_2$

c) $(CH_3CH_2)_2CCH_3$ with OH

d) $(CH_3)_2NCH_2CH_2COC_6H_5$

e) $CH_3CH_2CHCH_2CH_3$ with OH

f) $C_6H_5CH_2$ [dioxolane ring with C] $CH_2CH_2C_6H_5$

7-61 Contd...

g)  $C_6H_5CH{=}NOH$

n)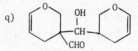

h)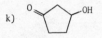
    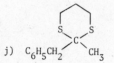

o)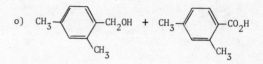

i)  $C_6H_5CH_2OH$ + $CH_3CH_3$
    (Grignard reagents readily
    react with the acidic hydro-
    gen atom of alcohols.)

p)  $C_6H_5\overset{OH}{\underset{|}{C}}HC_6H_5$

j)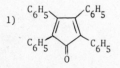

q)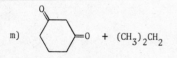

k)   (cyclopentanone with OH) 

r)  $C_6H_5CO_2H$ + $CH_4$

l)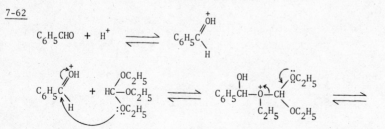

s)  cyclopentane ${=}CHCO_2CH_3$ + $(C_6H_5)_3P{=}O$

m)  (cyclohexane-1,3-dione) $O$ + $(CH_3)_2CH_2$

The 1,3-diketone has a $pK_a$ value near
9. The Grignard reagent functions as
a base to abstract an acidic proton
rather than as a nucleophile.

7-62

$C_6H_5CHO$ + $H^+$ $\rightleftharpoons$ $C_6H_5\overset{\overset{+}{O}H}{\underset{H}{C}}$

$C_6H_5\overset{\overset{+}{O}H}{\underset{H}{C}}$ + $HC\overset{OC_2H_5}{\underset{:OC_2H_5}{-OC_2H_5}}$ $\rightleftharpoons$ $C_6H_5CH{-}\overset{+}{O}{-}CH\overset{\ddot{O}C_2H_5}{\underset{OC_2H_5}{}}$ $\rightleftharpoons$

$\underset{C_2H_5}{}$

7-62 Contd...

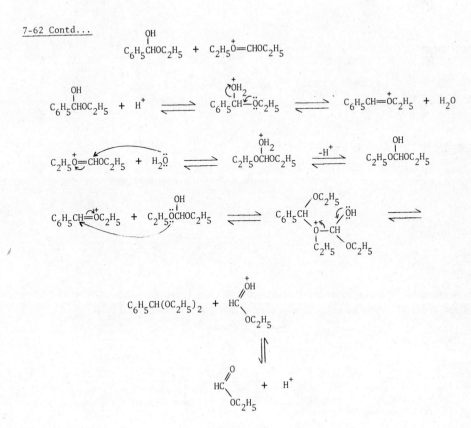

7-63

a)  Yes, because transfer of D shows that the source of D (or H) in the reduction is the α-D (or H) of the alkoxide group.

b)  The more favorable conformer has the methyl group equatorial. The complexed carbonyl group is large and prefers to be equatorial also. Thus D tends to approach from the axial side of the molecule to give predominately the trans isomer.

7-64  The formation and hydrolysis of the acetal does not involve cleavage of the C-O bond in 2-octanol so that configuration at the chiral center does not change.

7-65     $C_6H_5CH=C(CH_3)CHO$

α-Methylcinnamaldehyde

7-65 Contd...

a) $C_6H_5CH=C(CH_3)CH_2OH$

g) $C_6H_5CH=C(CH_3)\overset{\overset{OH}{|}}{C}HCH_3$

b) $C_6H_5CH=C(CH_3)CH_2OH$ + $C_6H_5CH=C(CH_3)CO_2H$

h) $C_6H_5CH=C(CH_3)CH=CHCH_3$

c) $C_6H_5CH=C(CH_3)CH(OC_2H_5)_2$

i) $C_6H_5CH=C(CH_3)\overset{S}{\underset{S}{CH}}$

d) $C_6H_5CH=C(CH_3)CH_2OH$

e) $C_6H_5CH=C(CH_3)CH=CHNO_2$

j) $C_6H_5CH=C(CH_3)CH=NNHC_6H_5$

k) $C_6H_5CH=C(CH_3)CH_2OH$

f) $C_6H_5CH=C(CH_3)CH$

l) $C_6H_5CH=C(CH_3)CH(OC_2H_5)_2$

7-66 Both $\overset{+}{N}$ and $\overset{+}{P}$ can stabilize the adjacent carbanion by an electrostatic inductive effect. In addition the $\overset{+}{P}$ can make use of empty $d$-orbitals to delocalize the negative charge.

7-67 Three successive aldol reactions with formaldehyde replace the three α-hydrogen atoms of acetaldehyde and give the triol-aldehyde. A subsequent Cannizzaro reaction with formaldehyde as the reducing agent leads to the product.

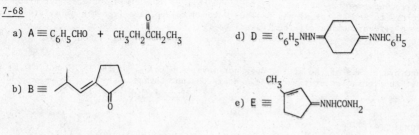

7-68

a) $A \equiv C_6H_5CHO$ + $CH_3CH_2\overset{\overset{O}{||}}{C}CH_2CH_3$

d) $D \equiv C_6H_5NHN=$⬡$=NNHC_6H_5$

b) $B \equiv$

e) $E \equiv$ =NNHCONH$_2$

c) $C \equiv (C_2H_5)_2C=O$ + $NCCH_2CO_2C_2H_5$

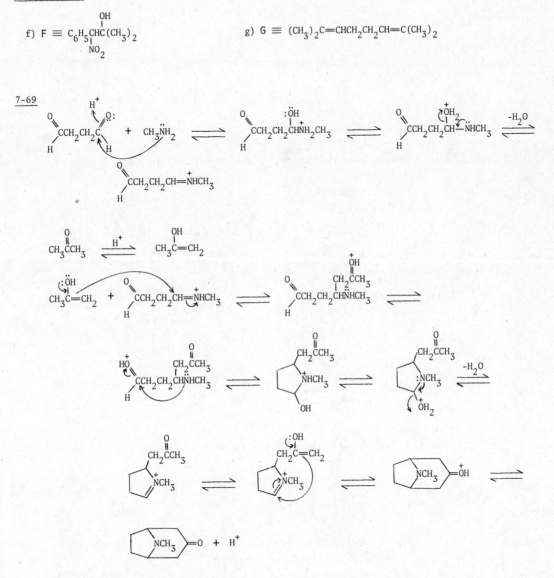

7-68 Contd...

f) F ≡ C₆H₅CHC(CH₃)₂ with OH and NO₂ substituents

g) G ≡ (CH₃)₂C=CHCH₂CH₂CH=C(CH₃)₂

7-69

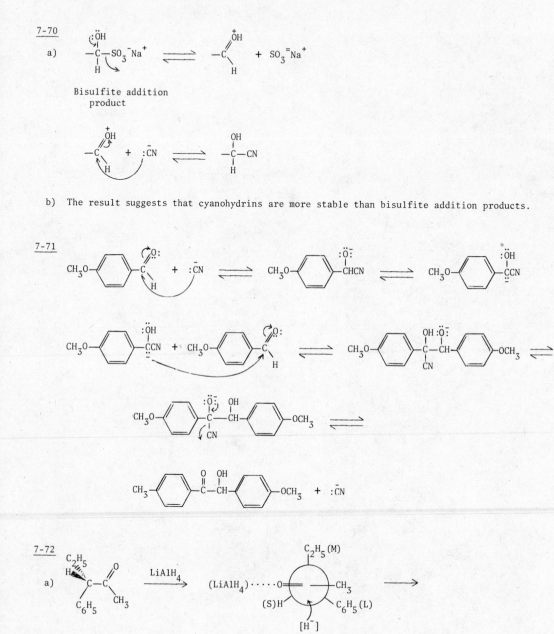

7-70

a)

Bisulfite addition
product

b) The result suggests that cyanohydrins are more stable than bisulfite addition products.

7-71

7-72

a)

7-72 Contd...

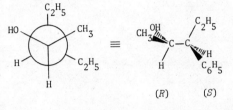

(R)          (S)

The carbonyl group is complexed with the LiAlH$_4$, thus is considered to be large. Sterically, it is best located between the small (S) and medium (M) groups. Hydride then attacks from the less hindered side of the C=O.

7-73  2,2-Dimethoxypropane is the ketal of acetone. Reaction with H$_2$O converts the ketal to acetone and methanol, both of which can be distilled away to complete this reaction.

$$CH_3\underset{\underset{OCH_3}{|}}{\overset{\overset{OCH_3}{|}}{C}}CH_3 + H_2O \longrightarrow CH_3\overset{O}{\overset{||}{C}}CH_3 + 2\ CH_3OH$$

7-74

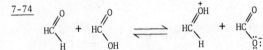

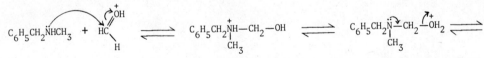

7-75

a)  $C_6H_5CHO + HOCH_2CH_2CH_2OH \xrightarrow[(-H_2O)]{p\text{-}TsOH} C_6H_5CH$

7-75 Contd...

b) $CH_3CH_2CH_2\overset{O}{\overset{\|}{C}}CH_3$ + $NaHSO_3$ $\longrightarrow$ $CH_3CH_2CH_2\underset{\underset{CH_3}{|}}{\overset{\overset{OH}{|}}{C}}SO_3^-Na^+$

c)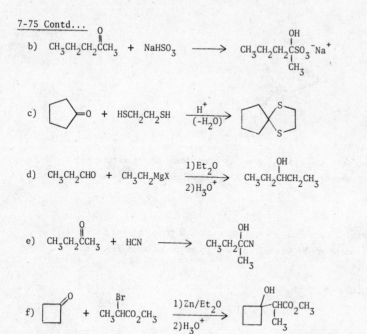

d) $CH_3CH_2CHO$ + $CH_3CH_2MgX$ $\xrightarrow[\text{2)}H_3O^+]{\text{1)}Et_2O}$ $CH_3CH_2\underset{\overset{|}{OH}}{CH}CH_2CH_3$

e) $CH_3CH_2\overset{O}{\overset{\|}{C}}CH_3$ + $HCN$ $\longrightarrow$ $CH_3CH_2\underset{\underset{CH_3}{|}}{\overset{\overset{OH}{|}}{C}}CN$

f) $\square$=O + $CH_3\underset{\overset{|}{Br}}{CH}CO_2CH_3$ $\xrightarrow[\text{2)}H_3O^+]{\text{1)}Zn/Et_2O}$ cyclobutane ring with $\underset{\underset{CH_3}{|}}{\overset{\overset{OH}{|}}{C}}CHCO_2CH_3$

7-76 A Cannizzaro reaction takes place with excess formaldehyde functioning as the reducing agent.

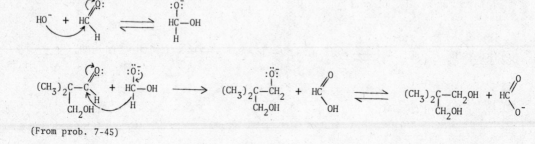

(From prob. 7-45)

7-77

a) $C_6H_5CH_2CN$ + $CH_3CH_2MgBr$ $\xrightarrow[\text{2)}H_3O^+]{\text{1)}Et_2O}$ $C_6H_5CH_2\overset{O}{\overset{\|}{C}}CH_2CH_3$

b) 2 $CH_3CHO$ $\xrightarrow[\Delta]{NaOH/H_2O}$ $CH_3CH=CHCHO$ $\xrightarrow[\text{2)}H_3O^+]{\text{1)}C_2H_5MgBr/Et_2O}$ $CH_3CH=CH\underset{\overset{|}{OH}}{CH}CH_2CH_3$

7-77 Contd...

c)  $C_6H_5CH_2CN$  $\xrightarrow[\text{2)H}_3O^+]{\text{1)LiAlH}_4/\text{Et}_2O}$  $C_6H_5CH_2CH_2NH_2$

d)  $2\ CH_3CHO$  $\xrightarrow[\Delta]{\text{NaOH/H}_2O}$  $CH_3CH{=}CHCHO$  $\xrightarrow[\text{2)H}_3O^+]{\text{1)NaBH}_4/\text{THF}}$  $CH_3CH{=}CHCH_2OH$

e)  $2\ CH_3\overset{\text{O}}{\overset{\|}{C}}CH_3$  $\xrightarrow[\Delta]{\text{NaOEt/EtOH}}$  $(CH_3)_2C{=}CH\overset{\text{O}}{\overset{\|}{C}}CH_3$  $\xrightarrow[\substack{\text{2)CH}_3\text{COCH}_3\\ \text{3) }\Delta}]{\text{1)NaOEt/EtOH}}$

Not isolated

$(CH_3)_2C{=}CH\overset{\text{O}}{\overset{\|}{C}}CH{=}C(CH_3)_2$  $\xrightarrow[\text{2)H}_3O^+]{\text{1)NaBH}_4/\text{THF}}$  $(CH_3)_2C{=}CHCH\overset{\text{OH}}{\overset{|}{}}CH{=}C(CH_3)_2$

f)  $C_6H_5CHO\ +\ CH_3CHO$  $\xrightarrow[\text{Not isolated}]{\text{NaOH/H}_2O}$  $C_6H_5CH{=}CHCHO$  $\xrightarrow[\text{2)CH}_3\text{CHO}]{\text{1)NaOH/H}_2O}$

$C_6H_5CH{=}CHCH{=}CHCHO$  $\xrightarrow[\text{2)H}_3O^+]{\text{1)NaBH}_4/\text{THF}}$  $C_6H_5CH{=}CHCH{=}CHCH_2OH$

g)  $CH_3CHO\ +\ 2\ C_2H_5SH$  $\xrightarrow[\text{(-H}_2O)]{\text{H}^+}$  $CH_3CH(SC_2H_5)_2$

7-78  Elemental analysis provides the empirical formula of $C_9H_{12}O$  *IHD* = 4.
The IR spectrum shows a hydroxy group at 3300-3400cm$^{-1}$ and the nmr spectrum shows $C_6H_5$- and $CH_3CH_2$- (triplet, quartet), as well as the -OH and a single proton deshielded (presumably by the oxygen atom) and split by two adjacent protons.

1-Phenyl-1-propanol

$C_6H_5MgBr\ +\ CH_3CH_2CHO$  $\xrightarrow[\text{2)H}_2O/\text{NH}_4\text{Cl}]{\text{1)Et}_2O}$  $C_6H_5\overset{\text{OH}}{\overset{|}{C}}HCH_2CH_3$

7-79  The IR spectrum shows a monosubstituted aromatic (680 cm$^{-1}$ and 740 cm$^{-1}$) and a possible C=O

7-79 Contd... shifted to 1660 cm$^{-1}$. Since both reactants have aromatic rings and carbonyl groups, the 1660 cm$^{-1}$ peak is consistent with a carbonyl group absorption shifted to lower energy by conjugation. The nmr spectrum shows protons in the aromatic region. If we are to account for the major components of the reactants, it is reasonable to assume that there are also some alkene protons in that same region. A plausible aldol-dehydration reaction gives a structure for chalcone consistent with the spectral data.

$$C_6H_5CHO + CH_3\overset{\overset{O}{\|}}{C}C_6H_5 \xrightarrow{NaOH/H_2O} C_6H_5CH=CH\overset{\overset{O}{\|}}{C}C_6H_5 + H_2O$$

Chalcone

(1,3-Diphenyl-2-propen-1-one)

7-80

a) The IR spectrum shows a conjugated C=O (1690 cm$^{-1}$) and possibly a C=C (1620 cm$^{-1}$). Those groups would be expected in the product of an aldol-dehydration sequence. The nmr spectrum confirms an alkene proton (6.0 ppm). Interpretation of the nmr peaks at 1.9 and 2.1 ppm is a little more complex. The peak areas of 6:3 (relative to the alkene proton) suggest a total of three methyl groups. Consideration of the reactants suggests that part of the peak at 2.1 ppm is due to $CH_3\overset{\overset{O}{\|}}{C}-$. Then a second and third methyl group must come at 1.9 and 2.1 ppm. Those peaks are both deshielded because they are attached to an alkene carbon but differ in chemical shift because one is in a Z and the other an E relationship to the acetyl group. There is a very small long range coupling evident in the peak at 1.9 ppm. These data and the mode of formation lead to the structure of mesityl oxide.

$$(CH_3)_2C=CH\overset{\overset{O}{\|}}{C}CH_3$$

Mesityl oxide

(4-Methyl-3-pentene-2-one)

b) 
$$CH_3\overset{\overset{O}{\|}}{C}CH_3 \underset{}{\overset{H^+}{\rightleftharpoons}} CH_2=\overset{\overset{OH}{|}}{C}CH_3 \quad \underline{and} \quad CH_3\overset{\overset{\overset{+}{OH}}{\|}}{C}CH_3$$

enol            protonated ketone

$$CH_3-\overset{\overset{+}{OH}}{\underset{CH_3}{\overset{\|}{C}}} + CH_2=\overset{\overset{:\ddot{O}H}{|}}{C}-CH_3 \rightleftharpoons (CH_3)_2\overset{\overset{OH}{|}}{C}-CH_2\overset{\overset{OH}{\|}}{C}CH_3 \rightleftharpoons (CH_3)_2\overset{\overset{+}{O}H_2}{C}{\overset{|}{\underset{H}{\rightleftharpoons}}}CH\overset{\overset{O}{\|}}{C}CH_3 \longrightarrow$$

$$(CH_3)_2C=CH\overset{\overset{O}{\|}}{C}CH_3 + H_3O^+$$

# 8 NUCLEOPHILIC SUBSTITUTIONS ON THE CARBONYL GROUP— THE CARBOXYLIC ACID FAMILY

<u>8-1</u>

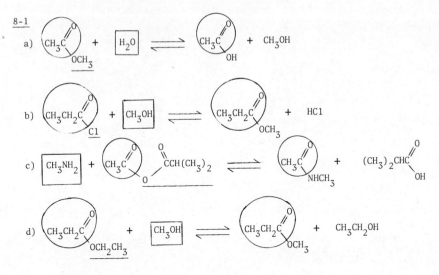

<u>8-2</u>

| Reactive leaving groups | $pK_a$ of conjugate acid | Groups converted to good leaving groups by protonation | $pK_a$ of conjugate acid | Not normally leaving groups | $pK_a$ of conjugate acid |
|---|---|---|---|---|---|
| :C̈l:⁻ | -7.0 | $H_2O$ | -1.7 | H:⁻ | - |
| HS̈:⁻ | 7.0 | ROH | ~ -2 | —C̈:⁻ | ~50 |
| RC(=O)Ö:⁻ | ~5 | $NH_3$ | 9.2 | | |
| | | $R_2NH$ | ~ 10 | | |

8-3

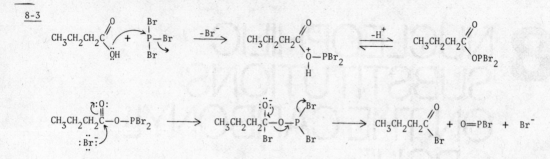

8-4

a) The positive charge on the nitrogen atom makes the carbon atom particularly reactive toward nucleophilic addition by a carboxy group. Loss of the original carboxy oxygen atom as the chloride ion adds is favored by loss of the stable molecule, DMF.

b) DMF is utilized, then regenerated. It is actually a catalyst.

c)

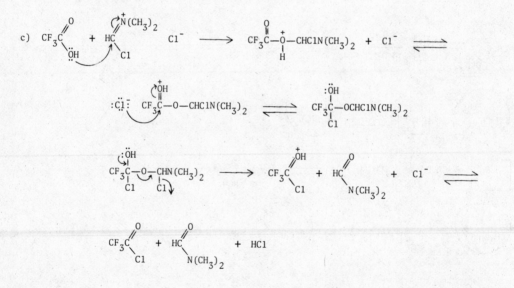

8-5  The desired acetyl chloride is the lowest boiling component in the reaction mixture. Warming the reaction mixture to above 51° will distill that product and shift the equilibrium concentrations.

8-6

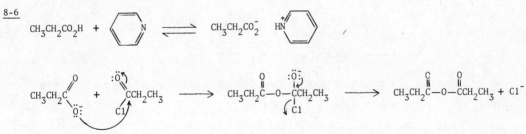

8-7

a) The entropy for cyclization of a single molecule to a nonstrained ring is more favorable than reaction of two molecules.

b)

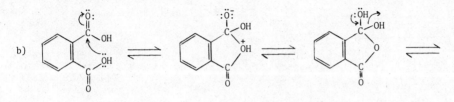

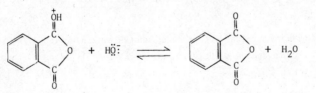

8-8

a)  $(C_6H_5CH_2CO)_2O$

b)  $C_6H_5CH_2COCl$

c)  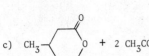 CH₃ + 2 CH₃CO₂H

d)  $CH_3COCH$ (with O O above)

e)  $(CH_3)_2CHCH_2COCl$

f)  $Cl_3CCOCl$

g)   + 2 CH₃CO₂H

8-9

a)  For the reaction

$$CH_3CO_2H \ + \ C_2H_5OH \ \underset{\longleftarrow}{\overset{K}{\longrightarrow}} \ CH_3CO_2C_2H_5 \ + \ H_2O$$

Let $X = [CH_3CO_2C_2H_5]$ and $[H_2O]$ at equilibrium

Then $1-X = [CH_3CO_2H]$ and $[C_2H_5OH]$ at equilibrium

$$K = 4 = \frac{[X][X]}{[1-X][1-X]} \qquad X = 0.67 \text{ moles/1}$$

b)  $K = 4 = \dfrac{[X][X]}{[10-X][1-X]}$ $\qquad X = 0.97$ moles/1

8-10

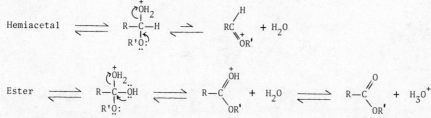

Hemiacetal

Ester

Loss of $H_2O$ from the hemiacetal adduct gives an unstable oxonium ion.  The ester adduct loses water to give a protonated carboxylic acid which readily loses $H^+$ to give the stable product.

8-11

a)  The nonbonding electrons of the carbonyl oxygen will be $sp^2$-like while those of the alcohol oxygen will be $sp^3$-like.  The greater the "s" character, the closer and tighter the electrons are held to the nucleus and the less available they are to act as a base.

b)  To the degree that structure B contributes to the resonance hybrid of the ester the alcohol oxygen atom is nonbasic.  Hybrid orbital considerations also suggest that there is more "s" character at the alcohol oxygen of B.  The electrons are held close to the nucleus and therefore the atom is less basic.

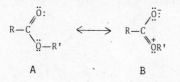

A                        B

Examination of the stability of each protonated species (the conjugate acids) leads to the same conclusions.  The ester protonated at the carbonyl oxygen is stabilized by resonance. Similar stabilization in the alcohol oxygen protonated species would be very unlikely.

8-11 Contd...

b) Contd...

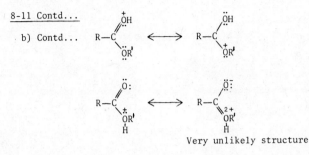

Very unlikely structure

8-12

a) $CH_3CH_2CH_2CO_2C_2H_5$

Ethyl butanoate

(Ethyl butyrate)

b) $C_6H_5COCl$

Benzoyl chloride

c)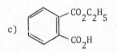

Ethyl hydrogen phthalate

d) $CH_3CO_2CH(CH_3)_2$

$i$-Propyl acetate

e) $(C_6H_5CO)_2O$

Benzoic anhydride

f) $C_6H_5CO_2C_6H_5$

Phenyl benzoate

8-13

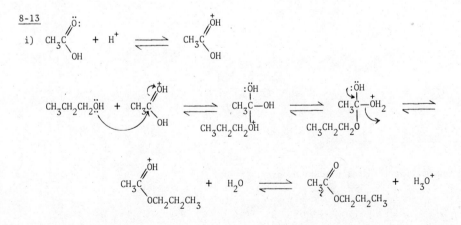

8-13 Contd...

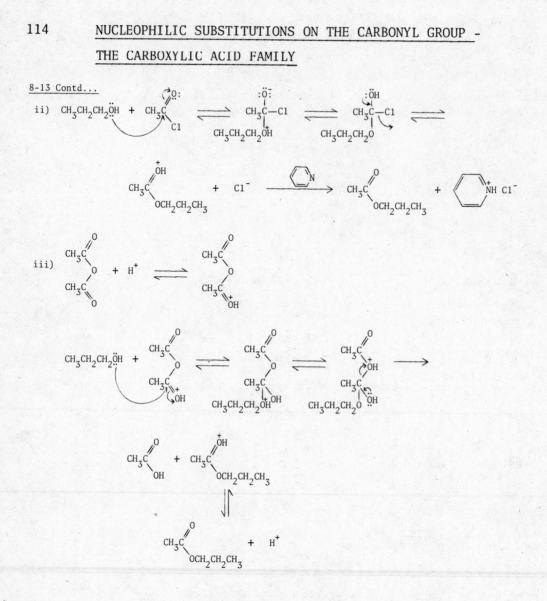

8-14

i) Use a large excess of the 1-butanol.

ii) Remove the low boiling methanol product by distillation.

8-15

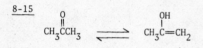

8-15 Contd...

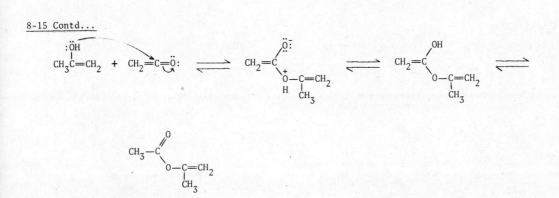

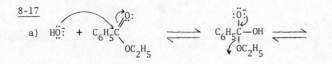

8-16

i) Exchange

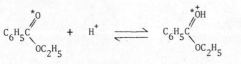

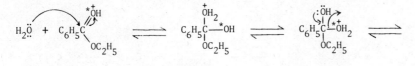

ii) Hydrolysis (or esterification)

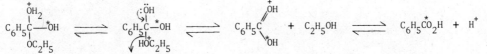

The exchange sequence must take place at a more rapid rate than does hydrolysis (or esterification).

8-17

a)   HÖ⁻ + C₆H₅C(=O)OC₂H₅ ⇌ C₆H₅C(Ö⁻)(OH)OC₂H₅ ⇌

8-17 Contd...

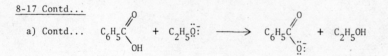

a) Contd...   $C_6H_5C\overset{O}{\underset{OH}{\Big\|}}$ + $C_2H_5\ddot{O}:^-$ $\longrightarrow$ $C_6H_5C\overset{O}{\underset{\ddot{O}:^-}{\Big\|}}$ + $C_2H_5OH$

b)  Base promoted esterification would involve addition of an alkoxide anion to the carboxylate anion.  That would form an electrostatically unfavorable dianion.

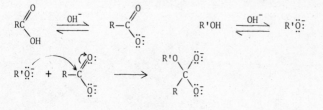

8-18

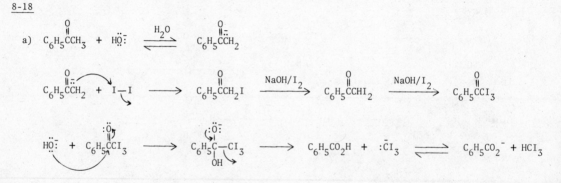

b)  Yes; it is a methyl carbonyl compound.

c)  $CH_3CH_2\overset{OH}{\underset{|}{C}}HCH_3$ $\xrightarrow[\text{(Oxidation)}]{NaOI}$ $CH_3CH_2\overset{O}{\overset{\|}{C}}CH_3$ $\xrightarrow[I_2]{NaOH/H_2O}$ $CH_3CH_2\overset{O}{\overset{\|}{C}}CI_3$ $\longrightarrow$

$CH_3CH_2CO_2^-Na$ + $HCI_3$

8-19

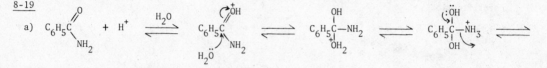

a)  $C_6H_5C\overset{O}{\underset{NH_2}{\Big\|}}$ + $H^+$ $\xrightarrow{H_2O}$ $C_6H_5C\overset{+OH}{\underset{NH_2}{\Big|}}$ $\underset{H_2\ddot{O}}{}$ $\rightleftharpoons$ $C_6H_5\overset{OH}{\underset{+OH_2}{\overset{|}{C}}}-NH_2$ $\rightleftharpoons$ $C_6H_5\overset{\ddot{O}H}{\underset{OH}{\overset{|}{C}}}-\overset{+}{N}H_3$ $\rightleftharpoons$

8-19 Contd...

a) Contd...

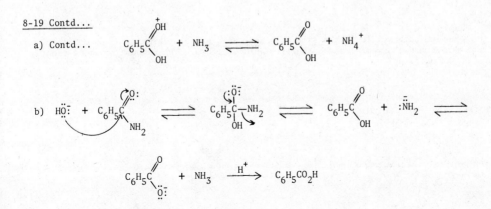

8-20 The strong bases hydrolyze the fats and oils usually found on dirty dishes.  The hydrolysis products are usually water soluble (glycerol and a soap).

8-21

a)  $C_6H_5CONH_2$  +  $H_2O$  $\xrightarrow[2)H_3O^+]{1)NaOH/\Delta}$  $C_6H_5CO_2H$

b)  $(CH_3)_3CCO_2CH_3$  +  $(CH_3)_2CHCH_2OH$  $\xrightarrow{p-CH_3C_6H_4SO_3H}$  $(CH_3)_3CCO_2CH_2CH(CH_3)_2$  +  $CH_3OH$

c)  cyclohexyl-$CO_2CH_3$  +  $H_2O$  $\xrightarrow[\Delta]{H_2SO_4}$  cyclohexyl-$CO_2H$  +  $CH_3OH$

d)  + $H_2O$(excess)  $\xrightarrow{NaOH}$  $CO_2^-Na^+$ / $CO_2^-Na^+$

e)  $C_6H_5$-COCl  +  $H_2O$  $\xrightarrow{THF}$  $C_6H_5$-$CO_2H$

f)  + $C_2H_5OH$  $\longrightarrow$  $HOCH_2CHCH_2CO_2C_2H_5$ (with $CH_3$ substituent)

8-22

a) Because an ammonium carboxylate is the salt of a weak acid and a weak base, a low equilibrium concentration of ammonia or amine and carboxylic acid can form. The ammonia or amine then functions as the nucleophile.

b) $CH_3CH_2CO_2^-\overset{+}{N}H_4 \rightleftharpoons CH_3CH_2CO_2H + NH_3$

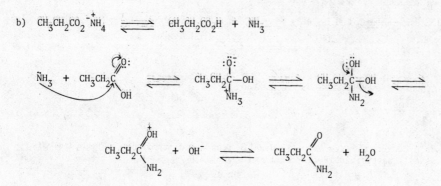

The unfavorable reaction is driven to completion by high temperature and loss of water.

8-23 HCl liberated as reaction occurs converts unreacted amine to a non-nucleophilic ammonium salt.

8-24

a) $CH_3CH_2CH_2CH_2CO_2H + NaOH \longrightarrow CH_3CH_2CH_2CH_2CO_2^- Na^+$

b) $CH_3CH_2CH_2CH_2CO_2H + SOCl_2 \longrightarrow CH_3CH_2CH_2CH_2COCl$

c) $CH_3CH_2CH_2CH_2CO_2H + CH_3NH_2 \xrightarrow{\Delta}$

      or + 1)$SOCl_2$; 2)excess $CH_3NH_2 \longrightarrow CH_3CH_2CH_2CH_2CONHCH_3$

d) $CH_3CH_2CH_2CH_2CO_2H + NH_3 \longrightarrow CH_3CH_2CH_2CH_2CO_2^-\overset{+}{N}H_4$

e) $CH_3CH_2CH_2CH_2CO_2H + CH_3OH(excess) \longrightarrow CH_3CH_2CH_2CH_2CO_2CH_3$

8-25

a)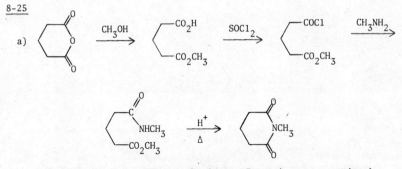

(N is better nucleophile.  Ester is more reactive.)

8-26

a) The departure of the alcohol must involve cleavage of the acyl-oxygen bond.  If the bond between the asymmetric carbon atom and oxygen were broken (alkyl-oxygen cleavage) some loss of optical purity would be expected to occur.

b.)

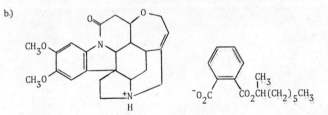

Brucine 2-octyl phthalate is the ammonium salt of the free carboxy group.  Note that the amino nitrogen atom is the basic center.  Amide nitrogen atoms are relatively nonbasic.

8-27  Addition of water could evolve hydrogen in a dangerously exothermic reaction if much LiAlH$_4$ remains.  Ethyl acetate, an ester, is reduced to ethyl alcohol in a mild reaction to consume any excess LiAlH$_4$.  Water can then be safely added.

8-28

a)  $C_6H_5CH_2CO_2H$ + LiAlH$_4$  $\xrightarrow[\text{2)H}_3\text{O}^+]{\text{1)THF}}$  $C_6H_5CH_2CH_2OH$

b)  $C_6H_5COCl$ or $C_6H_5CHO$ + NaBH$_4$  $\xrightarrow[\text{2) H}_3\text{O}^+]{\text{1)}i\text{-PrOH/H}_2\text{O/OH}^-}$  $C_6H_5CH_2OH$

8-28 Contd...

c)   $(CH_3)_2CHCONHCH_3$ + $(BH_3)_2$   $\xrightarrow[\text{2)HCl/H}_2\text{O}]{\text{1)Diglyme}}$   $(CH_3)_2CHCH_2NHCH_3$

d)   $OHC$—⬡—$COCl$ + $(BH_3)_2$   $\xrightarrow[\text{2)H}_3\text{O}^+]{\text{1)Diglyme}}$   $HOCH_2$—⬡—$COCl$

e)   $C_6H_5CO_2CH(CH_3)_2$ + $\underset{(BH_3)_2}{\overset{\text{LiAlH}_4}{\underset{\text{or}}{}}}$   $\xrightarrow[\text{2)H}_3\text{O}^+]{\text{1)THF}}$   $C_6H_5CH_2OH$ + $(CH_3)_2CHOH$

f)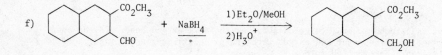

8-29

a)   $Cl—\overset{\overset{O}{\|}}{C}—Cl$ + 2 $CH_3OH$   $\longrightarrow$   $CH_3O\overset{\overset{O}{\|}}{C}OCH_3$

b)   $CH_3I$ + $Mg$   $\xrightarrow{\text{Et}_2\text{O}}$   $CH_3MgI$

    3 $CH_3MgI$ + $CH_3O\overset{\overset{O}{\|}}{C}OCH_3$   $\xrightarrow[\text{2)H}_2\text{O/NH}_4\text{Cl}]{\text{1)Et}_2\text{O}}$   $(CH_3)_3COH$

Note that the weakly acidic workup is necessary to avoid elimination of water from tertiary alcohols.

8-30

a)   $C_6H_5CH_2CO_2C_2H_5$ ⟨

    $\xrightarrow[\text{2)H}_3\text{O}^+]{\text{1)LiAlH}_4}$   $C_6H_5CH_2CH_2OH$ + $C_2H_5OH$

    $\xrightarrow[\text{2)H}_2\text{O/NH}_4\text{Cl}]{\text{1)C}_2\text{H}_5\text{MgI}}$   $C_6H_5CH_2\overset{\overset{OH}{|}}{C}(C_2H_5)_2$ + $C_2H_5OH$

8-30 Contd...

b)   $CH_3CH_2CCH_2CO_2H$  (with C=O)

1)$LiAlH_4$
2)$H_3O^+$
→ $CH_3CH_2CHCH_2CH_2OH$ (with OH on CH)   (Assumes sufficient reagent to abstract the acidic hydrogen.)

1)$C_2H_5MgI$
2)$H_2O/NH_4Cl$
→ $(CH_3CH_2)_2CCH_2CO_2H$ (with OH)

c)   (γ-butyrolactone ring)

1)$LiAlH_4$
2)$H_3O^+$
→ $HOCH_2CH_2CH_2CH_2OH$

1)$C_2H_5MgI$
2)$H_2O/NH_4Cl$
→ $HOCH_2CH_2CH_2C(C_2H_5)_2$ (with OH)

d)   $CH_3CH_2CH_2C$ (with C=O and $NHC_6H_5$)

1)$LiAlH_4$
2)$H_2O$
→ $CH_3CH_2CH_2CH_2NHC_6H_5$

1)$C_2H_5MgI$
2)$H_2O/NH_4Cl$
→ $CH_3CH_2CH_2C(C_2H_5)_2$ (with OH)  +  $C_6H_5NH_2$

8-31   The ketone and organometallic reagents are both so crowded that addition of another *t*-butyl reagent is sterically inhibited.

8-32   When $CO_2$ is bubbled through the reaction mixture a large excess of Grignard reagent is present.  Excess reagent adds to the initial adduct to form some tertiary alcohol.

8-33   Other approaches to the following syntheses are also possible.

a)   $C_2H_5Br$  +  $Mg$  $\xrightarrow{Et_2O}$  $C_2H_5MgBr$

$2\ C_2H_5MgBr$  +  $HCO_2C_2H_5$  $\xrightarrow[2)H_3O^+]{1)Et_2O}$  $CH_3CH_2CHCH_2CH_3$ (with OH)

8-33 Contd...

b)  $C_6H_5Br$ + Mg  $\xrightarrow{Et_2O}$  $C_6H_5MgBr$

2 $C_6H_5MgBr$ + $CdCl_2$  $\longrightarrow$  $(C_6H_5)_2Cd$

$(C_6H_5)_2Cd$ + $C_6H_5COCl$  $\xrightarrow[2)H_3O^+]{1)Et_2O}$  $(C_6H_5)_2C{=}O$

c)  2 $C_2H_5MgBr$ + 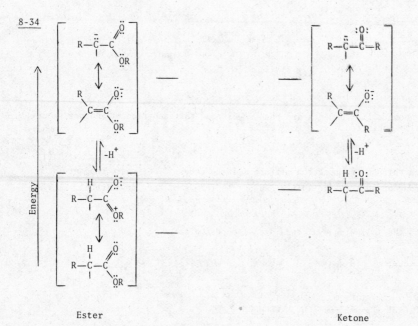  $\xrightarrow[2)H_2O/NH_4Cl]{1)THF}$  $HOCH_2CH_2CH_2\overset{\overset{\displaystyle OH}{|}}{C}(CH_2CH_3)_2$

d)  $n\text{-}C_4H_9Br$ + Mg  $\xrightarrow{Et_2O}$  $n\text{-}C_4H_9MgBr$

2 $n\text{-}C_4H_9MgBr$ + $(CH_3)_3CCH_2CO_2CH_3$  $\xrightarrow[2)H_3O^+]{1)Et_2O}$  $(CH_3)_3CCH_2\overset{\overset{\displaystyle OH}{|}}{C}(C_4H_9\text{-}n)_2$

8-34

Ester                                      Ketone

Acidity is a measure of the difference in energy between the acid and its conjugate base.

8-35  If we assume that resonance stabilization of the conjugate bases of amides and esters are
similar, then acidity differences must reflect different ground state stabilities.  Resonance
between the nitrogen electron pair and the carbonyl group is more important than that of the
ester oxygen atom.  The nitrogen atom accommodates the positive charge better than does an
oxygen atom.

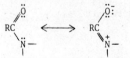

The difference in energy is therefore greater between the neutral amide and its conjugate
base than between the neutral ester and its conjugate base.

8-36  The conjugate base of the β-keto ester is stabilized by delocalization of the negative
charge by two carbonyl groups, those of the keto and the ester groups.

8-37  Both experiments are consistent with initial formation of the ester enolate anion.

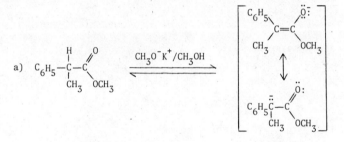

Racemic intermediate

(Condensation may not occur with this compound since the equilibrium cannot be shifted by
formation of a new enolate anion.)

b)  $CH_3C$
    $OC_2H_5$
    $\xrightarrow{C_2H_5O^-Na^+/C_2H_5OD}$  Ester enolate  $\xrightarrow{C_2H_5OD}$  $DCH_2CO_2C_2H_5$
    Partially exchanged
    ester

8-38  To avoid any possibility of transesterification which would give a mixture of ester products.

8-39
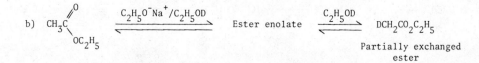

<u>8-39 Contd...</u>

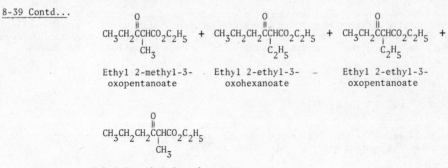

Ethyl 2-methyl-3-    Ethyl 2-ethyl-3-    Ethyl 2-ethyl-3-
oxopentanoate       oxohexanoate        oxopentanoate

$$CH_3CH_2CH_2\overset{O}{\overset{\|}{C}}\overset{}{\underset{\underset{CH_3}{|}}{C}}HCO_2C_2H_5$$

Ethyl 2-methyl-3-oxohexanoate

<u>8-40</u>   The strong base converts all of the ester to its enolate anion. (An alkoxide base gives an equilibrium mixture of ester and alkoxide.) The enolate anion is not electrophilic so that self condensation doesn't occur.

<u>8-41</u>

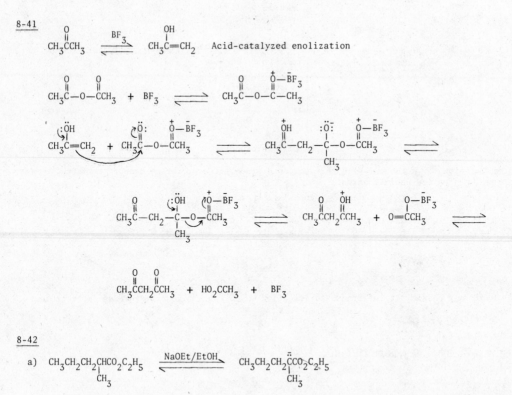

<u>8-42</u>

a) $CH_3CH_2CH_2\underset{\underset{CH_3}{|}}{C}HCO_2C_2H_5 \xrightarrow{\text{NaOEt/EtOH}} CH_3CH_2CH_2\underset{\underset{CH_3}{|}}{\overset{..}{C}}CO_2C_2H_5$

The enolate anion forms but no condensation reaction takes place with NaOEt/EtOH because the

8-42 Contd...

a) Contd...    final equilibrium is too unfavorable.

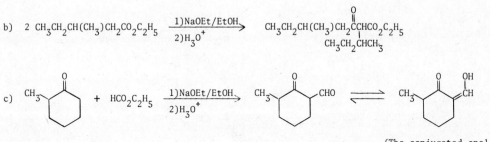

b) 2 $CH_3CH_2CH(CH_3)CH_2CO_2C_2H_5$ $\xrightarrow[2)H_3O^+]{1)NaOEt/EtOH}$ 

$$CH_3CH_2CH(CH_3)CH_2\overset{O}{\overset{\|}{C}}\underset{CH_3CH_2CHCH_3}{\overset{|}{C}}HCO_2C_2H_5$$

c) CH₃-cyclohexanone + $HCO_2C_2H_5$ $\xrightarrow[2)H_3O^+]{1)NaOEt/EtOH}$ CH₃-cyclohexanone-CHO ⇌ CH₃-cyclohexanone=CH-OH

(The conjugated enol is more stable.)

d) $C_6H_5\overset{O}{\overset{\|}{C}}CH_3$ + $(CH_3)_2CHCO_2C_2H_5$ $\xrightarrow[2)H_3O^+]{1)NaOEt/EtOH}$ $C_6H_5\overset{O}{\overset{\|}{C}}CH_2\overset{O}{\overset{\|}{C}}CH(CH_3)_2$

e) cyclobutane-$CH_2CO_2C_2H_5$ + $O{=}C(OC_2H_5)_2$ $\xrightarrow[2)H_3O^+]{1)NaOEt/EtOH}$ cyclobutane-$CH(CO_2C_2H_5)_2$

f) $H_5C_2O_2CCH(CH_3)CH_2CH_2CH_2CH_2CO_2C_2H_5$ $\longrightarrow$ CH₃-cyclohexanone-$CO_2C_2H_5$

8-43

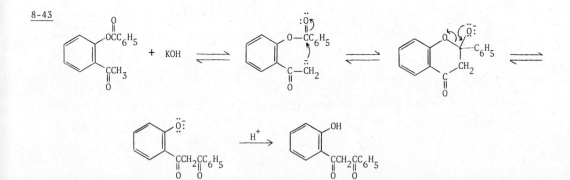

8-44

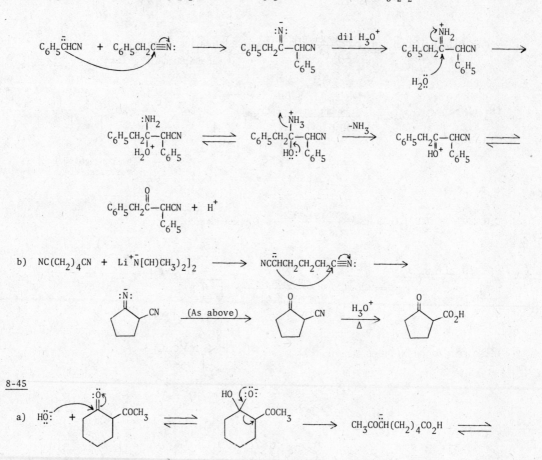

a) $C_6H_5CH_2CN$ + $Li^+\bar{N}[CH(CH_3)_2]_2$ ⟶ $C_6H_5\bar{C}HCNLi^+$ + $HN[CH(CH_3)_2]_2$

b) Addition of hydroxide to the acetyl carbonyl group followed by cleavage gives cyclohexanone and acetic acid.

8-45 Contd...

b) Contd...

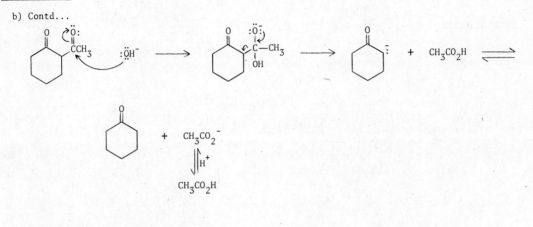

8-46

| Bonds broken | kcal/mol | kJ/mol | Bonds formed | kcal/mol | kJ/mol |
|---|---|---|---|---|---|
| C—C | 83 | 347 | C—H | -99 | -414 |
| O—H | 111 | 464 | C=O | -192 | -803 |
| C—O | 86 | 359 | | -291 kcal/mol | -1217 kJ/mol |
| | 280 kcal/mol | 1170 kJ/mol | | | |

$\Delta H° = 280 - 291 = -11$ kcal/mol ($-46$ kJ/mol)

8-47 The results are similar to evidence used to support enol formation in carbonyl compounds. In this case the enol formed by decarboxylation is readily brominated.

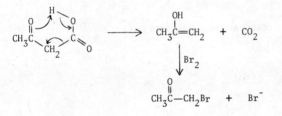

8-48 β-Keto esters form the enolate of a ketone which is more stable than the enolate of the carboxylic acid which forms in the *gem*-diacid decarboxylation.

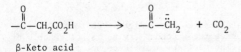

β-Keto acid

8-48 Contd...

$$HO-\overset{\overset{\displaystyle O}{\|}}{C}-CH_2CO_2H \longrightarrow HO-\overset{\overset{\displaystyle O}{\|}}{C}-\bar{C}H_2 + CO_2$$

*gem*-Diacid

8-49

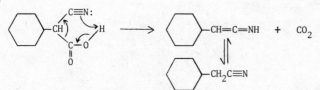

8-50

a)   $CH_3CH=CHCH=CHCH_2CO_2H$

3,5-Heptadienoic acid

d)   $O_2NCH_3$

Nitromethane

b)   $C_6H_5CH_2\overset{\overset{\displaystyle CH_3}{|}}{C}HCO(CH_2)_3CO_2CH_3$

Methyl 6-methyl-5-oxo-7-
phenylheptanoate

e)   

Acetophenone

c)   $C_6H_5COCH\overset{\overset{\displaystyle CH_3}{|}}{C}HCH_2CH_3$

2-Methyl-1-phenyl-1-butanone

f)   $K^+ \; \bar{O}_2CCH_2\overset{\overset{\displaystyle CH_3}{|}}{C}HCH_2CH_2CO_2^- K^+$

Dipotassium 3-methyladipate

8-51

$$C_6H_5SO_2Cl + RNH_2 \longrightarrow C_6H_5SO_2NHR \xrightarrow[H_2O]{NaOH} C_6H_5SO_2\ddot{N}R \; Na^+$$

$$C_6H_5SO_2Cl + R_2NH \longrightarrow C_6H_5SO_2NR_2$$

$$C_6H_5SO_2Cl + R_3N \longrightarrow \text{No reaction}$$

The sulfonamide of a primary amine has an acidic hydrogen atom which is abstracted by base
to give a water soluble salt. The sulfonamide from the secondary amine is not capable of
forming a salt and remains insoluble in water. The tertiary amine does not form a
sulfonamide since one alkyl group would have to depart from the nitrogen atom.

8-52  One -OH group is not esterified thus can give up a proton to produce a stabilized anion (conjugate base).

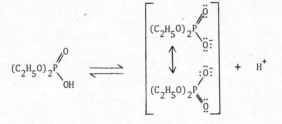

8-53  Absence of $^{18}O$ exchange suggests a direct displacement mechanism rather than an addition-elimination.

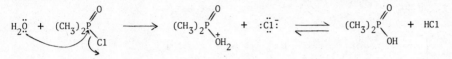

8-54

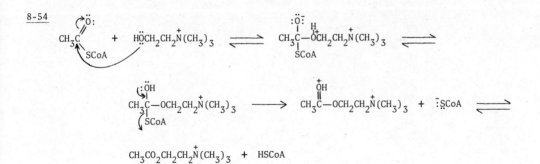

$$CH_3CO_2CH_2CH_2\overset{+}{N}(CH_3)_3 \ + \ HSCoA$$

8-55

a)  $C_2H_5O_2CCH_2COCOCH_2CO_2C_2H_5$

d)  $(CH_3)_2CHCH_2CO_2CH_2CH(CH_3)_2$

b)  $CH_3CO_2H \ + \ (C_6H_5)_2CHOH$

e)  $CH_3CH_2COCH(CN)_2$

c)  ⬠—$CO_2CH_3 \ + \ C_2H_5OH$

f)  $CH_3CH_2C\overset{O}{\underset{SCH_3}{\big\langle}}$

8-55 Contd...

g) $p\text{-}CH_3C_6H_4SO_3\overset{\overset{\textstyle CH_3}{|}}{C}HCH_2CH_3$

q) $CH_3CH_2CO_2H$

h) $C_6H_5\overset{\overset{\textstyle CHO}{|}}{C}HCO_2CH_3$

r) $CH_3CH_2CH_2CH_2\overset{\overset{\textstyle O}{||}}{C}CH_3$

i) $CH_3CHOHCH_2CO_2C_2H_5$

s) $C_6H_5COCH_2COC_6H_5$

j) $CH_2(CO_2H)_2 \;+\; 2\;C_2H_5OH$

t) $HO_2CCH_2CH_2CO_2CH_3$

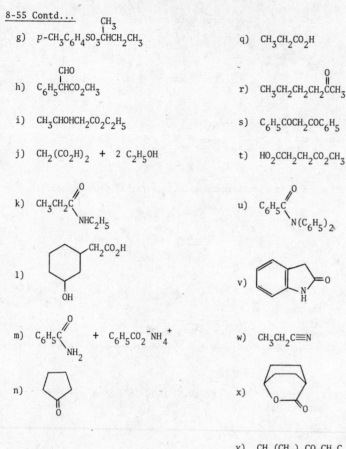

k) $CH_3CH_2\overset{\overset{\textstyle O}{||}}{C}{\diagdown}_{NHC_2H_5}$

u) $C_6H_5\overset{\overset{\textstyle O}{||}}{C}{\diagdown}_{N(C_6H_5)_2}$

l)

v)

m) $C_6H_5\overset{\overset{\textstyle O}{||}}{C}{\diagdown}_{NH_2} \;+\; C_6H_5CO_2^-NH_4^+$

w) $CH_3CH_2C\equiv N$

n)

x)

y) $CH_3(CH_2)_5CO_2CH_2C_6H_5 \;+\; C_2H_5OH$

o) $CH_3NH\overset{\overset{\textstyle O}{||}}{C}CH_2CH_2CO_2H$

z) $C_6H_5CO_2CH(CH_3)_2 \;+\; C_6H_5CO_2H$

p)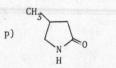

8-56  Esters hydrolyze (saponification) in aqueous base.  If the ester is not soluble in the basic
solution, the saponification reaction is markedly decreased.

8-57

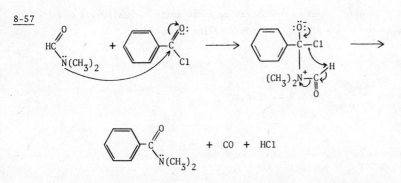

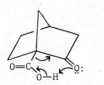   + CO + HCl

The sequence of bond breaking is driven to completion by the high temperature and loss of CO. Note that the process can be envisioned as proceeding via a 5-atom cyclic pathway.

8-58

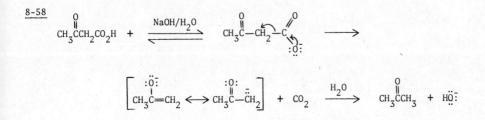

8-59  A cyclic, six-membered ring transition state proposed for the decarboxylation reaction would require formation of a double bond at the bridgehead of the small bicyclic compound. Such bridgehead double bonds are forbidden because excess angle strain is large (Bredt's rule).

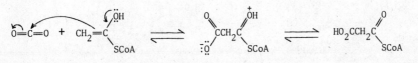

8-60

8-61   Loss of $CO_2$ from the carbamic acid involves the departure of an amine. Decarboxylation of the carbamate salt would require loss of the very poor leaving group, $R_2N:^-$ .

8-62

a)   $C_6H_5CO_2CH_3$ + 2 $CH_3MgBr$ $\xrightarrow[\text{2)}H_2O/NH_4Cl]{\text{1)}Et_2O}$ $C_6H_5\overset{\underset{|}{OH}}{C}H(CH_3)_2$

b)   (structure) + $\xrightarrow[\text{2)}CH_3COCl]{\text{1)}NaOEt/Et_2O}$ (structure with —$COCH_3$)

c)   $CH_3CO_2H$ + $C_2H_5OH$ $\xrightarrow{H^+}$ $CH_3CO_2C_2H_5$

     2 $CH_3CO_2C_2H_5$ $\xrightarrow{NaOEt/EtOH}$ $CH_3COCH_2CO_2C_2H_5$ $\xrightarrow[\text{2)}H_3O^+]{\text{1)}LiAlH_4/Et_2O}$ $CH_3CHOHCH_2CH_2OH$

d)   $(CH_3)_2CHCH_2CO_2H$ $\xrightarrow[\text{2)}CH_3NH_2]{\text{1)}SOCl_2}$ $(CH_3)_2CHCH_2\overset{\overset{\displaystyle O}{\|}}{C}{\underset{\displaystyle NHCH_3}{}}$

e)   $HO_2CCO_2H$ + $C_2H_5OH$(excess) $\xrightarrow{H^+}$ $C_2H_5O_2CCO_2C_2H_5$

     $CH_3CH_2CH_2CO_2C_2H_5$ $\xrightarrow[\text{2)}C_2H_5O_2CCO_2C_2H_5]{\text{1)}NaOEt/EtOH}$ $CH_3CH_2\overset{\overset{\displaystyle CO_2C_2H_5}{|}}{C}HCOCO_2C_2H_5$

f)   2 $C_2H_5O_2CCH_2CH_2CO_2C_2H_5$ $\xrightarrow[\text{2)}H_3O^+/\Delta]{\text{1)}NaOEt/EtOH}$ $O=$(six-membered ring)$=O$

Cyclization to form a six-membered ring is relatively favorable. Reaction is carried out in very dilute solution so that the initial substitution is followed by intra rather than intermolecular reaction.

8-63

a)

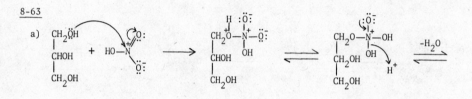

8-63 Contd...

a) Contd...

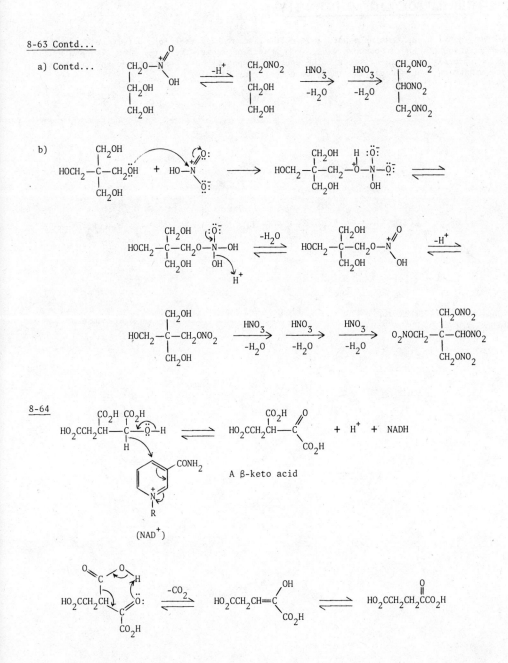

b)

8-64

A β-keto acid

(NAD⁺)

8-65   The *tert*-butyl group remains equatorial in both isomers and therefore determines configuration of the carboethoxy group. In the trans isomer the ester group is equatorial and it is axial in the cis isomer. The equatorial position is less crowded and can better accommodate the tetrahedral intermediate of ester hydrolysis.

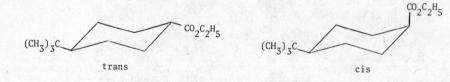

8-66

a)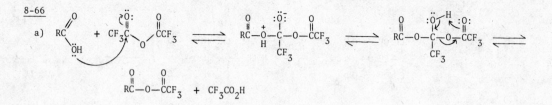

b) Trifluoroacetate is a better leaving group than HO$^-$ since it is the conjugate base of a strong acid

8-67

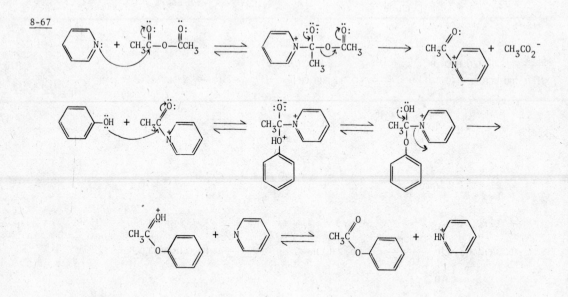

<u>8-68</u>  One equivalent of base forms the more stable enolate anion which is acylated by ethyl
benzoate. Two equivalents of strong base produce a dianion.

$$:\overset{-}{C}H_2-\overset{\overset{O}{\|}}{C}-\overset{..}{C}H-CHO$$

Acylation takes place at the less stable (more reactive) terminal carbanion.


<u>8-69</u>

a)  In the Knoevenagel condensation the α-hydrogen atoms are activated by two ester groups. An
enolate anion is formed under very mild basic conditions so that self condensation of the
aldehyde is minimal.

b)  In the Perkin reaction the carboxylate salt functions as the base which abstracts an
α-hydrogen atom from the anhydride. Hydrolysis provides a cinnamic acid (a 3-phenyl-2-
propenoic acid) in the most common examples of the Perkin reaction.

c)  In the Stobbe condensation the anion formed from diethyl succinate adds to a ketone. The
intermediate undergoes an intramolecular substitution on the more remote ester group to give
a five-membered lactone. Reaction of the lactone with base generates a new carbanion which
leads to a relatively stable carboxylate anion on ring opening.

$$C_2H_5O_2CH_2CH_2CO_2C_2H_5 \;+\; (CH_3)_3CO^- \;\rightleftharpoons\; C_2H_5O_2CH_2\overset{..}{C}HCO_2C_2H_5 \;+\; (CH_3)_3COH$$

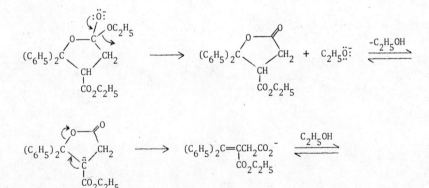

8-69 Contd...

$$(C_6H_5)_2C=CCH_2CO_2H \ + \ C_2H_5O^-$$
$$\quad\quad\quad\quad | $$
$$\quad\quad\quad CO_2C_2H_5$$

8-70

a)

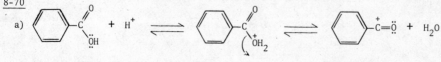

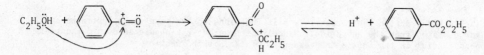

An acylium ion

The intermediate acylium ion is a high energy species.  It would only be expected in special cases of esterification.

b)  The usual addition-elimination would involve a very crowded tetrahedral intermediate in this sterically hindered compound.  The acylium ion pathway does not involve any significant increase in crowding and actually decreases steric interaction during the elimination step.

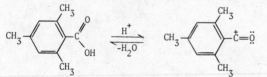

8-71

a)   $CH_3CO_2H \ + \ CH_3OH \ \xrightarrow{H^+} \ CH_3CO_2CH_3$

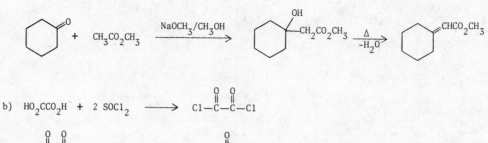

b)   $HO_2CCO_2H \ + \ 2 \ SOCl_2 \ \longrightarrow \ Cl-\overset{O}{\overset{||}{C}}-\overset{O}{\overset{||}{C}}-Cl$

   $Cl-\overset{O}{\overset{||}{C}}-\overset{O}{\overset{||}{C}}-Cl \ + \ 1 \ CH_3OH \ \longrightarrow \ ClC\overset{O}{\overset{||}{}}CO_2CH_3$

8-71 Contd...

b) Contd...

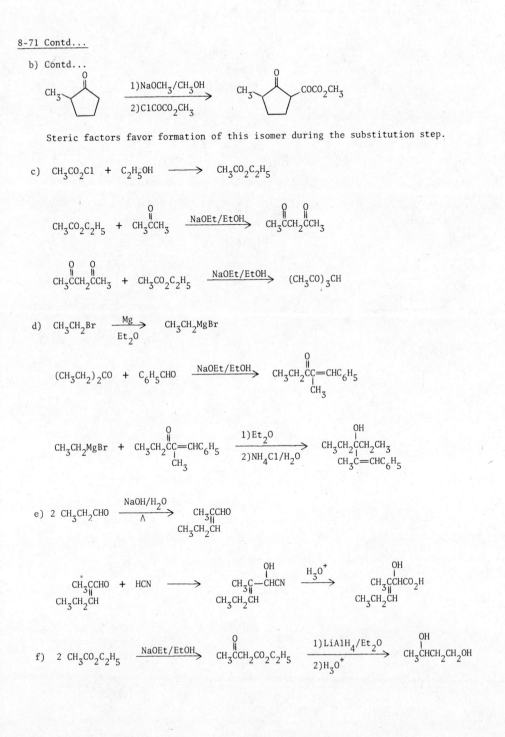

Steric factors favor formation of this isomer during the substitution step.

c)  $CH_3CO_2Cl$ + $C_2H_5OH$ $\longrightarrow$ $CH_3CO_2C_2H_5$

$CH_3CO_2C_2H_5$ + $CH_3\overset{O}{\overset{\|}{C}}CH_3$ $\xrightarrow{\text{NaOEt/EtOH}}$ $CH_3\overset{O}{\overset{\|}{C}}CH_2\overset{O}{\overset{\|}{C}}CH_3$

$CH_3\overset{O}{\overset{\|}{C}}CH_2\overset{O}{\overset{\|}{C}}CH_3$ + $CH_3CO_2C_2H_5$ $\xrightarrow{\text{NaOEt/EtOH}}$ $(CH_3CO)_3CH$

d)  $CH_3CH_2Br$ $\xrightarrow[\text{Et}_2O]{\text{Mg}}$ $CH_3CH_2MgBr$

$(CH_3CH_2)_2CO$ + $C_6H_5CHO$ $\xrightarrow{\text{NaOEt/EtOH}}$ $CH_3CH_2\overset{O}{\overset{\|}{C}}\underset{CH_3}{\overset{}{C}}=CHC_6H_5$

$CH_3CH_2MgBr$ + $CH_3CH_2\overset{O}{\overset{\|}{C}}\underset{CH_3}{\overset{}{C}}=CHC_6H_5$ $\xrightarrow[\text{2)NH}_4Cl/H_2O]{\text{1)Et}_2O}$ $\underset{CH_3C=CHC_6H_5}{CH_3CH_2\overset{OH}{\overset{\|}{C}}CH_2CH_3}$

e)  2 $CH_3CH_2CHO$ $\xrightarrow[\Lambda]{\text{NaOH/H}_2O}$ $\underset{CH_3CH_2CH}{CH_3\overset{}{\underset{\|}{C}}CHO}$

$\underset{CH_3CH_2CH}{CH_3\overset{*}{\underset{\|}{C}}CHO}$ + HCN $\longrightarrow$ $\underset{CH_3CH_2CH}{CH_3\overset{OH}{\underset{\|}{C}}-CHCN}$ $\xrightarrow{H_3O^+}$ $\underset{CH_3CH_2CH}{CH_3\overset{OH}{\underset{\|}{C}}CHCO_2H}$

f)  2 $CH_3CO_2C_2H_5$ $\xrightarrow{\text{NaOEt/EtOH}}$ $CH_3\overset{O}{\overset{\|}{C}}CH_2CO_2C_2H_5$ $\xrightarrow[\text{2)H}_3O^+]{\text{1)LiAlH}_4/\text{Et}_2O}$ $CH_3\overset{OH}{\underset{\|}{C}}HCH_2CH_2OH$

8-71 Contd...

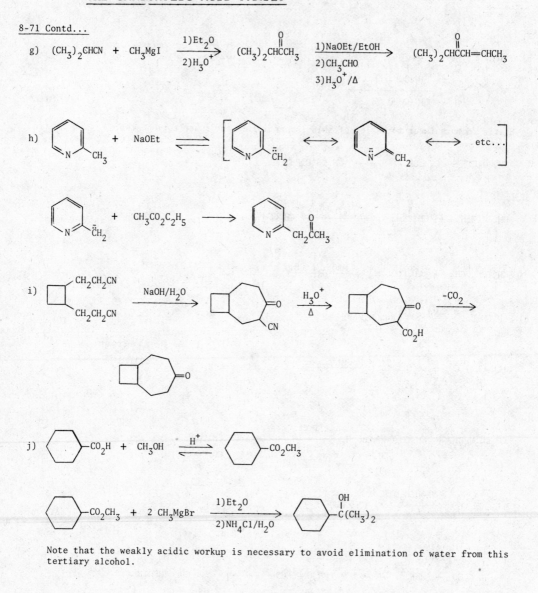

Note that the weakly acidic workup is necessary to avoid elimination of water from this tertiary alcohol.

8-71 Contd...

k) Contd...

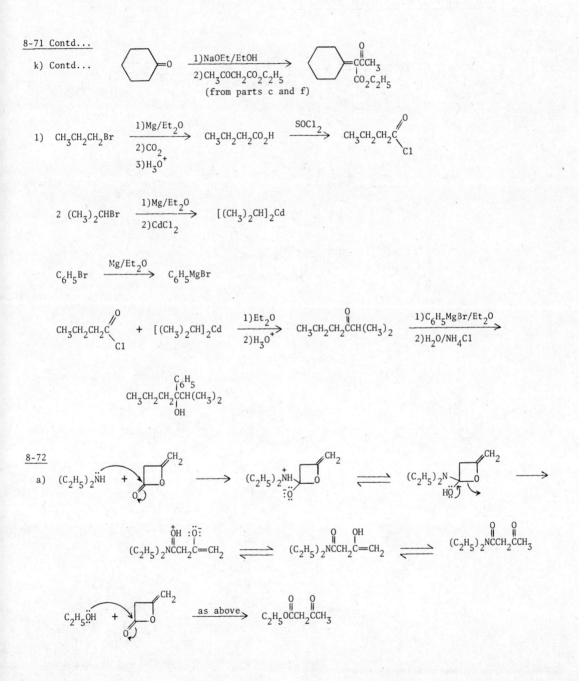

8-72

a)

8-72 Contd...

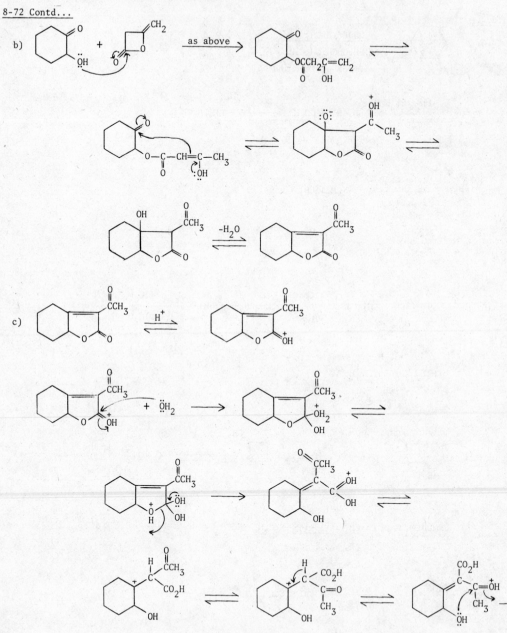

(Protonation-deprotonation of the carbon-carbon double bond allows cis-trans
isomerization to take place.)

8-72 Contd...

c)   Contd...

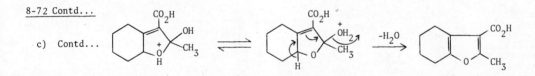

8-73  *IHD* = 5

The peak at 7.3 ppm with an area of 5 indicates a monosubstituted aromatic and accounts for

*IHD* = 4.  The singlet peak at 2.0 suggests $CH_3\overset{O}{\underset{}{C}}$— and accounts for *IHD* = 1.  The two triplets

of area = 2 suggest a —$CH_2$—$CH_2$— fragment.  Both of those multiplets are deshielded so

that the structure must be

2-Phenylethyl acetate

8-74  The IR carbonyl absorptions suggest 4-ring lactones which can account for at least $C_3O_2$ of
the molecular formula.  The eight H's must actually be in a ratio of 6:2.  Since they are
both singlet peaks, $>CH_2$ and $>C(CH_3)_2$ are suggested.  Chemical shifts show that the
equivalent $CH_3$ groups are not deshielded but that the $CH_2$ groups are markedly deshielded in
B and slightly deshielded in A.  The compounds are

A                                  B

β-Methyl-β-butylrolactone      α,α-Dimethyl-β-propiolactone

8-75

a)  *IHD* = 5.  A substituted aromatic ring (nmr = 6.7 - 7.7) accounts for *IHD* = 4 and some type
of conjugated carbonyl group (IR = 1680 cm$^{-1}$) accounts for *IHD* = 1.  The nmr peak at 9.7 ppm
which is lost on exchange with $D_2O$ is consistent with N-H.  Since the compound can be
prepared from p-bromotoluene, one nmr peak at 2.8 or 2.9 ppm must be a methyl group on the
aromatic ring.  The other peak would be consistent with an -$NHCH_3$ since only one H is located
on the nitrogen atom.  The compound is

8-75 Contd...

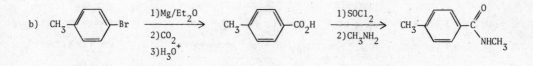

*N,p*-Dimethylbenzamide

b)

# 9 NUCLEOPHILIC SUBSTITUTIONS AT SATURATED CARBON

9-1  The rate-controlling step for the $S_N1$ reaction is a dissociation.  The position of equilibrium can be shifted back to undissociated starting material by increasing  the concentration of one of the products (mass law effect).  The leaving group and the added nucleophile compete for the intermediate carbocation.

9-2  The reaction proceeds by an $S_N1$ mechanism.  The reaction rate depends on the formation of the carbocation, not on the nature of the nucleophile.

9-3

a)  Rate = $k_2[C_6H_5CH_2Br][N_3^-]$

b)  The rate would double.

c)  The rate would increase by four (2 x 2).

9-4  The reaction of two molecules would randomly give a mixture of enantiomeric products. Reaction of two molecules ($k_e$) would result in no  optical rotation for a mixture of those two molecules ($k_\alpha$).   Thus $k_\alpha : k_e$ = 1.

9-5  When 50% of the original 2-iodooctane has reacted, the reaction mixture will, on the average, be racemic.  Any further chemical reaction will take place with equal probability on the $R$ and $S$ enantiomers.  No optical rotation is generated from this racemic mixture.

9-6

a)  Azide replaces chloride by an $S_N2$ mechanism, $\therefore$ inversion.

b)  Reduction of azide to amine does not affect the asymmetric carbon atom, $\therefore$ retention.

9-7

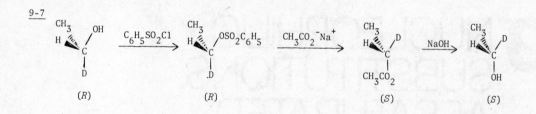

9-8  The solvolysis reaction of the tertiary organohalogen proceeds via an $S_N1$ mechanism. The polar solvent system enhances loss of $Br^-$ to give a symmetrically solvated carbocation. The intermediate carbocation is easily attacked by the nucleophile $H_2O$ from either side to give racemic product.

9-9

a)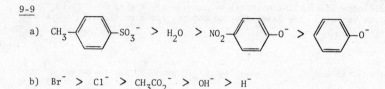

b)  $Br^- > Cl^- > CH_3CO_2^- > OH^- > H^-$

9-10  Hydroxide is a very poor leaving group. However, in the presence of acid the hydroxy group is protonated and the good leaving group, water, departs.

9-11

i)  In the oxygen and nitrogen series anions are better nucleophiles than neutral species.

ii)  Delocalization of electrons decreases nucleophilicity.

iii)  Nitrogen is a better nucleophile than oxygen because oxygen is more electronegative and holds its electrons more tightly.

9-12  A nucleophile must have a nonbonding electron pair to share in bond making; $BF_4^-$ does not.

9-13

a)  $(CH_3)_3P > (CH_3)_3B$        The boron atom has no unshared electron pair. It is actually a Lewis acid.

9-13 Contd...

b) $C_6H_5O^- > C_6H_5OH$      Anions are usually better nucleophiles than analogous noncharged species.

c) $(CH_3)_2NH > CH_3NH_2$      The electron donating methyl groups enhance nucleophilicity. Steric factors are not important in this specific reaction.

d) $p\text{-}CH_3C_6H_4O^- > p\text{-}NO_2C_6H_4O^-$      Nitro delocalizes the electron pair and decreases nucleophilicity.

e) $CH_3SH > CH_3OH$      The sulfur atom is the more nucleophilic.

f) $n\text{-}C_4H_9O^- > t\text{-}C_4H_9O^-$      The tertiary anion leads to steric hindrance.

g) $H_3N > H_4\overset{+}{N}$      Cations are not nucleophilic.

h)      $> (C_2H_5)_3N$      The alkyl groups are "tied back" in the bicyclic compound so that no steric interactions occur.

9-14 Steric hindrance to the $S_N2$ reaction accounts for the slower rates in the 2-substituted pyridines. The greater rate of the 4-methyl pyridine can be attributed to electron donation by the methyl group which enhances the nitrogen nucleophilicity.

9-15 The rate of reaction is the rate of carbocation formation and is independent of the nucleophile. However the product mixture will depend on the nucleophilicity of $Br^-$ and $Cl^-$ even though the addition occurs after the slow step of the overall reaction. $Br^-$ is a better nucleophile than $Cl^-$ in this reaction.

9-16

a) $(CH_3)_2\ddot{N}\text{—}CH_2Cl \xrightarrow{H_2O} [(CH_3)_2\ddot{N}\text{—}\overset{+}{C}H_2 \longleftrightarrow (CH_3)_2\overset{+}{N}\text{=}CH_2] Cl^- \xrightarrow[-H^+]{H_2O} (CH_3)_2\ddot{N}\text{—}CH_2OH$

b) Resonance stabilization of the intermediate cation involves an important contributing structure in which the positive charge is located on the heteroatom. A nitrogen atom is less electronegative than oxygen and can better accommodate the positive charge.

9-17

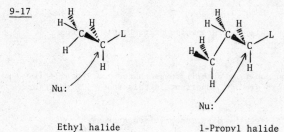

Ethyl halide          1-Propyl halide

In the ethyl halides, back-side attack of the nucleophile is sterically hindered by H-atoms on the β-carbon atom.  With the propyl systems at least 1/3 of the rotamer populations involve blocking of the back-side of the reaction center by a methyl group.

9-18

a) $(p\text{-MeOC}_6H_4)_3CCl$ > Chlorodiphenylmethane > 2-Chloro-2,3-dimethylbutane > 3-Chloro-2-methylpropene > 2-Chloropropane.

b) Chloromethyl methyl ether > Chlorophenylmethane > Chloromethane > 2-Chloropropane > 1-Chloro-2,2-dimethylpropane.

9-19  A is a very crowded molecule.  Dissociation into a carbocation relieves strain as the molecule changes from a tetrahedral to a trigonal geometry.  The rate controlling step is favored by "steric acceleration".

9-20  Ring opening occurs readily with ethylene oxide because the protonation makes the oxygen atom a good leaving group and ring strain is relieved.

9-21  The reactants and products will have essentially the same energies in the two solvent systems.  The major difference will be in the transition states and intermediates where the charged species are more stable in the solvent containing a higher percentage of water.

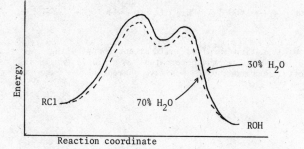

9-22

a) Water is a more polar solvent than methanol and dissociation to a more symmetrically solvated carbocation is favored. A higher degree of racemization results.

b) Reaction of this benzylic halide proceeds by an $S_N1$ mechanism in ethanol-$H_2O$. When the good nucleophile methoxide is used, an $S_N2$ pathway is favored on the secondary carbon atom and inversion stereochemistry results.

9-23

i)   $R—L \xrightarrow{\phantom{xxx}} \overset{\delta+ \quad \delta-}{R----L}$      Formation of charge

ii)  $Nu:^- + R—L \xrightarrow{\phantom{xxx}} \overset{\delta- \qquad \delta-}{Nu----R----L}$      Dispersal of charge

iii) $Nu: + R—L \xrightarrow{\phantom{xxx}} \overset{\delta+ \qquad \delta-}{Nu----R----L}$      Formation of charge

iv)  $Nu:^- + R—L^+ \xrightarrow{\phantom{xxx}} \overset{\delta- \qquad \delta+}{Nu----R----L}$      Destruction of charges

9-24  The hydration of $F^-$ is the most exothermic. Hydration is very favorable so that it is difficult to desolvate the ion to free the nucleophile. Iodide is the least strongly solvated and therefore is most easily freed to function as a nucleophile.

9-25  Bond energies C—Cl = 81 kcal/mol (339 kJ/mol)

$\phantom{Bond energies}$ C—Br = 68 kcal/mol (284 kJ/mol)

Activation energies in the aprotic solvent DMSO reflect bond strengths since solvation is relatively unimportant. Bond strengths and the rate of bond formation (kinetics) are in the same order.

9-26  The $S_N1$ pathway becomes relatively more important in both cases as solvent becomes more polar and capable of enhancing an ionization pathway. The benzylic substrate can form the more stable carbocation, thus gives relatively more $S_N1$ reaction while $S_N2$ predominates with the secondary propyl substrate.

9-27  A skeletal rearrangement produces the same relatively stable tertiary carbocation in each case.

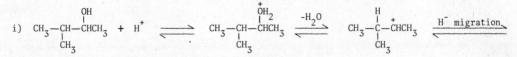

9-27 Contd...

i) Contd..        $(CH_3)_2\overset{+}{C}CH_2CH_3$

ii)  $CH_3-\underset{\underset{CH_3}{|}}{\overset{\overset{CH_3}{|}}{C}}-CH_2-OH \;+\; H^+ \;\rightleftharpoons\; CH_3-\underset{\underset{CH_3}{|}}{\overset{\overset{CH_3}{|}}{C}}-CH_2-\overset{+}{O}H_2 \;\underset{}{\overset{-H_2O}{\rightleftharpoons}}\; CH_3-\underset{\underset{CH_3}{|}}{\overset{\overset{CH_3}{|}}{C}}-\overset{+}{C}H_2 \;\overset{CH_3^- \text{migration}}{\underset{}{\rightleftharpoons}}$

        $(CH_3)_2\overset{+}{C}CH_2CH_3$

$(CH_3)_2\overset{+}{C}CH_2CH_3 \;+\; :\overset{..}{\underset{..}{C}l}\overline{:} \;\longrightarrow\; (CH_3)_2\overset{\overset{Cl}{|}}{C}CH_2CH_3$

9-28  In aqueous base these allylic halides are expected to react by an $S_N1$ mechanism. The
nucleophile can add to the allylic carbocation at either of two carbon atoms.

$CH_3CH{=}CH-CH_2Cl$ ⎤

$CH_3\overset{\overset{Cl}{|}}{C}H-CH{=}CH_2$ ⎦  $\longrightarrow$  $[CH_3CH{=}CH{-}\overset{+}{C}H_2 \longleftrightarrow CH_3\overset{+}{C}H{-}CH{=}CH_2]\; Cl^-$

                    $\downarrow$ $H_2O$
                    $(-H^+)$

        $CH_3CH{=}CHCH_2OH \;+\; CH_3\overset{\overset{OH}{|}}{C}HCH{=}CH_2$

9-29  Neighboring group participation by the sulfur is considerably better than by oxygen. One
reason is that the sulfur atom is a better nucleophile than oxygen. A second factor is that
sulfur is a larger atom with longer bonds. The three ring intermediate formed by the sulfur
atom is less strained (easier to form in the rate-controlling step) than that of the oxygen
atom.

9-30  In concentrated base the large excess of hydroxide substitutes for bromide with typical
$S_N2$ inversion. In the dilute base the intramolecular substitution by carboxylate is the
favored first step.

9-31  The stereospecific reactions proceed through epoxides. Opening of the epoxide in a second
stereospecific step gives the product of overall retention.

9-31 Contd...

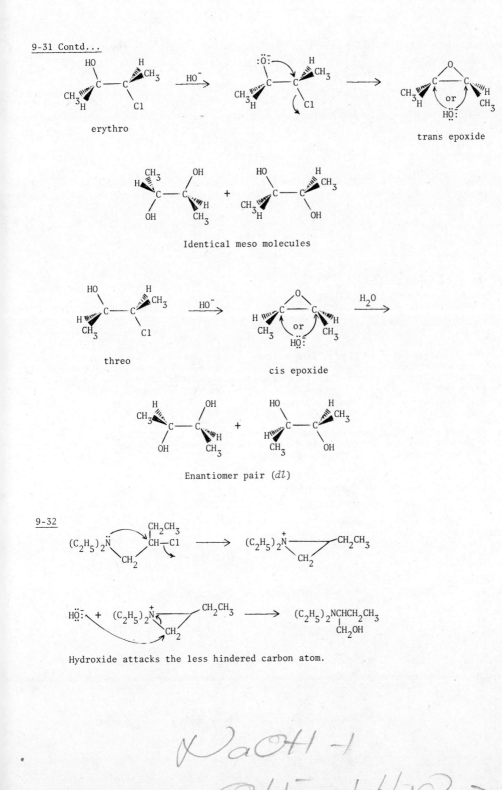

erythro

trans epoxide

Identical meso molecules

threo

cis epoxide

Enantiomer pair (*dl*)

9-32

Hydroxide attacks the less hindered carbon atom.

NaOH →

OH⁻ + H₂O →

<u>9-33</u>  The reactivity order reflects the ease in forming a carbocation in this acid catalyzed reaction.

<u>9-34</u>

a)  $C_6H_5CH_2OH \xrightarrow{PBr_3} C_6H_5CH_2Br$

b)  (R)-$C_6H_5\overset{\underset{\textstyle |}{OH}}{C}HCH_3 \xrightarrow[\text{or } SOCl_2/\text{pyridine}]{PCl_3}$ (S)-$C_6H_5\overset{\underset{\textstyle |}{Cl}}{C}HCH_3$

c)  $CH_3CH_2OH \xrightarrow[(P + I_2)]{PI_3} CH_3CH_2I$

d)  (R)-$CH_3\overset{\underset{\textstyle |}{OH}}{C}HCH_2CH_3 \xrightarrow[Et_2O]{SOCl_2}$ (R)-$CH_3\overset{\underset{\textstyle |}{Cl}}{C}HCH_2CH_3$

<u>9-35</u>  Formation of a haloalkane from an alcohol (the reverse of the hydrolysis reaction) requires that hydroxy be converted to a good leaving group. Acid produced in the neutral hydrolysis can be the catalyst for a reverse reaction. Basic hydrolysis produces alcohol and the halide anion so that no acid catalyst is available for the reverse reaction.

<u>9-36</u>  Iodide is a better nucleophile than water and a better leaving group than chloride. Iodide substitutes for chloride, then water displaces iodide. Only a catalytic amount of iodide is added since it is regenerated as the alcohol product forms.

$CH_3CH_2CH_2Cl + :\overset{..}{\underset{..}{I}}:^- \longrightarrow CH_3CH_2CH_2I + :\overset{..}{\underset{..}{Cl}}:^-$     fast

$CH_3CH_2CH_2I + H_2\overset{..}{\underset{..}{O}} \longrightarrow CH_3CH_2CH_2OH + HI$     fast

<u>9-37</u>

i)  $(CH_3)_3C\overset{..}{\underset{..}{O}}:^- Na^+ + CH_3\overset{\frown}{-}OSO_3CH_3 \longrightarrow (CH_3)_3COCH_3 + CH_3OSO_3^-Na^+$

ii) 

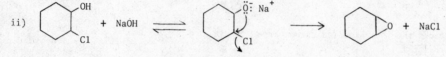

9-38   $N,N,N$-Trimethylphenylammonium ethoxide functions as both base and alkylating agent.  The ethoxide, working as a base, preferentially forms an alkoxide (phenoxide) from the phenolic hydroxy group of morphine.  The trimethylammonium group then is the methylating agent since dimethylaniline becomes the good leaving group.

$$R\overset{..}{\underset{..}{O}}\text{:}^- \quad + \quad CH_3\text{—}\overset{+}{N}(CH_3)_2C_6H_5 \quad \longrightarrow \quad ROCH_3 \quad + \quad (CH_3)_2\overset{..}{N}C_6H_5$$

9-39   Alcohol is protonated by the acid in either mechanism so that the initial leaving group is unchanged.  Since bisulfate is the better nucleophile, we would expect the alkyl sulfate to form more readily.

9-40   The ether cleaves under acidic conditions so as to give the more stable carbocation or the more favorable carbocation-like transition state.  In this case, the benzylic carbocation is favored.

$$C_6H_5CH_2OCH_3 \quad \xrightarrow{\ HI\ } \quad C_6H_5CH_2I \quad + \quad CH_3OH$$

9-41   Although the alcohol initially forms on ether cleavage, excess HI rapidly converts alcohol to an iodoalkane.

9-42   In acid, the protonated epoxide first opens ($S_N1$) to give the more favorable secondary carbocation, then the alcohol adds.  In base, an $S_N2$ reaction takes place as alkoxide attacks at the less substituted carbon atom of the epoxide.

9-43

a)   $CH_3CH_2CH_2OCH_3$

d)   $C_2H_5OCH\text{—}\overset{OH}{\underset{CH_3}{|}}CHCH_3$

b)   [structure: benzene ring with $\text{—}CH_2OH$ and $OC_2H_5$ substituents]

e)   [structure: tetrahydropyran ring with O]

c)   $(CH_3)_2CHI \quad + \quad C_6H_5OH$

f)   $(CH_3)_3CI \quad + \quad CH_3OH$

(or $CH_3I$)

9-44   If alkyl-oxygen cleavage takes place, the oxygen atom of the alcohol product must come from the water.

9-44 Contd...

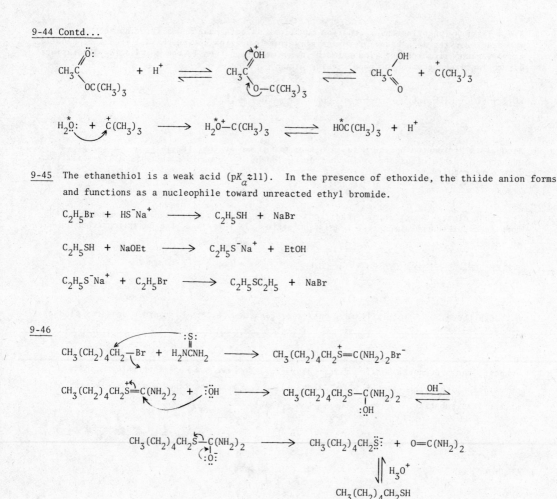

9-45  The ethanethiol is a weak acid ($pK_a \approx 11$).  In the presence of ethoxide, the thiide anion forms and functions as a nucleophile toward unreacted ethyl bromide.

$$C_2H_5Br + HS^-Na^+ \longrightarrow C_2H_5SH + NaBr$$

$$C_2H_5SH + NaOEt \longrightarrow C_2H_5S^-Na^+ + EtOH$$

$$C_2H_5S^-Na^+ + C_2H_5Br \longrightarrow C_2H_5SC_2H_5 + NaBr$$

9-46

9-47

a)  Trimethyloxonium fluoroborate is an excellent methylating agent.

b)  Fluoroborate is not a nucleophilic anion  (see problem solution 9-12).  A better nucleophile such as the halides would immediately undergo substitution on the cation and destroy the salt.

$$X^- + CH_3-\overset{+}{O}(CH_3)_2 \longrightarrow CH_3X + O(CH_3)_2$$

9-48  The product has a plane of symmetry.

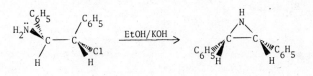

9-49  Formation of the diazonium ion requires that the amino nitrogen atom lose two hydrogen atoms. This is not possible with secondary amines and the reaction sequence stops at the *N*,*N*-disubstituted nitrosoamine.

9-50

a)  The critical distance between the two quaternary ammonium groups is the same as in decamethonium dibromide (and curare).

b)  Succinyl choline is a diester.  Many methods of metabolic degradation of esters are available in biological systems.

9-51

$$(CH_3)_3N: + HO-OH\ H^+ \xrightarrow{H_2O} (CH_3)_3\overset{+}{N}-OH + H_2O \rightleftharpoons (CH_3)_3\overset{+}{N}-\overset{..}{\overset{..}{O}}: + H_3O^+$$

9-52  The first methyl group increases the electron density at the nitrogen atom to which it is attached.  That nitrogen atom is the better nucleophile in the second alkylation step.

9-53

a)  $CH_3CH_2CH_2CH_2OH + HCl \longrightarrow . CH_3CH_2CH_2CH_2Cl \xrightarrow{NH_3 \text{(excess)}} CH_3CH_2CH_2CH_2NH_2$

b)  $CH_3CH_2CH_2Br + (CH_3)_2NH \xrightarrow{Na_2CO_3} CH_3CH_2CH_2N(CH_3)_2$

c)  $H_2NNH_2 + (CH_3)_2CHCl \xrightarrow{Na_2CO_3} H_2NNHCH(CH_3)_2 \xrightarrow[Na_2CO_3]{CH_3CH_2Br} CH_3CH_2NHNHCH(CH_3)_2$

(The more bulky isopropyl group inhibits substitution of the second alkyl group on the same nitrogen atom.)

d)  $C_6H_5CH_2Cl + (CH_3)_3N \longrightarrow C_6H_5CH_2\overset{+}{N}(CH_3)_3 \ Cl^-$

9-53 Contd...

e)  $(CH_3)_2NH + C_2H_5I \xrightarrow{Na_2CO_3} (CH_3)_2NC_2H_5 \xrightarrow{H_2O_2} (CH_3)_2\overset{+}{\underset{O^-}{N}}C_2H_5$

9-54

$[CH_3CH_2CH(CH_3)O]_3P: + CH_3{-}I \longrightarrow [CH_3CH_2CH(CH_3)O]_3\overset{+}{P}CH_3 \ I^-$

(R)                                                              (R)

$[CH_3CH_2CH(CH_3)O]_2\overset{+}{\underset{CH_3}{P}}{-}O{-}CH(CH_3)CH_2CH_3 + I^- \xrightarrow{(S_N2 \ \text{inversion})}$

(R)                              (R)

$[CH_3CH_2CH(CH_3)O]_2\underset{CH_3}{P}{=}O + CH_3CH_2CH(CH_3)I$

(R)                              (S)

9-55

a)
$\underset{\displaystyle (R)}{}$

$(CH_3)_2\underset{Cl}{\overset{|}{C}H}CHCO_2H + NH_3 \text{(excess)} \xrightarrow{H_2O} (CH_3)_2CH\overset{NH_2}{\overset{|}{C}}HCO_2H$

2-Amino-3-methylbutanoic acid

(Valine)

b)  $ClCH_2CH_2OH + (C_2H_5)_2NH \longrightarrow (C_2H_5)_2NCH_2CH_2OH$

2-Diethylaminoethanol

c)  $C_6H_5CH_2Cl + C_6H_5NH_2 \longrightarrow C_6H_5CH_2NHC_6H_5$

N-Phenylbenzylamine

d) $3 \ CH_3I + C_6H_5CH_2NH_2 \longrightarrow C_6H_5CH_2\overset{+}{N}(CH_3)_3 \ I^-$

N,N,N-Trimethylbenzylammonium
iodide

e)  $C_2H_5Br + (C_6H_5CH_2)_3P \longrightarrow (C_6H_5CH_2)_3\overset{+}{P}C_2H_5 \ Br^-$

Ethyltribenzylphosphonium
bromide

f)  $C_6H_5\overset{O}{\overset{\|}{C}}CH_2Br + (CH_3)_2S \longrightarrow C_6H_5\overset{O}{\overset{\|}{C}}CH_2\overset{+}{S}(CH_3)_2 \ Br^-$

Dimethylphenacylsulfonium
bromide

9-56

$$CH_3CCH_2CCH_3 + K_2CO_3 \longrightarrow (CH_3\overset{O}{\overset{||}{C}})_2\overset{..}{\overset{-}{C}}H$$

(with carbonyl O's on first structure)

$$(CH_3\overset{O}{\overset{||}{C}})_2\overset{..}{\overset{-}{C}}H + CH_3\overset{\frown}{-}I \longrightarrow (CH_3\overset{O}{\overset{||}{C}})_2CHCH_3$$

9-57

a)  $CH_2(CO_2C_2H_5)_2$  $\xrightarrow[\text{2) 2 }CH_3CH_2I]{\text{1)NaOEt/EtOH}}$  $(CH_3CH_2)_2C(CO_2C_2H_5)_2$

b)  $CH_2(CO_2C_2H_5)_2$  $\xrightarrow[\text{2) }CH_3CH_2CH_2Cl]{\text{1) 1 NaOEt/EtOH}}$  $CH_3CH_2CH_2CH(CO_2C_2H_5)_2$  $\xrightarrow[\text{2)}CH_3I]{\text{1)NaOEt/EtOH}}$

$$CH_3CH_2CH_2\underset{\underset{CH_3}{|}}{C}(CO_2C_2H_5)_2 \xrightarrow{H_3O^+/\Delta} CH_3CH_2CH_2\underset{\underset{CH_3}{|}}{C}HCO_2H$$

c)  $CH_3\overset{O}{\overset{||}{C}}CH_2CO_2C_2H_5$  $\xrightarrow{\text{1)NaOEt/EtOH}}$  $CH_3\overset{O}{\overset{||}{C}}CH_2$—(cyclopentyl)

2) (cyclopentyl)—Cl

3)$H_3O^+/\Delta$

d)  $CH_2(CO_2C_2H_5)_2$  $\xrightarrow{\text{1)NaOEt/EtOH}}$  (cyclopentyl)—$CO_2H$

2)$Br(CH_2)_4Br$

3)$H_3O^+/\Delta$

9-58  The $S_N2$ reaction depends on a good nucleophile.  Carbon is less electronegative than an oxygen atom so that the nonbonding electrons of the anion are more available than those on the oxyanion.  In the $S_N1$ reaction a reactive carbocationic intermediate is involved.
Reaction is less selective and the relative importance of O-alkylation increases.

9-59

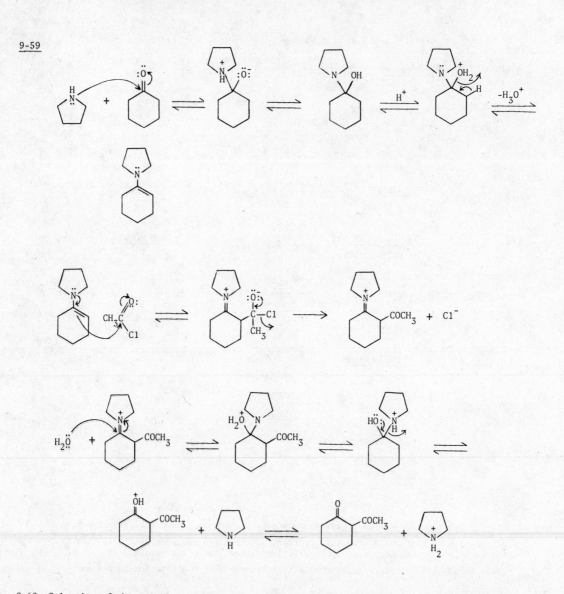

9-60  Solvation of the cyanide ion through hydrogen bonding to ethanol decreases the effective
nucleophilicity of the anion.  Aprotic solvents minimize such anion solvation.

9-61

$C_6H_5CH_2CH_2Br$ $\xrightarrow[\substack{2)H_2C\diagtriangle CH_2 \\ 3)H_3O^+}]{1)Mg/Et_2O}}$ $C_6H_5CH_2CH_2CH_2CH_2OH$ $\xrightarrow{HBr}$

$C_6H_5CH_2CH_2CH_2CH_2Br$ $\xrightarrow[\substack{2)H_2C\diagtriangle CH_2 \\ 3)H_3O^+}]{1)Mg/Et_2O}}$ $C_6H_5(CH_2)_5CH_2OH$

9-62 Three products will form, in addition to a usually poor overall yield in the Wurtz reaction;

$CH_3CH_2Br$ + $CH_3CH_2CH_2Br$ $\xrightarrow[\Delta]{Na/C_6H_6}$ $n\text{-}C_4H_{10}$ + $n\text{-}C_5H_{12}$ + $n\text{-}C_6H_{14}$

9-63 Some of the Grignard reagent initially formed reacts with still unreacted haloalkane in a process resembling the Wurtz reaction. Thus two moles of haloalkane are consumed for only one mol of magnesium. In Grignard formation the stoichiometry is based on one mol of magnesium per one mol of the organohalogen compound.

9-64

a) $CH_3CH_2C\equiv CH$ + $NaNH_2$ $\xrightarrow[\substack{2)CH_3(CH_2)_4CH_2Br}]{1)NH_3/-33°}}$ $CH_3CH_2C\equiv C(CH_2)_5CH_3$

b) 2 $n\text{-}C_4H_9Li$ + CuI $\xrightarrow{THF/0°}$ $(n\text{-}C_4H_9)_2CuLi$ $\xrightarrow{}$ (cyclohexene with $C_4H_9\text{-}n$)

c) $CH_3Br$ + NaCN $\xrightarrow{DMSO}$ $CH_3CN$

d) $HC\equiv CH$ + $NaNH_2$ $\xrightarrow[\substack{2)CH_3(CH_2)_6CH_2Br}]{1)NH_3/-33°}}$ $HC\equiv C(CH_2)_7CH_3$

9-65

$H:^-$ + $RC\overset{O}{\underset{L}{\diagdown}}$ $\xrightarrow{}$ $RC\overset{O}{\underset{H}{\diagdown}}$ $\xrightarrow{}$ $R\overset{OH}{\underset{}{C}}H_2$

Aldehyde        Alcohol

9-65 Contd...

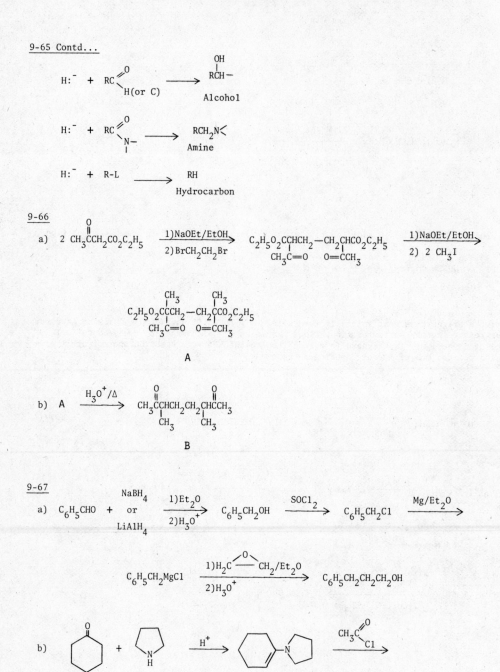

9-66

a) $2\ CH_3CCH_2CO_2C_2H_5 \xrightarrow[2)BrCH_2CH_2Br]{1)NaOEt/EtOH} C_2H_5O_2CCHCH_2-CH_2CHCO_2C_2H_5 \xrightarrow[2)\ 2\ CH_3I]{1)NaOEt/EtOH}$

$$C_2H_5O_2CCCH_2-CH_2CCO_2C_2H_5$$

A

b) $A \xrightarrow{H_3O^+/\Delta} CH_3CCHCH_2CH_2CHCCH_3$

B

9-67

a) $C_6H_5CHO + \begin{array}{c} NaBH_4 \\ or \\ LiAlH_4 \end{array} \xrightarrow[2)H_3O^+]{1)Et_2O} C_6H_5CH_2OH \xrightarrow{SOCl_2} C_6H_5CH_2Cl \xrightarrow{Mg/Et_2O}$

$C_6H_5CH_2MgCl \xrightarrow[2)H_3O^+]{1)H_2C-CH_2/Et_2O} C_6H_5CH_2CH_2CH_2OH$

b)

(Use of the enamine avoids polyacylation)

9-67 Contd...

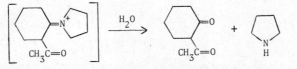

c)   CH₃CCH₂CO₂C₂H₅  $\xrightarrow[2)CH_3CH_2Br]{1)NaOEt/EtOH}$  CH₃CCHCO₂C₂H₅  $\xrightarrow{H_3O^+/\Delta}$  CH₃CCH₂CH₂CH₃
         ‖O                                                    ‖O  |CH₂CH₃                              ‖O

d)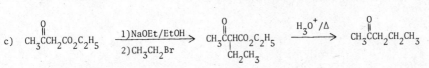

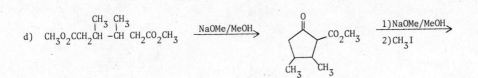

e)   HO₂CCH₂CH₂CO₂H + C₂H₅OH(excess)  $\xrightarrow{H_3O^+}$  C₂H₅O₂CCH₂CH₂CO₂C₂H₅

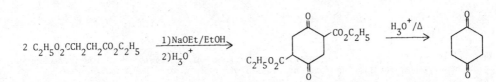

9-68

a)   (CH₃)₂CHCH₂Br

b)   ⬡—CHOHCH₂OH

c)   ⬡—N⁺(C₂H₅)₃Br⁻

d)   CH₃CHCH₃
          |Br

e)   (CH₃)₂CHI

f)   CH₃CH₂CCHCCH₃
            ‖  |  ‖
            O C₂H₅ O

g)   CH₃C≡CCH₂CH₂CH₂Cl

h)   ⬡

i)   CH₃CH₂CH₂I

j)   CH₃OCH₃

9-68 Contd...

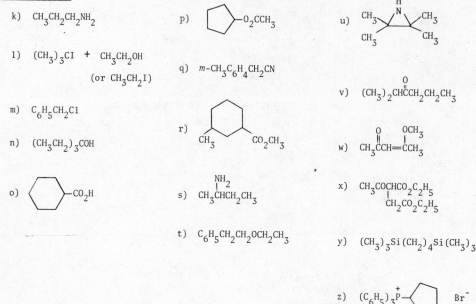

k)   $CH_3CH_2CH_2NH_2$

l)   $(CH_3)_3CI$ + $CH_3CH_2OH$

       (or $CH_3CH_2I$)

m)   $C_6H_5CH_2Cl$

n)   $(CH_3CH_2)_3COH$

o)   ⬡—$CO_2H$

p)   ⬠—$O_2CCH_3$

q)   $m$-$CH_3C_6H_4CH_2CN$

r)   $CH_3$ ⬡ $CO_2CH_3$

s)   $CH_3\overset{NH_2}{\underset{|}{CH}}CH_2CH_3$

t)   $C_6H_5CH_2CH_2OCH_2CH_3$

u)   $CH_3$ $\overset{H}{\underset{}{N}}$ $CH_3$ / $CH_3$ $CH_3$

v)   $(CH_3)_2\overset{O}{\overset{||}{CH}C}CH_2CH_2CH_3$

w)   $CH_3\overset{O}{\overset{||}{C}}CH{=}\overset{OCH_3}{\underset{|}{C}}CH_3$

x)   $CH_3COCHCO_2C_2H_5$ / $CH_2CO_2C_2H_5$

y)   $(CH_3)_3Si(CH_2)_4Si(CH_3)_3$

z)   $(C_6H_5)_3\overset{+}{P}$—⬠   $Br^-$

9-69   Departure of acetic acid from A forms a tertiary carbocation. That planar intermediate leads to a racemic alcohol product on reaction with water.

9-70

a)   As the nucleophile becomes less solvated it is freer for reaction. When reactions are carried out under identical conditions, substitution in aprotic HMPT proceeds more effectively.

b)   Inversion of configuration provides strong evidence for substitution by the $S_N2$ mechanism.

Apparently the enhanced nucleophilicity in HMPT overcomes the severe steric inhibition to back sided attack on the primary carbon atom of the neopentyl group.

9-71

A $\longrightarrow$ B   $S_N2$ - inversion

B $\longrightarrow$ C   No effect on asymmetric carbon atom - retention

C $\longrightarrow$ D   $S_N2$ - inversion

D $\longrightarrow$ E   No effect on asymmetric carbon atom - retention

} Overall retention

9-72

a)  A = HC≡C:⁻ Na⁺

   B = HC≡CCH₂CH₂CH₂OH

   C = SOCl₂

   D = HC≡CCH₂CH₂CH₂CN

b)  E = CH₃CH₂Br

   F = CH₃CH₂NH₂

c)  G = CH₂(CO₂C₂H₅)₂

   H = CH₃CH(CO₂C₂H₅)₂

   I = CH₃C̈(CO₂C₂H₅)₂ Na⁺

   J = CH₃(CH₂)₃C(CO₂C₂H₅)₂
                    |
                   CH₃

d)  K = CH₂=CHCH₂O⁻Na⁺

   L =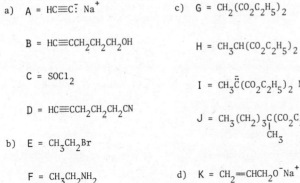

   M = PBr₃

   N = CH₂=CHCH₂OCH₂CH₃

e)  O =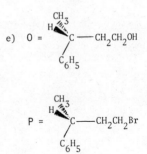

   P = 
   $$\begin{array}{c} CH_3 \\ H\cdots C - CH_2CH_2Br \\ C_6H_5 \end{array}$$

   Q = LiAlH₄/Et₂O

9-73

a)  With silver nitrate, tertiary haloalkanes ionize to form a tertiary carbocation and a precipitate forms rapily.  The speed of ionization and hence precipitate formation decreases in the order: tertiary > secondary > primary,  The reverse is true for $S_N2$ substitution of I⁻ for Br⁻ where primary > secondary > tertiary.  If the unknown reacts rapidly with AgNO₃/EtOH and not at all with NaI/acetone it is tertiary; if a precipitate forms slowly with both tests then the unknown is secondary.  If the unknown reacts rapidly with NaI/acetone and not with AgNO₃/EtOH it is primary.

b)  CH₃CH₂Br        AgNO₃/EtOH - no reaction        NaI/Acetone - fast

   (CH₃)₂CHBr       AgNO₃ - slow                    NaI/Acetone - slow

   (CH₃)₃CCl        AgNO₃/EtOH - fast               NaI/Acetone - no reaction

9-74

   Cl₂CHCHCHCl₂
        |
        Cl

9-74 Contd...   The doublet-triplet with an area ratio of 2:1 indicates two equivalent protons split by one proton and the one proton split by the other two.  Since the doublet is deshielded the most, the protons it represents must be deshielded by a greater number of chlorine atoms than the proton which accounts for the triplet.

9-75

$$(C_2H_5O)_3P \; + \; C_6H_5CH_2Cl \; \longrightarrow \; (C_2H_5O)_3\overset{+}{P}CH_2C_6H_5 \; Cl^- \; \longrightarrow \; (C_2H_5O)_2\overset{O}{\overset{\|}{P}}CH_2C_6H_5 \; + \; C_2H_5Cl$$

$$\qquad\qquad\qquad\qquad\qquad\qquad\qquad\qquad\qquad A \qquad\qquad\qquad\qquad\qquad\qquad\qquad\qquad\qquad B$$

$$B \; \xrightarrow[\text{DMF}]{\text{NaOMe}} \; (C_2H_5O)_2\overset{O}{\overset{\|}{P}}-\overset{..}{C}HC_6H_5 \; \xrightarrow{C_6H_5CHO} \; C_6H_5CH\!=\!CHC_6H_5 \; + \; (C_2H_5O)_2\overset{O}{\overset{\|}{P}}-O^-Na^+$$

$$\qquad\qquad\qquad\qquad\qquad\qquad\qquad C$$

The phosphonium salt A is unstable and forms B by the Arbusov reaction.  Addition of base forms the phosphonate ylid which undergoes a Wittig type reaction with benzaldehyde.

9-76

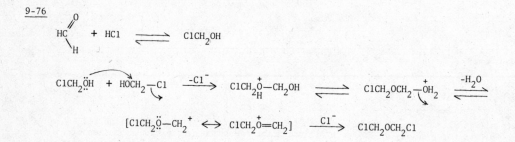

9-77

a)  In the highly polar solvent formic acid, the benzylic alcohol solvolyzes by an $S_N1$ pathway with racemization stereochemistry.

b)  In this case bromide replaces bromide in an $S_N2$ reaction.  Each substitution gives an inverted molecule which cancels the rotation of an unreacted molecule.

c)  In the trans isomer the carbonyl oxygen atom can assist in displacing the bromide by a neighboring group effect.  This is not possible in the cis isomer.

9-77 Contd...

c)

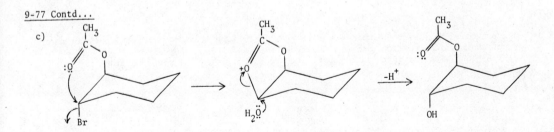

d) In azide the negative charge is more delocalized than in the amide anion.  Charge is spread over three atoms.

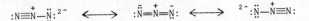

e)

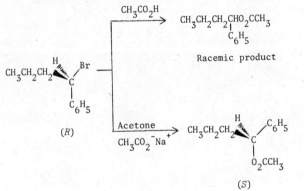

CH₃CO₂H → CH₃CH₂CH₂CHO₂CCH₃
                                    C₆H₅

Racemic product

The highly polar solvent and moderate nucleophile result in solvolysis by an $S_N1$ pathway.

Acetone
CH₃CO₂⁻ Na⁺

The moderately polar solvent and excellent nucleophile favor an $S_N2$ mechanism.

(*S*)

Inverted product

f) The structure of the rigid bicyclic molecule inhibits backsided attack of a nucleophile by an $S_N2$ pathway.  Formation of a carbocation in an $S_N1$ process is inhibited because the bridgehead carbon atom cannot become planar.

g) Only the trans isomer can undergo a backsided $S_N2$ cyclization.

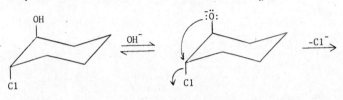

<u>9-78</u>

a) In approaching this synthesis we recognize that a tertiary alcohol with two identical alkyl groups can be prepared from a Grignard reagent plus an ester. The ester, methylcyclohexylcarboxylate, is a substituted acetate. It can be prepared from diethylmalonate.

$H_2C(CO_2C_2H_5)_2$ $\xrightarrow[\text{2)}Br(CH_2)_5Br]{\text{1)}NaOEt/EtOH}$ [cyclohexane ring with $CO_2C_2H_5$ and $CO_2C_2H_5$] $\xrightarrow{H_3O^+/\Delta}$

[cyclohexane]$-CO_2H$ $\xrightarrow{CH_3OH/H^+}$ [cyclohexane]$-CO_2CH_3$ $\xrightarrow[\text{2)}NH_4Cl/H_2O]{\text{1)}C_2H_5MgBr/Et_2O}$ [cyclohexane]$-\overset{\overset{\text{OH}}{|}}{C}(C_2H_5)_2$

b) In this example the ketone precursor to the alcohol product is a substituted acetone. It can be prepared from ethyl acetoacetate.

$CH_3\overset{\overset{\text{O}}{\|}}{C}CH_2CO_2C_2H_5$ $\xrightarrow[\text{2) 2 }C_2H_5Br]{\text{1)}NaOEt/EtOH}$ $CH_3\overset{\overset{\text{O}}{\|}}{C}C(C_2H_5)_2CO_2C_2H_5$ $\xrightarrow[\Delta]{H_3O^+}$

$CH_3\overset{\overset{\text{O}}{\|}}{C}CH(C_2H_5)_2$ $\xrightarrow[\text{2)}NH_4Cl/H_2O]{\text{1)}C_2H_5MgBr/Et_2O}$ $CH_3\overset{\overset{\text{OH}}{|}}{\underset{\underset{C_2H_5}{|}}{C}}CH(C_2H_5)_2$

c) To minimize steric problems, add the larger group ($CH_3CH_2$) first, then the smaller group ($CH_3$).

$CH_3\overset{\overset{\text{O}}{\|}}{C}CH_2CO_2C_2H_5$ $\xrightarrow[\text{2)}CH_3CH_2Br]{\text{1)}NaOEt/EtOH}$ $CH_3\overset{\overset{\text{O}}{\|}}{C}-\overset{\overset{\text{CH}_2\text{CH}_3}{|}}{C}HCO_2C_2H_5$ $\xrightarrow[\text{2)}CH_3I]{\text{1)}NaOEt/EtOH}$

$CH_3\overset{\overset{\text{O}}{\|}}{C}-\overset{\overset{\text{CH}_2\text{CH}_3}{|}}{\underset{\underset{CH_3}{|}}{C}}CO_2C_2H_5$ $\xrightarrow[\Delta]{H_3O^+}$ $CH_3\overset{\overset{\text{O}}{\|}}{C}\overset{}{\underset{\underset{CH_3}{|}}{C}}HCH_2CH_3$

d) $CH_2(CO_2C_2H_5)_2$ $\xrightarrow[\text{2) 2 }C_2H_5Br]{\text{1)}NaOEt/EtOH}$ $(C_2H_5)_2C(CO_2C_2H_5)_2$ $\xrightarrow[\Delta]{H_3O^+}$ $(C_2H_5)_2CHCO_2H$

e) $CH_2(CO_2C_2H_5)_2$ $\xrightarrow[\text{2)}C_6H_5CH_2Cl]{\text{1)}NaOEt/EtOH}$ $C_6H_5CH_2CH(CO_2C_2H_5)_2$ $\xrightarrow{H_3O^+/\Delta}$

9-78 Contd...

e) Contd...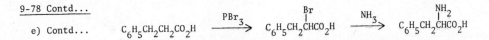

9-79  The anion forms at the more acidic position with one mol of base.  When two moles of strong
base are used, a second, less favorable anion also forms.  The less stable carbanion is the
more reactive nucleophile and is alkylated first.

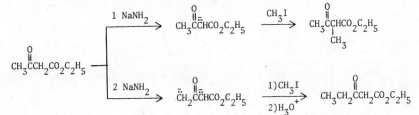

9-80  The molecular weight of ethyl acetoacetate is 130.  The addition of four carbon atoms and
associated hydrogens would be required to give a molecular weight near 186.  The nmr singlet

at 2.1 ppm could account for $CH_3\overset{O}{\overset{\|}{C}}$— while the quartet at 4.2 ppm and triplet at 1.3 are due

to the $CH_3CH_2O$— group.  Both of these groups are essentially unchanged from ethyl
acetoacetate.  Alkylation must have taken place at the methylene next to the carbonyl.  The
triplet at 0.8 ppm with integral area of 6 is consistent with two equivalent methyl groups.
If four carbon atoms were actually added in the alkylation, then two equivalent ethyl groups
are indicated.  That would lead to a molecular weight of 186.  However, the quartet expected
for the —$CH_2$— groups is not initially obvious.  Careful examination of integral areas

shows that the singlet at 2.1 ppm is somewhat larger than 3 protons while the *apparent*
*triplet* at 1.9 ppm does not fit the structure which seems to require alkylation of ethyl
acetoacetate by two ethyl groups.  Actually the total area of the peaks between 1.6 and
2.1 ppm corresponds to 7 protons.  The pattern observed results from the overlap of a
singlet at 2.1 ppm and a quartet with skewed multiplet areas centered at 1.9 ppm.

singlet

quartet

Combine to give

b)   $CH_3\overset{O}{\overset{\|}{C}}CH_2CO_2CH_2CH_3$  $\xrightarrow[\text{2) 2 }CH_3CH_2Br]{\text{1)NaOEt/EtOH}}$  $CH_3\overset{O}{\overset{\|}{C}}-\underset{\underset{CH_2CH_3}{|}}{\overset{\overset{CH_2CH_3}{|}}{C}}-CO_2CH_2CH_3$

9-81

a)

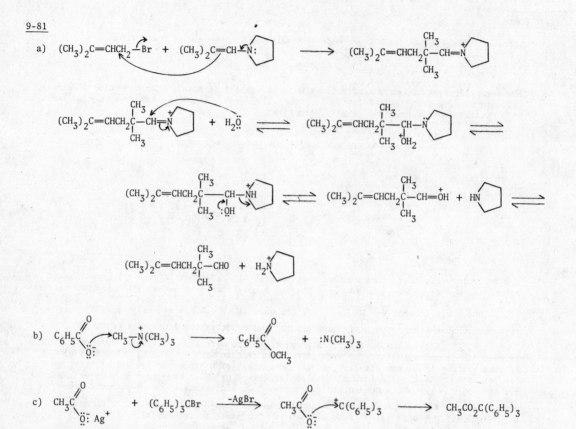

b)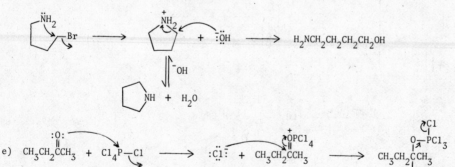

c)

d) The nitrogen atom acts as a neighboring group to displace Br⁻. The cyclic product can be recovered, or re-opened to give substitution.

e)

9-81 Contd...

e) Contd...

$$\left[ \begin{array}{c} CH_3CH_2\overset{+}{\underset{}{C}}CH_3 \\[2pt] \overset{\displaystyle :\ddot{C}l:}{\Big\updownarrow} \\[2pt] CH_3CH_2\underset{\overset{}{\underset{+}{C}l}}{\overset{O}{\underset{\parallel}{C}}}CH_3 \end{array} \right] + Cl^- \longrightarrow CH_3CH_2\underset{Cl}{\overset{Cl}{\underset{\mid}{\overset{\mid}{C}}}}CH_3$$

9-82

a) Use of the enamine insures monoalkylation in the first step.

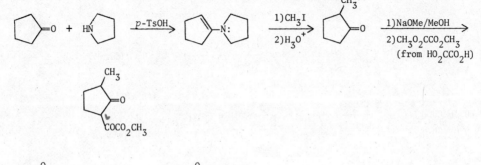

b) 

$$C_6H_5\overset{O}{\overset{\parallel}{C}}CH_3 \xrightarrow[\text{2) 2 } CH_3CH_2I]{\text{1)NaH/}C_6H_6} C_6H_5\overset{O}{\overset{\parallel}{C}}\underset{\overset{\mid}{CH_2CH_3}}{C}HCH_2CH_3$$

c) $HO_2C(CH_2)_5CO_2H + C_2H_5OH(\text{excess}) \longrightarrow C_2H_5O_2C(CH_2)_5CO_2C_2H_5 \xrightarrow{\text{NaOEt/EtOH}}$

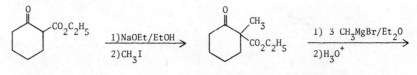

9-82 Contd...

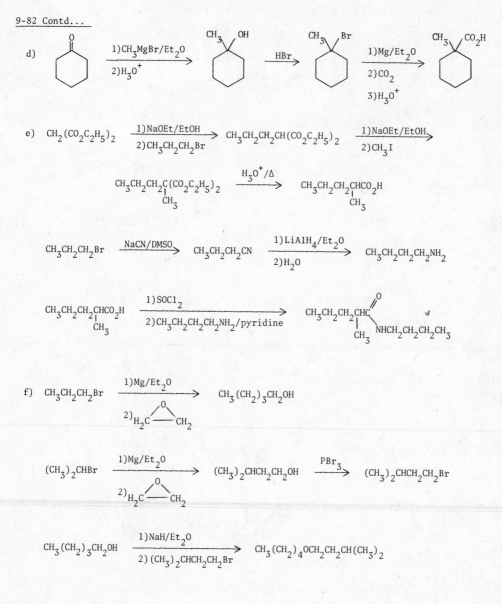

d)

e) $CH_2(CO_2C_2H_5)_2$ $\xrightarrow[\text{2)}CH_3CH_2CH_2Br]{\text{1)NaOEt/EtOH}}$ $CH_3CH_2CH_2CH(CO_2C_2H_5)_2$ $\xrightarrow[\text{2)}CH_3I]{\text{1)NaOEt/EtOH}}$

$CH_3CH_2CH_2\underset{\underset{CH_3}{|}}{C}(CO_2C_2H_5)_2$ $\xrightarrow{H_3O^+/\Delta}$ $CH_3CH_2CH_2\underset{\underset{CH_3}{|}}{CH}CO_2H$

$CH_3CH_2CH_2Br$ $\xrightarrow{NaCN/DMSO}$ $CH_3CH_2CH_2CN$ $\xrightarrow[\text{2)}H_2O]{\text{1)}LiAlH_4/Et_2O}$ $CH_3CH_2CH_2CH_2NH_2$

$CH_3CH_2CH_2\underset{\underset{CH_3}{|}}{CH}CO_2H$ $\xrightarrow[\text{2)}CH_3CH_2CH_2CH_2NH_2/\text{pyridine}]{\text{1)}SOCl_2}$ $CH_3CH_2CH_2\underset{\underset{CH_3}{|}}{CH}\overset{\overset{O}{||}}{C}NHCH_2CH_2CH_2CH_3$

f) $CH_3CH_2CH_2Br$ $\xrightarrow[\text{2)}H_2C\overset{O}{-\!-\!-}CH_2]{\text{1)}Mg/Et_2O}$ $CH_3(CH_2)_3CH_2OH$

$(CH_3)_2CHBr$ $\xrightarrow[\text{2)}H_2C\overset{O}{-\!-\!-}CH_2]{\text{1)}Mg/Et_2O}$ $(CH_3)_2CHCH_2CH_2OH$ $\xrightarrow{PBr_3}$ $(CH_3)_2CHCH_2CH_2Br$

$CH_3(CH_2)_3CH_2OH$ $\xrightarrow[\text{2)}(CH_3)_2CHCH_2CH_2Br]{\text{1)}NaH/Et_2O}$ $CH_3(CH_2)_4OCH_2CH_2CH(CH_3)_2$

9-83

a) Elemental analysis provides an empirical formula of $C_6H_{13}NO_2$ and the mass spectrum confirms this as the molecular formula. The IR spectrum suggests some type of carbonyl group. The mode of formation of A suggests that dimethylamine has displaced a halogen in a substitution reaction, thus compound B must also have the carbonyl group.

9-83 Contd...

a) Contd...  The nmr spectrum is consistent with a dimethylamino group (singlet at 2.3 ppm) and the ethyl group of an ester (triplet-quartet at 1.2 and 4.2 ppm).  The singlet at 3.2 ppm must be a —CH$_2$— deshielded by a carbonyl group.

b)  $(CH_3)_2NH$  +  $XCH_2CO_2C_2H_5$  $\xrightarrow{Na_2CO_3}$  $(CH_3)_2NCH_2CO_2C_2H_5$

   B                                              A

   (X = halogen)

9-84

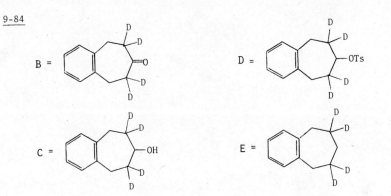

The IR peak at 2160 cm$^{-1}$ is due to C—D stretching.

# 10 ELIMINATION REACTIONS- ALKENES AND ALKYNES

10-1

a) $t\text{-BuÖ:}^-$ + H–CH$_2$–CH$_2$–Br $\xrightarrow[\Delta]{\text{DMSO}}$ CH$_2$=CH$_2$

b) EtÖ:$^-$ + H–CH$_2$–C(CH$_3$)(CH$_3$)–Br $\xrightarrow[\Delta]{\text{EtOH}}$ CH$_2$=C(CH$_3$)$_2$

c) HÖ:$^-$ + H–CH$_2$–CH$_2$–$\overset{+}{N}$(C$_2$H$_5$)$_3$ $\longrightarrow$ CH$_2$=CH$_2$ + N(C$_2$H$_5$)$_3$

d) 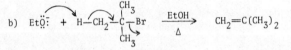 $\longrightarrow$ CH$_3$CH=CHCO$_2$H

(Acid regenerates the carboxylic acid from the salt formed with pyridine.)

10-2

a) (CH$_3$)$_3$C–Cl $\xrightarrow{\text{EtOH}}$ (CH$_3$)$_3$C$^+$ + Cl$^-$

EtÖH + H–CH$_2$–$\overset{+}{C}$(CH$_3$)$_2$ $\longrightarrow$ CH$_2$=C(CH$_3$)$_2$

b) C$_6$H$_5$CH(CH$_3$)–$\overset{+}{N}$(CH$_3$)$_3$ $\xrightarrow{\text{H}_2\text{O}}$ C$_6$H$_5$$\overset{+}{C}$HCH$_3$ + N(CH$_3$)$_3$

C$_6$H$_5$$\overset{+}{C}$H–CH$_2$–H + :ÖH$_2$ $\longrightarrow$ C$_6$H$_5$CH=CH$_2$

c) CH$_3$CH$_2$$\overset{+}{C}$(CH$_3$)(CH$_3$)–S(CH$_3$)$_2$ $\xrightarrow{\text{EtOH/H}_2\text{O}}$ CH$_3$CH$_2$$\overset{+}{C}$(CH$_3$)(CH$_3$) + S(CH$_3$)$_2$

10-2 Contd...

c) Contd..

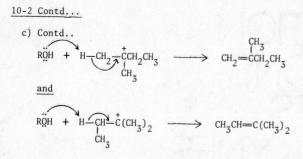

and

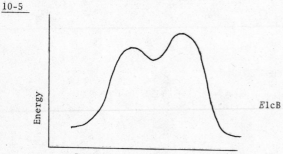

10-3 The exchange of deuterium for a proton takes place via the initially formed carbanion intermediate. Since departure of a fluoride ion is the rate-controlling step, hydrogen-deuterium exchange occurs during an initial pre-equilibrium step.

10-4 The carbonyl group and chlorine atom enhance the acidity of the adjacent hydrogen atom. Carbanion formation should be rapid.

10-5

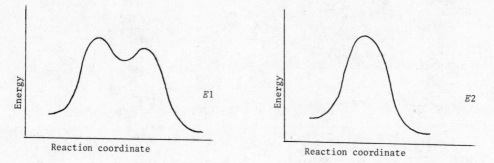

To account for the hydrogen-deuterium exchange, the carbanion intermediate must return to starting material more rapidly than it goes to product in this example of an *E*1cB reaction.

10-6    The smaller nitrogen kinetic isotope effect for the β-phenylethylammonium salt demonstrates
that C—N⁺ bond breaking is not as important in forming the transition state.  This is
expected for an "E1cB like" E2 process where cleavage of the β-hydrogen bond is kinetically
more important.  The phenyl group enhances the acidity of the β-hydrogen atom relative to
that of the ethylammonium salt.

10-7    (Refer to fig. 10-1)
For the threo isomer, the rotamer which can undergo anti elimination (A) is also the most
stable rotamer, thus is available in the highest concentration for reaction.  For the
erythro isomer, the rotamer which can undergo anti elimination (A') is not the most stable
rotamer in regard to steric interaction, thus is not available in high concentration for
reaction.

10-8

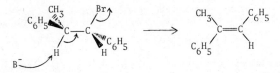

        Erythro (1R, 2R)

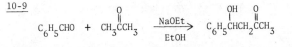

        Threo (1S, 2R)

10-9

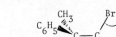 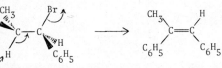

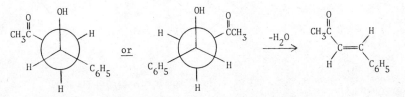

Anti elimination of H-OH from the most favorable rotamers of the enantiomeric aldol adducts
leads to the E stereoisomer.

10-10

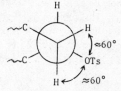

10-11    Only the cis isomer has the H atom and OTs group antiperiplanar.  The trans isomer must change to an unfavorable diaxial conformation for *anti-E*2 elimination to occur, and then a less acidic β-hydrogen atom is removed.  An *E*1 process is more likely to take place from the trans diequatorial conformation.

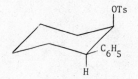                 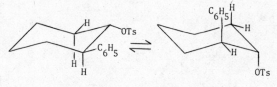

*cis*-2-Phenylcyclohexyl tosylate              *trans*-2-Phenylcyclohexyl tosylate

10-12 _____

a)    Because of the large size of the *t*-butyl group, flipping the ring of *trans-4-t-* butylcyclohexyl  tosylate to all axial substitutents is much less favorable than a similar ring flip by menthyl chloride.

b)    If an *E*1 mechanism were involved, the elimination could have occured from a β-hydrogen atom on either side of the carbocation intermediate to give a mixutre of 2- and 3-menthenes. (See sec. 10-3 for further discussion of alkene stability.)

10-13    One isomer has no H and Cl atoms anti to each other in either ring conformation.  *E*2 elimination is very unfavorable.

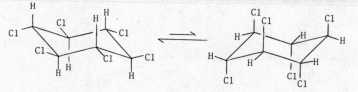

10-14    The H and Cl atoms are coplanar in A, but in B their dihedral angle is about 60°.  The *E*2 process is favored in the coplanar system, A.

10-15  Formation of the 2-pentenes proceeds preferentially through the less crowded transition
state to give the more stable *E* isomer.  The 1-pentene, though the less substituted alkene,
forms through a less crowded pathway than the *Z*-2-pentene.

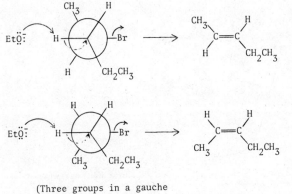

(Three groups in a gauche
orientation.)

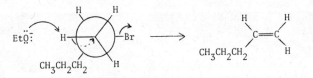

10-16  An *E*1 reaction is expected to occur because of the good leaving group on a secondary carbon
atom, crowding at the β-carbon, and the nonbasic solvolytic conditions.  The more highly
substituted products predominate with the *E*-2-alkene being favored over the *Z* isomer
because of steric crowding in the transition state leading to the *Z* isomer.

10-17  The 1-phenylpropene is stabilized by conjugation of the double bond with the benzene ring.

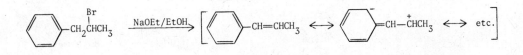

10-18  As the size of the leaving group increases, more product of Hofmann orientation is observed.
Note that the tosylate is effectively smaller than the $-\overset{+}{S}(CH_3)_2$ or $-SO_2CH_3$ groups.

Though tosylate is a large group,  attachment to the carbon atom at which reaction occurs
involves a single C—O—S bond.  The largeness of OTs is further away from the reaction
center.

10-19   The 1-alkene product increases as the size of the base increases because the hydrogen at
the number three carbon becomes more crowded and more difficult to abstract.

10-20

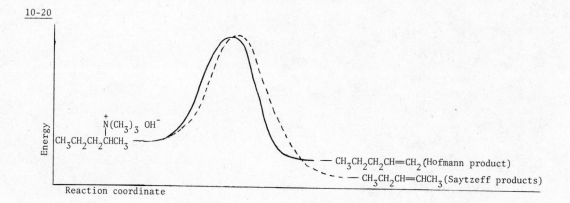

10-21   These anions are the conjugate bases of reasonably strong acids.   They are weak bases,
but good nucleophiles.

10-22   Acetate is a stronger base than chloride.   (Acetate is the conjugate base of a weaker
acid.)   Elimination is favored relative to substitution with the stronger base.

10-23   The reactivity order is the order of alkene stability.   The results suggest that product
stability is reflected in transition state stability as is typical for elimination
reactions that proceed with Saytzeff orientation.

10-24   Alkene stability will depend, in part, on the number of C-H bonds adjacent to the double
bond if stabilization of the alkene by hyperconjugation is considered.   Product A has eight
C-H bonds (two methyl and one ethyl group) adjacent to the double bond while B has only
seven.

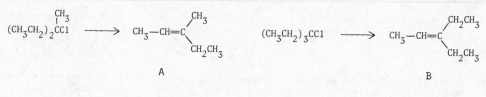

10-25

a)   Solvent will have no effect on the $S_N1:E1$ rate ratio since both mechanisms have the same
rate-controlling step; formation of a carbocation.   Partition between elimination or
substitution products occurs after the slow step.

10-25 Contd...

b) $S_N1$:  $\overset{\delta-}{Nu:}$------$\overset{\delta+}{C}$

E1 :  $\overset{\delta-}{B}$-------H------$\overset{|}{C}$=====$\overset{\delta+}{C}$

10-26

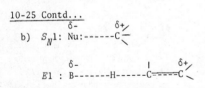

$CH_3CH_2\overset{\underset{|}{CH_3}}{\overset{|}{C}}Cl$  $\xrightarrow{\text{NaOH/H}_2\text{O/EtOH}}$  $CH_3CH=C(CH_3)_2$ + $CH_3CH_2\overset{\underset{}{\phantom{x}}}{\overset{CH_3}{C}}=CH_2$ + $CH_3CH_2\overset{\underset{|}{CH_3}}{\overset{|}{C}}-OH$ + $CH_3CH_2\overset{\underset{|}{CH_3}}{\overset{|}{C}}-OC_2H_5$

10-27  Only the 3,3-dimethyl-1-butene could have come from an E2 reaction, though the absence of a reasonable base in the system makes this unlikely.  The other two products result from rearrangement of an initially formed carbocation followed by elimination.  An E1 pathway can account for all three products.

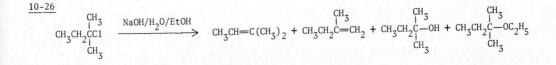

$CH_3\overset{\underset{|}{OH}}{\overset{|}{C}}HC(CH_3)_3$  $\xrightleftharpoons{\text{H}_2\text{SO}_4}$  $CH_3\overset{\underset{|}{\overset{+}{OH}_2}}{\overset{|}{C}}HC(CH_3)_3$  $\rightleftharpoons$  $CH_3\overset{+}{C}HC(CH_3)_3$

$HSO_4^-$ + $H-CH_2-\overset{+}{C}HC(CH_3)_3$  $\longrightarrow$  $CH_2=CHC(CH_3)_3$

$CH_3\overset{\underset{|}{CH_3}}{\overset{+}{C}}HC(CH_3)_2$  $\longrightarrow$  $(CH_3)_2CH\overset{+}{C}(CH_3)_2$

$HSO_4^-$ + $(CH_3)_2\overset{H}{\underset{}{C}}-\overset{+}{C}(CH_3)_2$  $\longrightarrow$  $(CH_3)_2C=C(CH_3)_2$

$(CH_3)_2CH\overset{+}{C}-CH_2-H$ + $HSO_4^-$  $\longrightarrow$  $(CH_3)_2CH\overset{\underset{|}{CH_3}}{\overset{|}{C}}=CH_2$

10-28

$CH_3CH_2\overset{..}{O}CH_2CH_3$  $\xrightleftharpoons{\text{H}_2\text{SO}_4}$  $CH_3CH_2\overset{\underset{|}{H}}{\overset{+}{O}}CH_2CH_3$ + $HSO_4^-$

$HSO_4^-$ + $H-CH_2-CH_2-\overset{\underset{|}{H}}{\overset{+}{O}}CH_2CH_3$  $\longrightarrow$  $CH_2=CH_2$ + $HOCH_2CH_3$

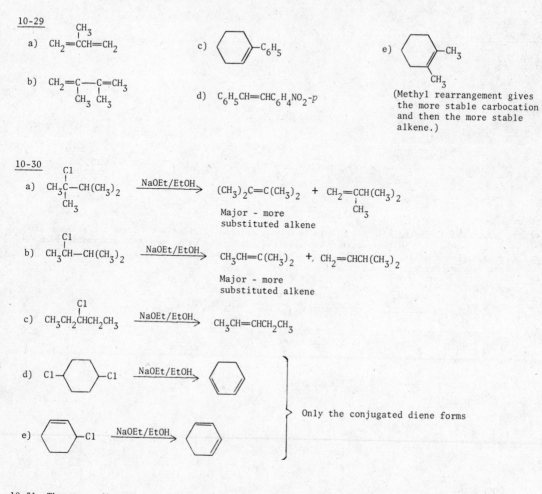

10-29

a) CH$_2$=CCH=CH$_2$ (with CH$_3$ on center carbon)

b) CH$_2$=C—C=CH$_3$ (with CH$_3$ and CH$_3$ below)

c) cyclohexene with C$_6$H$_5$ substituent

d) C$_6$H$_5$CH=CHC$_6$H$_4$NO$_2$-$p$

e) cyclohexene ring with two CH$_3$ groups

(Methyl rearrangement gives
the more stable carbocation
and then the more stable
alkene.)

10-30

a) CH$_3$C—CH(CH$_3$)$_2$ (with Cl above, CH$_3$ below) $\xrightarrow{\text{NaOEt/EtOH}}$ (CH$_3$)$_2$C=C(CH$_3$)$_2$ + CH$_2$=CCH(CH$_3$)$_2$ (with CH$_3$)

Major - more
substituted alkene

b) CH$_3$CH—CH(CH$_3$)$_2$ (with Cl above) $\xrightarrow{\text{NaOEt/EtOH}}$ CH$_3$CH=C(CH$_3$)$_2$ +, CH$_2$=CHCH(CH$_3$)$_2$

Major - more
substituted alkene

c) CH$_3$CH$_2$CHCH$_2$CH$_3$ (with Cl above) $\xrightarrow{\text{NaOEt/EtOH}}$ CH$_3$CH=CHCH$_2$CH$_3$

d) Cl—⬡—Cl $\xrightarrow{\text{NaOEt/EtOH}}$ cyclohexadiene

e) cyclohexene—Cl $\xrightarrow{\text{NaOEt/EtOH}}$ cyclohexadiene

}  Only the conjugated diene forms

10-31  The trans diaxial isomer has a more favorable molecular dipole moment because the moments
of each C-Br bond are in opposite directions and cancel each other.  The bond dipole
moments of the diequatorial isomer add together to give the molecule a significant dipole
moment.

or

10-32  The bromine atoms of $cis$-1,2-dibromocyclohexane cannot attain the $anti$-periplanar

10-32 Contd...
arrangement preferred for elimination.  However $S_N2$ displacement of one bromide by iodide
gives a trans product from which *anti*-elimination can occur after a ring flip.

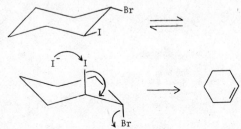

(More favorable equatorial
 approach of I⁻)

10-33

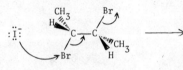     

Z-2-Butene

10-34

a)  $C_6H_5CH=CHCH(CH_3)C_6H_5$

    1,3-Diphenyl-1-butene

b)  $CH_3CH=C=CH_2$

    1,2-Butadiene
    (Methylallene)

c)

    Cyclopentene

d)  $(CH_3)_2C=C=O$

    2-Methyl-1-oxopropene
    (Dimethylketene)

10-35  The trans isomer has no β-hydrogen atoms coplanar with the quaternary nitrogen atom.  Ring
       flip would force two large groups into axial positions.  Substitution by hydroxide on an
       $N$-methyl group is the preferred reaction.  The cis isomer can undergo anti-periplanar
       elimination.

10-36

a)  The reactions are both anti $E2$ eliminations.

10-36 Contd...

a) Contd...

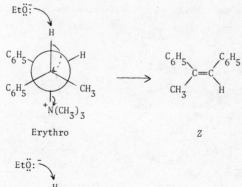

Erythro                    Z

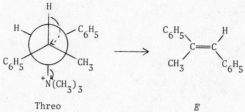

Threo                      E

b) The threo configuration undergoes anti elimination from its most favorable conformation. The erythro isomer must rotate to a less favorable conformation for reaction to occur.

10-37

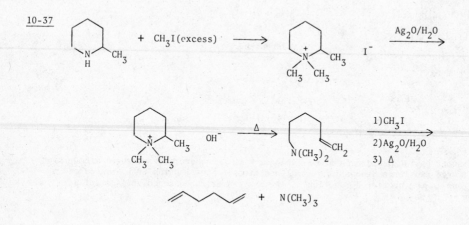

<u>10-38</u>

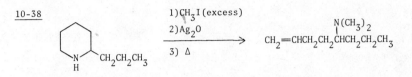

1)CH$_3$I(excess)
2)Ag$_2$O
3) Δ

$$CH_2=CHCH_2CH_2\overset{\overset{\displaystyle N(CH_3)_2}{|}}{CH}CH_2CH_2CH_3$$

The alternate direction of elimination would produce the optically inactive product
$(CH_3)_2N(CH_2)_3CH=CHCH_2CH_2CH_3$.

<u>10-39</u>

a) and b)

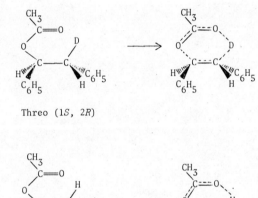

Threo (1S, 2R)

Erythro (1S, 2S)

c)  The transition state leading to the E isomer is of lower energy in both cases. Syn coplanarity can be attained from erythro or threo and lead to E products.

<u>10-40</u>

a)  The high temperatures at which pyrolysis is usually carried out results in very little selectivity in the choice of β-hydrogen atoms.

b)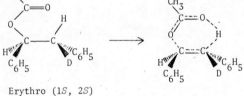

$$CH_2=CHCH_2CH_3 \quad + \quad CH_3CH=CHCH_3$$
$$60\% \qquad\qquad\qquad 40\%$$

Two internal H's
Three terminal H's

10-40 Contd...

b) Contd...

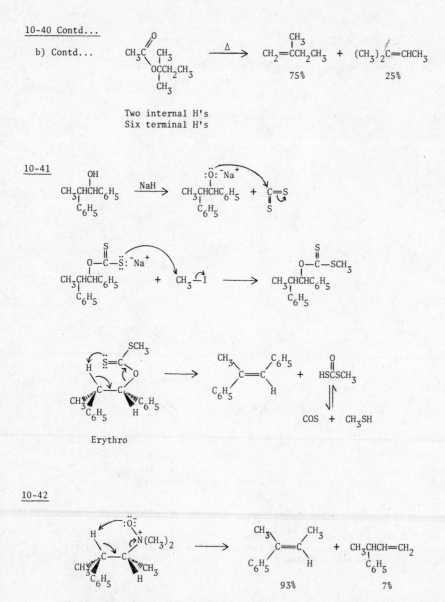

Two internal H's
Six terminal H's

10-41

Erythro

10-42

The E alkene is readily produced via a syn elimination. A syn elimination can also produce the less stable terminal alkene. Formation of the Z alkene would require an anti-elimination which cannot occur with the amine oxide.

10-43  The amine oxide pyrolysis proceeds by a syn elimination to give $Z$ product.  The Hofmann elimination predominately is an anti elimination giving $E$ product.

10-44  Only the $Z$ isomer has the H and Cl atoms in an anti-periplanar configuration favorable for $E2$ elimination.

10-45

$$CH_3(CH_2)_5C\equiv CCH_3 \;\underset{\longleftarrow}{\overset{NaNH_2}{\longrightarrow}}\; \left[\begin{array}{c} CH_3(CH_2)_5C\equiv C-\ddot{C}H_2 \\ \updownarrow \\ CH_3(CH_2)_5\ddot{C}=C=CH_2 \end{array}\right] Na^+ \;+\; NH_3 \;\rightleftharpoons$$

$$CH_3(CH_2)_5CH=C=CH_2 \;+\; NaNH_2 \;\rightleftharpoons\; \left[\begin{array}{c} CH_3(CH_2)_5CH=C=\ddot{C}H \\ \updownarrow \\ CH_3(CH_2)_5\ddot{C}H-C\equiv CH \end{array}\right] Na^+ \;+\; NH_3 \;\rightleftharpoons$$

$$CH_3(CH_2)_6C\equiv CH \;+\; NaNH_2$$

10-46

a)  $n\text{-}C_5H_{11}C\equiv CH$

    1-Heptyne

b)  $C_6H_5C\equiv CH$

    Phenylacetylene

    (Phenylethyne)

c)  $\langle\hspace{-2pt}\rangle-CH_2CH_2C\equiv CH$

    4-Cyclohexyl-1-butyne

d)  $CH_3C\equiv CCH_3$

    2-Butyne

10-47  The isotope effect indicates a slower rate for the reaction of deuterio compared to protio alcohol.  This shows that the C-H (or C-D) bond must break in the rate-controlling step of the oxidation.  An $E2$ process is consistent with this result.

10-48   The process is analogous to elimination via acetate esters.

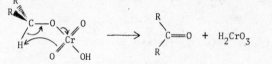

10-49

a)

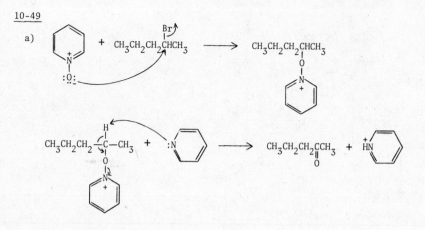

b)

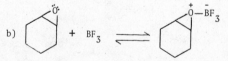

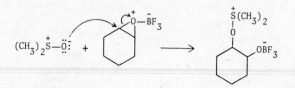

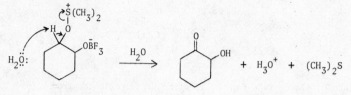

10-50   The cyclic iodate ester proposed as the oxidation intermediate requires a cis arrangement of the two hydroxy groups. A trans isomer must isomerize to the cis isomer for oxidation to occur.

10-51

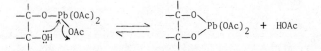

This step is second order.  Additional HOAc would reverse the reaction by a mass action effect.

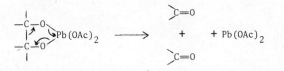

Cis glycol is required to form the cyclic ester.

$$-\overset{|}{\underset{|}{C}}-O \\ \quad\quad Pb(OAc)_2 \longrightarrow \quad + \quad + Pb(OAc)_2$$

with products $\overset{}{\underset{}{>}}C=O$ and $\overset{}{\underset{}{>}}C=O$

10-52

$$CH_4 \xrightarrow{\;e^-\;} [CH_4]^{+}$$
$$m/e = 16$$

The molecular ion is relatively stable and is the base peak.  The peak at $m/e = 17$ is due to the presence of the $^{13}C$ isotope.

$$[CH_4]^{+} \longrightarrow [CH_3]^{+} + H\cdot$$
$$m/e = 15$$

Loss of a hydrogen atom is also relatively favorable.

The remaining processes do not lead to important fragments, thus have low relative intensities.

$$[CH_3]^{+} \longrightarrow [CH_2]^{+} + H\cdot \qquad [CH_4]^{+} \longrightarrow CH_2 + [H_2]^{+}$$
$$m/e = 14 \qquad\qquad\qquad\qquad\qquad m/e = 2$$

$$[CH_2]^{+} \longrightarrow [CH]^{+} + H\cdot \qquad [CH_4]^{+} \longrightarrow CH_3\cdot + [H]^{+}$$
$$m/e = 13 \qquad\qquad\qquad\qquad\qquad m/e = 1$$

$$[CH]^{+} \longrightarrow [C]^{+} + H\cdot$$
$$m/e = 12$$

10-53

a)  $CH_3CH_2CH_2CH_2CH_2CH_2CH_2CH_3$

Peaks come in fairly regular groupings, 14 units apart.

10-53 Contd...

b) $CH_3C(CH_3)_2CH_2CH(CH_3)CH_3$

Fragmentation readily leads to the relatively stable tertiary carbocation.

$$CH_3\overset{\overset{CH_3}{|}}{\underset{\underset{CH_3}{|}}{C}}{}^+ \qquad m/e = 57$$

c) $(CH_3)_2CHCH_2CH_2CH_2CH_2CH_3$

The most intense peak is fragmentation to give the 2-propyl cation.

$(CH_3)_2CH^+ \qquad m/e = 43$

10-54

a)

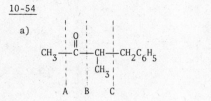

$$CH_3\overset{}{\underset{}{\vdots}}\overset{O}{\overset{\|}{C}}\overset{}{\vdots}CH\overset{}{\vdots}CH_2C_6H_5$$
$$\underset{A}{\quad}\underset{B}{\quad}\underset{C}{\quad}CH_3$$

$\longrightarrow$ Molecular ion $m/e = 162$

A $\longrightarrow$ $\overset{O}{\overset{\|}{{}^+CCHCH_2C_6H_5}}$ $\qquad m/e = 147$
$\qquad\qquad\quad \underset{CH_3}{}$

B $\longrightarrow$ $CH_3\overset{O}{\overset{\|}{C}}{}^+$ $\qquad m/e = 43$

C $\longrightarrow$ ${}^+CH_2C_6H_5$ $\qquad m/e = 91$

b)

$$CH_3O\overset{}{\vdots}\overset{O}{\overset{\|}{C}}\overset{}{\vdots}CH_2\overset{}{\vdots}CH_2CH_2\overset{}{\vdots}CH_2N(CH_3)_2$$
$$\quad\ \underset{A}{\quad}\underset{B}{\quad}\underset{C}{\quad}\underset{D}{\quad}$$

$\longrightarrow$ Molecular ion $\qquad m/e = 159$

A $\longrightarrow$ $\overset{O}{\overset{\|}{{}^+C(CH_2)_4N(CH_3)_2}}$ $\quad m/e = 128$

B $\longrightarrow$ $CH_3O\overset{O}{\overset{\|}{C}}{}^+$ $\qquad m/e = 59$

C $\longrightarrow$ $CH_3O\overset{{}^+OH}{\overset{\|}{C}}CH_2$ $\qquad m/e = 74$

(This fragmentation involves abstraction of a hydrogen atom $\gamma$ to the carbonyl - see sec. 10-8C.)

D $\longrightarrow$ ${}^+CH_2-\ddot{N}(CH_3)_2$ $\qquad m/e = 58$

10-55

a)  i)

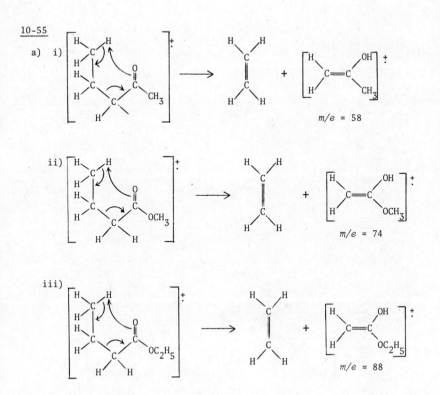

*m/e* = 58

ii)

*m/e* = 74

iii)

*m/e* = 88

b)  The nitrogen atom is tricoordinate, thus amides lead to a fragment with an odd *m/e* value.

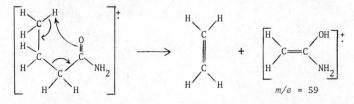

*m/e* = 59

10-56

a)  Cleavage of a methyl free radical from the ethyl group at the four position produces a radical anion that can be resonance stabilized by the nitro group.

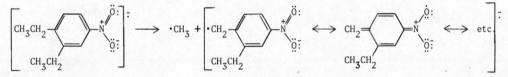

10-56 Contd...

b) Deuterium could be used to label the methyl of the ethyl group at the four position as a $CD_3$. If this were the group which cleaved, the radical anion would differ in $m/e$ value by three units relative to cleavage at the other position.

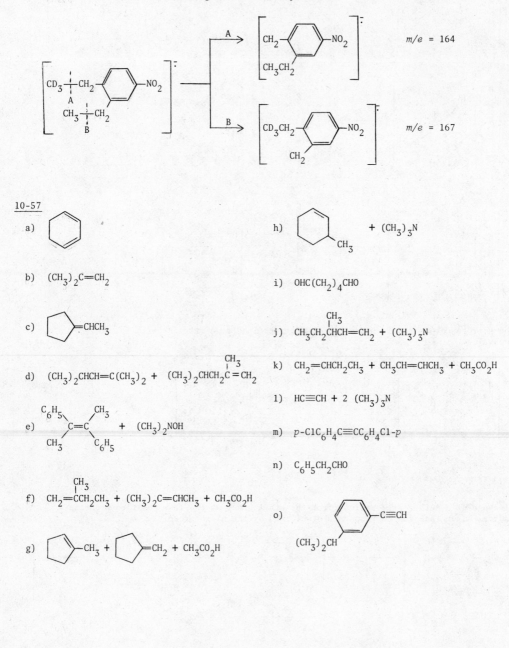

10-57

a)

b) $(CH_3)_2C{=}CH_2$

c) =CHCH_3

d) $(CH_3)_2CHCH{=}C(CH_3)_2$ + $(CH_3)_2CHCH_2\overset{CH_3}{\underset{|}{C}}{=}CH_2$

e)  + $(CH_3)_2NOH$

f) $CH_2{=}\overset{CH_3}{\underset{|}{C}}CH_2CH_3$ + $(CH_3)_2C{=}CHCH_3$ + $CH_3CO_2H$

g) —$CH_3$ + =$CH_2$ + $CH_3CO_2H$

h)  + $(CH_3)_3N$

i) $OHC(CH_2)_4CHO$

j) $CH_3CH_2\overset{CH_3}{\underset{|}{C}}HCH{=}CH_2$ + $(CH_3)_3N$

k) $CH_2{=}CHCH_2CH_3$ + $CH_3CH{=}CHCH_3$ + $CH_3CO_2H$

l) $HC{\equiv}CH$ + 2 $(CH_3)_3N$

m) $p{-}ClC_6H_4C{\equiv}CC_6H_4Cl{-}p$

n) $C_6H_5CH_2CHO$

o) —$C{\equiv}CH$

10-57 Contd...

p) 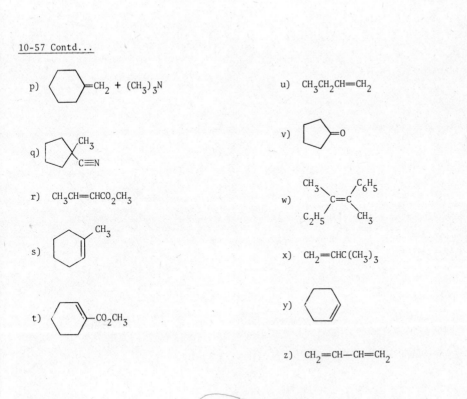=CH$_2$ + (CH$_3$)$_3$N

u)  CH$_3$CH$_2$CH=CH$_2$

q) [cyclopentane ring with CH$_3$ and C≡N substituents]

v) [cyclopentanone]=O

r)  CH$_3$CH=CHCO$_2$CH$_3$

w) [structure: CH$_3$ and C$_6$H$_5$ on C=C with C$_2$H$_5$ and CH$_3$]

s) [cyclohexene ring with CH$_3$]

x)  CH$_2$=CHC(CH$_3$)$_3$

t) [cyclohexene ring]—CO$_2$CH$_3$

y) [cyclohexene]

z)  CH$_2$=CH—CH=CH$_2$

10-58

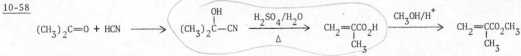

$$(CH_3)_2C=O + HCN \longrightarrow (CH_3)_2\overset{OH}{\underset{}{C}}-CN \xrightarrow[\Delta]{H_2SO_4/H_2O} CH_2=\underset{CH_3}{\overset{}{C}}CO_2H \xrightarrow{CH_3OH/H^+} CH_2=\underset{CH_3}{\overset{}{C}}CO_2CH_3$$

(The commercial process accomplishes elimination, hydrolysis, and esterification in one step by treating the cyanohydrin with acidic methanol.)

10-59  Because of free rotation about the single bond either of the two hydrogen atoms can be abstracted from the number 3 carbon atom.

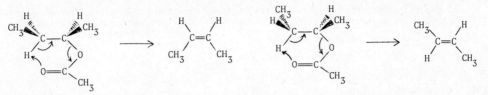

10-60

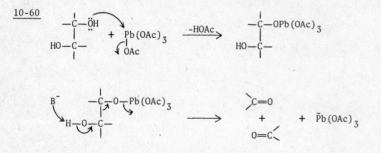

10-61 The negative oxygen atom of the amine oxide is solvated strongly by hydrogen bonding to water molecules. The oxyanion must loose much of this water solvation before it can effectively act as a base. Under anhydrous conditions with an aprotic solvent, the oxygen atom is relatively free.

10-62

$$CH_3CH_2CO_2C(CH_3)_3 \rightleftharpoons \overset{H_3O^+}{\longrightarrow} CH_3CH_2C\overset{O}{\underset{\overset{+}{O}-C(CH_3)_3}{\diagdown}} \rightleftharpoons CH_3CH_2C\overset{O}{\underset{OH}{\diagdown}} + \overset{CH_3}{\underset{CH_3}{\overset{+}{C}-CH_3}}$$

$$\overset{CH_3}{\underset{CH_3}{\overset{+}{C}-CH_2-H}} + \overset{..}{O}H_2 \rightleftharpoons (CH_3)_2C=CH_2 + H_3O^+$$

10-63 In the polar neutral medium, $E1$ and $S_N1$ solvolysis processes occur. Substitution predominates in the absence of base. The smaller water molecule is a more effective nucleophile than ethanol so that the alcohol is the major substitution product.

10-64 The amino group in A can act as an internal base to remove the β-hydrogen atom. A six-membered cyclic transition state results in formation of the 1-alkene. Compound B reacts via a normal bimolecular $E2$ process in which steric factors favor removal of the less hindered terminal β-hydrogen atom.

10-65

a) 
$$Br-CH_2-\underset{CH_3}{\overset{CH_3}{C}}-C\overset{O}{\underset{OH}{\diagup}} + Na_2CO_3 \rightleftharpoons Br-CH_2-\underset{CH_3}{\overset{CH_3}{C}}-C\overset{O}{\underset{\ddot{O}:}{\diagup}} \xrightarrow{\Delta} CH_2{=}C(CH_3)_2 + CO_2$$

b) In this reaction the driving force is formation of a stable alkene. Decarboxylation of β-keto acids depends on formation of an enolate anion which has a similarly placed double bond.

10-66

a) Elimination takes place as one carbon-halogen bond is converted to the organolithium.

$$Li + X-\overset{|}{\underset{|}{C}}-\overset{|}{\underset{|}{C}}-X \longrightarrow Li^+ \ :\overset{|}{\underset{|}{C}}{\to}\overset{|}{\underset{|}{C}}{\to}X \longrightarrow \diagup\!\!\!C{=}C\!\!\!\diagdown$$

b) Loss of $H_2O$ in the fragmentation proceeds in the direction expected for formation of the more stable benzylic cation.

$$(C_6H_5)_2\underset{OH}{\overset{|}{C}}C(CH_3)_2\underset{OH}{\overset{|}{C}}(CH_3)_2 \underset{H^+}{\rightleftharpoons} (C_6H_5)_2\underset{\overset{+}{OH}_2}{\overset{|}{C}}C(CH_3)_2\underset{OH}{\overset{|}{C}}(CH_3)_2 \xrightarrow{-H_2O}$$

$$(C_6H_5)_2\overset{+}{C}{-}\underset{CH_3}{\overset{CH_3}{\underset{|}{C}}}{-}\overset{:\ddot{O}H}{\overset{|}{C}}(CH_3)_2 \xrightarrow{-H^+} (C_6H_5)_2C{=}C(CH_3)_2 + O{=}C(CH_3)_2$$

rather than

$$(C_6H_5)_2\underset{OH}{\overset{|}{C}}C(CH_3)_2\underset{OH}{\overset{|}{C}}(CH_3)_2 \underset{H^+}{\rightleftharpoons} (C_6H_5)_2\underset{OH}{\overset{|}{C}}C(CH_3)_2\underset{\overset{+}{OH}_2}{\overset{|}{C}}(CH_3)_2 \xrightarrow{-H_2O}$$

$$(C_6H_5)_2\overset{:\ddot{O}H}{\overset{|}{C}}{-}\underset{CH_3}{\overset{CH_3}{\underset{|}{C}}}{-}\overset{+}{C}(CH_3)_2 \xrightarrow{-H^+} (C_6H_5)_2C{=}O + (CH_3)_2C{=}C(CH_3)_2$$

c) The more acidic β-hydrogen atom is adjacent to the phenyl ring. Acidity factors govern the the direction of elimination in this example.

$$\xrightarrow{\Delta} C_6H_5{-}CH{=}CH_2 + (CH_3)_2NC_2H_5 + H_2O$$

10-66 Contd...

d) Small bicyclic molecules with bridgehead double bonds such as G have never been prepared. Bredt's rule states that introduction of a double bond at the bridgehead of small bicyclic systems is prohibited.

10-67

a) $CH_3CH_2CH_2Br \xrightarrow{Mg/Et_2O} CH_3CH_2CH_2MgBr \xrightarrow[2)H_3O^+]{1)(C_6H_5)_2C=O/Et_2O}$

$CH_3CH_2CH_2\overset{\overset{\displaystyle OH}{|}}{C}(C_6H_5)_2 \xrightarrow{-H_2O} CH_3CH_2CH=C(C_6H_5)_2$

The tertiary benzylic alcohol readily dehydrates during acid workup.

b) $CH_3CHO + H_2NOH \longrightarrow CH_3CH=NOH \xrightarrow[(-H_2O)]{SOCl_2} CH_3C\equiv N$

$CH_3C\equiv N + CH_3CHO \xrightarrow{NaOEt/EtOH} CH_3\overset{\overset{\displaystyle OH}{|}}{C}HCH_2CN \xrightarrow{H_3O^+ \text{ or } HO^-/H_2O} CH_3CH=CHCN$

c) $BrCH_2CH_2CH_2Br \xrightarrow{t-BuOK/t-BuOH} CH_2=CHCH_2Br$

$2\ CH_2=CHCH_2Br \xrightarrow[\substack{2)HCO_2Et \\ 3)H_3O^+}]{1)Mg/Et_2O} CH_2=CHCH_2\overset{\overset{\displaystyle OH}{|}}{C}HCH_2CH=CH_2 \xrightarrow[\substack{2)LiAlH_4THF \\ 3)H_3O^+}]{1)p-TsCl/pyridine}$

$CH_2=CHCH_2CH_2CH_2CH=CH_2$

d) $\xrightarrow[2)H_3O^+]{1)NaBH_4/THF}$ $\xrightarrow[\Delta]{H_3PO_4}$

e) $C_6H_5\overset{\overset{\displaystyle O}{||}}{C}CH_3 \xrightarrow[2)H_3O^+]{1)LiAlH_4/Et_2O} C_6H_5\overset{\overset{\displaystyle OH}{|}}{C}HCH_3 \xrightarrow{PBr_3} C_6H_5\overset{\overset{\displaystyle Br}{|}}{C}HCH_3$

$HC\equiv CH + NaNH_2 \longrightarrow NaC\equiv CH$

10-67 Contd...

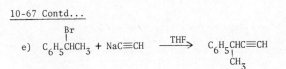

e)   $C_6H_5CHCH_3$ + NaC≡CH   $\xrightarrow{THF}$   $C_6H_5CHC≡CH$
      (Br)                                              (CH₃)

10-68   The IR absorption of A suggests a ketone.  By making the reasonable assumption that the
        product should have some similarity to the starting material we deduce that the integral
        areas of the nmr must correspond to 6:4:4.  Again relying on the starting material
        structure, we propose that there are two methyl groups (0.9 ppm), two methylene groups
        adjacent to a carbonyl (2.3 ppm)  and two other similar methylene groups (1.2 - 1.7 ppm).
        We conclude that A is formed by an elimination reaction followed by tautomerization of the
        initially formed enol to a more stable ketone.

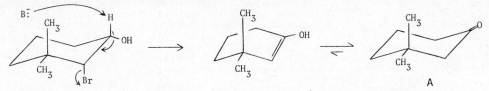

        The notable feature about the nmr spectrum of B is that there are two protons (using the
        same deductions as above about the actual numbers of protons) deshielded as if they were
        adjacent to an oxygen atom.  The absence of functional group IR absorption suggests an
        ether, in this case an epoxide.  The trans isomer has Br and OH anti and can readily form
        an epoxide through intramolecular displacement of bromide.

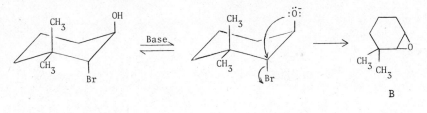

10-69   The IR spectrum suggests that A is an alcohol and the nmr spectrum, when adjusted to the
        integral areas corresponding to the molecular formula, indicates two methyl groups (1.2 ppm),
        two phenyl groups, and two deshielded protons.  The structure is symmetrical and must be -

        $$C_6H_5-\underset{\underset{CH_3}{|}}{\overset{\overset{OH}{|}}{C}}-\underset{\underset{CH_3}{|}}{\overset{\overset{OH}{|}}{C}}-C_6H_5$$

              A

        Periodic acid accomplishes oxidative cleavage of glycols.  Compound B must be acetophenone.

        $$C_6H_5\overset{\overset{O}{||}}{C}CH_3$$

              B

<u>10-70</u>  *IHD* = 6

The nmr spectrum indicates an aromatic ring, an alkene proton deshielded to 6.6 - 6.8 ppm and possible a methyl ketone.  The IR suggests a double bond ($\approx$1600 cm$^{-1}$) and possibly a conjugated carbonyl group ($\approx$1680 cm$^{-1}$).  Conjugation is further suggested by the presence of one alkene proton which must be under the aromatic resonance to account for the peak areas (5 + 1 = 6)  The compound is 4-phenyl-3-buten-2-one (benzalacetone).

$$C_6H_5CH=CHCCH_3 \overset{O}{\overset{\|}{\phantom{C}}}$$

<u>10-71</u>  Elemental analysis and the mass spectrum lead to a molecular formula of $C_{10}H_{14}N_2$.

Nicotine must be an amine and possess a pyridine ring with a substituent at the C-3 carbon atom.  Formation of a dichloride indicates two basic nitrogen atoms are present.  The nmr spectrum shows aromatic protons (the peaks deshielded to 8.6 pppm are a part of this), some deshielded aliphatic protons and a possible deshielded methyl singlet.  The Hofmann degradation sequence is most helpful since it indicates that the substituent on the pyridine ring of nicotine has at least four carbon atoms.  Furthermore, the fact that one Hofmann elimination still retains the nitrogen atom shows that the substituent is a cyclic amine containing four carbon atoms.  The structure of nicotine is...

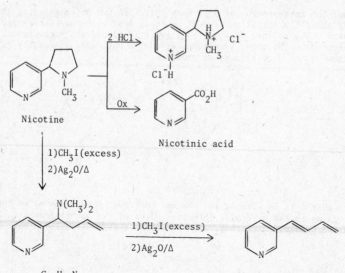

# 11 ELECTROPHILIC ADDITIONS TO UNSATURATED CARBON

11-1

a)

| Bonds broken | kcal/mol | kJ/mol |
|---|---|---|
| *C=C | 146 | 610 |
| O—H | 111 | 464 |
| | 257 kcal/mol | 1074 kJ/mol |

| Bonds formed | | |
|---|---|---|
| C—H | 99 | 414 |
| *C—C | 83 | 347 |
| C—O | 86 | 359 |
| | 268 kcal/mol | 1120 kJ/mol |

$\therefore \Delta H° = 257 - 268 = -11$ kcal/mol

$(= 1074 - 1120 = -46$ kJ/mol$)$

b)

| Bonds broken | kcal/mol | kJ/mol |
|---|---|---|
| *C=O | 179 | 748 |
| O—H | 111 | 464 |
| | 290 kcal/mol | 1212 kJ/mol |

| Bonds formed | | |
|---|---|---|
| *2 C—O | 172 | 718 |
| O—H | 111 | 464 |
| | 283 kcal/mol | 1182 kJ/mol |

$\therefore \Delta H° = 290 - 283 = 7$ kcal/mol

$(= 1212 - 1182 = 30$ kJ/mol$)$

The hydration of ethylene is thermodynamically more favorable than the hydration of acetone.

*The calculations use data for breaking a double bond and forming a single bond. The difference accounts for the actual change which is the loss of a pi bond.

11-2  If the initial protonation step were a rapid acid-base reaction as is observed in most carbonyl addition reactions, H and D would exchange faster than hydration occurs.  The slow electrophilic addition of $H^+$ must be followed by a rapid product-forming step.

11-3  Electron donating groups enhance reactivity while electron withdrawing groups decrease reactivity at the double bond.

$p$-$CH_3OC_6H_4CH$=$CHCO_2H$ > $C_6H_5CH$=$CHCO_2H$ > $p$-$ClC_6H_4CH$=$CHCO_2H$ > $p$-$NO_2C_6H_4CH$=$CHCO_2H$

11-4  The more stable intermediate dication formed on addition of $H^+$ has positive charges the furthest from each other.

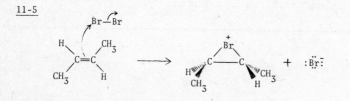

11-5

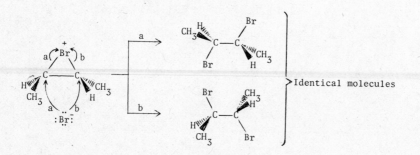

> Identical molecules

11-6  The phenyl group stabilizes the carbocation by resonance delocalization of the positive charge.

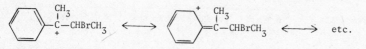

11-7

a)

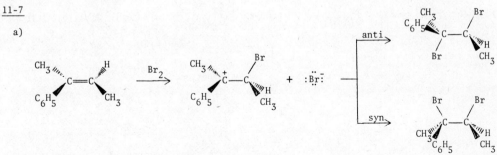

Each stereochemical pathway leads to a mixture of enantiomers.  Only one enantiomer is shown in each sequence above.

b)  Anti addition leads to the more favorable arrangement of large, medium, and small groups. The cationic transition state leading to that product is expected to be of lower energy.

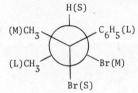

(More stable rotamer)

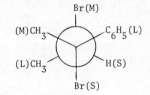

11-8

a)

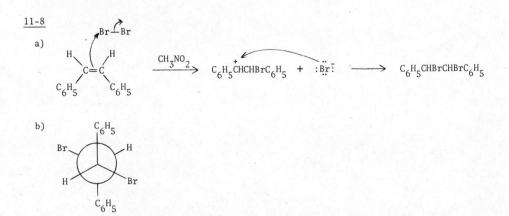

b)

The meso isomer has the more favorable spatial arrangement of large, medium and small groups.

11-9  The phenyl group provides stability to a noncyclic cationic intermediate.  Addition of the
chloride to that benzylic cation favors formation of the less crowded product.

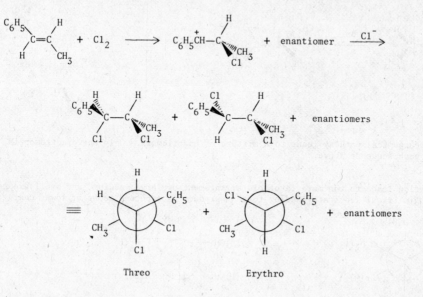

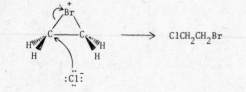

Threo            Erythro

11-10  The intermediate bromonium ion reacts with bromide formed in the reaction or with the
added chloride ion.

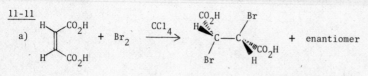

11-11

a)

dl-2,3-Dibromosuccinic acid
(dl-2,3-Dibromobutanedioic acid)

11-11 Contd...

b) 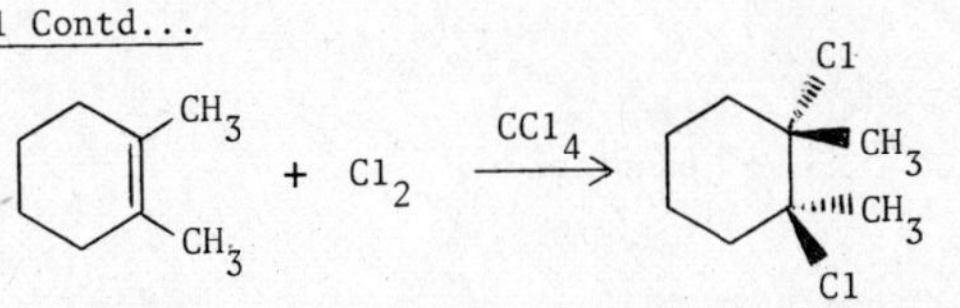 + Cl$_2$ $\xrightarrow{CCl_4}$ + enantiomers

*trans*-1,2-Dichloro-1,2-dimethylcyclohexane

c) CH$_2$=CHCH$_2$C≡CH + Br$_2$ $\xrightarrow{CCl_4}$ BrCH$_2$CH(Br)CH$_2$C≡CH

4,5-Dibromo-1-pentyne

d) 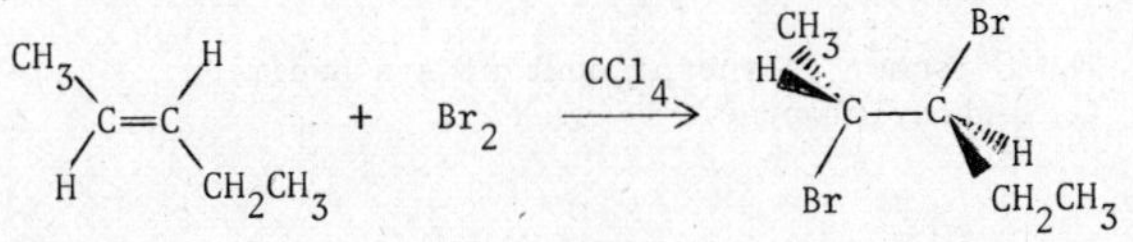 + Br$_2$ $\xrightarrow{CCl_4}$ + enantiomer

*erythro*-2,3-Dibromopentane

e) 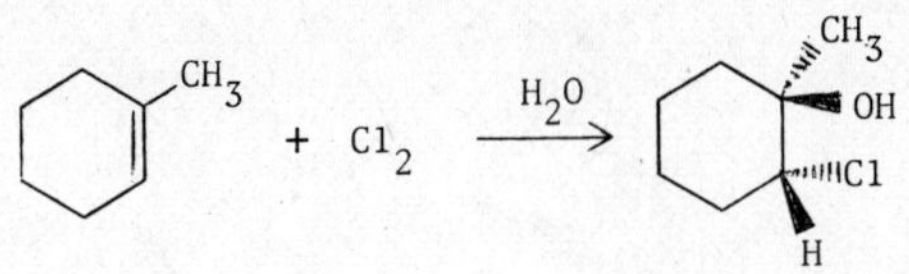 + Cl$_2$ $\xrightarrow{H_2O}$

1-Methyl-2-chlorocyclohexanol

f) CH$_2$=CHCN + HOCl $\longrightarrow$ HOCH$_2$CHCN
with Cl on the CHCN carbon

1-Chloro-2-hydroxypropanenitrile

11-12  When an acid reacts with an aldehyde or ketone, rapid and reversible addition of the proton to the carbonyl oxygen atom takes place. The reaction is normally catalyzed by the acid. Reaction of acid with an alkene double bond produces a new sigma bond to the proton in the slow, rate-controlling step.

11-13  Acetate from the solvent competes with bromide as the potential nucleophile that adds to the initially formed cation.

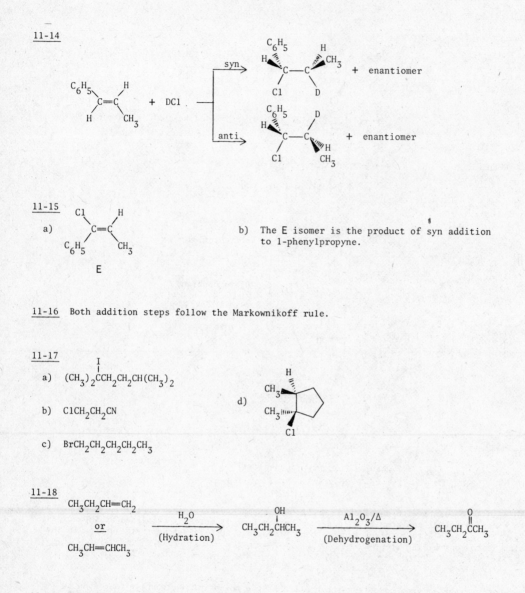

11-14

11-15

a) [structure: E isomer of 1-chloro-1-phenyl-propene] E

b) The E isomer is the product of syn addition to 1-phenylpropyne.

11-16  Both addition steps follow the Markownikoff rule.

11-17

a)  $(CH_3)_2CCH_2CH_2CH(CH_3)_2$ (with I substituent)

b)  $ClCH_2CH_2CN$

c)  $BrCH_2CH_2CH_2CH_2CH_3$

d) [cyclopentane structure with CH₃, H, CH₃, Cl substituents]

11-18

$CH_3CH_2CH{=}CH_2$

or

$CH_3CH{=}CHCH_3$

$\xrightarrow[\text{(Hydration)}]{H_2O}$

$CH_3CH_2\overset{OH}{\underset{}{C}}HCH_3$

$\xrightarrow[\text{(Dehydrogenation)}]{Al_2O_3/\Delta}$

$CH_3CH_2\overset{O}{\overset{\|}{C}}CH_3$

11-19  The addition of $H^+$ to the double bond is more favorable when a tertiary rather than a secondary carbocation is formed.

11-20

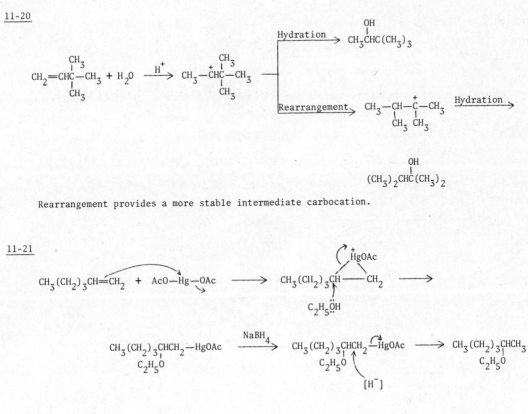

Rearrangement provides a more stable intermediate carbocation.

11-21

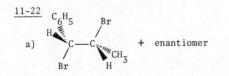

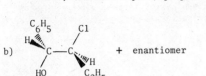

11-22

a) 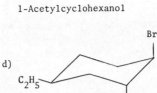 + enantiomer

*threo*-1,2-Dibromo-1-phenylpropane

c) 1-Acetylcyclohexanol

b) 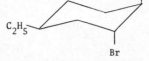 + enantiomer

2-Chloro-1-phenyl-1-butanol

d) 1,2-Dibromo-4-ethylcyclohexane

11-22 Contd...

e)   CH$_3$OCCH$_2$CH$_3$
     Cl (above), CH$_3$ (below)

2-Chloro-2-methoxybutane

g)   1-Methylcyclohexanol

f)   (CH$_3$)$_2$CHCH$_2$CH$_2$CH$_2$Br

1-Bromo-4-methylpentane

11-23

a)   CH$_3$CH$_2$CH=CH$_2$   $\xrightarrow[\text{2)H}_2\text{O}_2/\text{H}_2\text{O/NaOH}]{\text{1) (BH}_3)_2/\text{THF}}$   CH$_3$CH$_2$CH$_2$CH$_2$OH

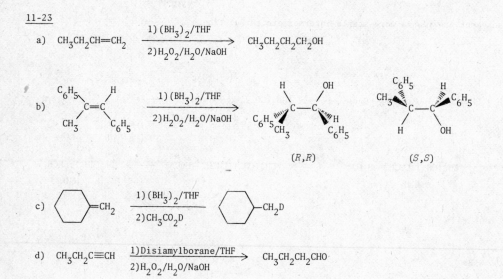

b)   $\xrightarrow[\text{2)H}_2\text{O}_2/\text{H}_2\text{O/NaOH}]{\text{1) (BH}_3)_2/\text{THF}}$

(R,R)          (S,S)

c)   =CH$_2$   $\xrightarrow[\text{2)CH}_3\text{CO}_2\text{D}]{\text{1) (BH}_3)_2/\text{THF}}$   —CH$_2$D

d)   CH$_3$CH$_2$C≡CH   $\xrightarrow[\text{2)H}_2\text{O}_2/\text{H}_2\text{O/NaOH}]{\text{1)Disiamylborane/THF}}$   CH$_3$CH$_2$CH$_2$CHO

11-24

a)   The meso product is formed by permanganate oxidation; a syn hydroxylation.  The *dl* product is formed from hydrolysis of the epoxide; an anti hydroxylation.

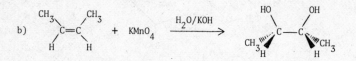

b)   + KMnO$_4$   $\xrightarrow{\text{H}_2\text{O/KOH}}$

11-24 Contd...

b) Contd...

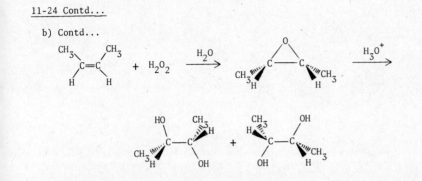

11-25 The aldehyde group can be converted to a ketal which will be stable under the basic conditions. After completion of the oxidation, the ketal protecting group is readily removed by using dilute acid.

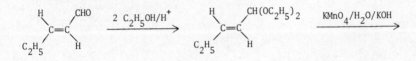

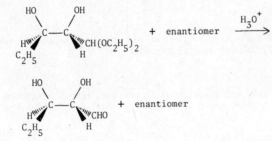

11-26

a) $n\text{-}C_4H_9Li + H_2CCl_2 \rightleftharpoons n\text{-}C_4H_{10} + H\ddot{C}Cl_2$

$H-\overset{..}{C}-Cl \longrightarrow H-\ddot{C}-Cl + Cl^-$
$\quad\;\; |$
$\quad\; Cl$

b) $Cl-\overset{Cl}{\underset{Cl}{\overset{|}{C}}}-\overset{O}{\overset{\|}{C}}\ddot{O}{:}^-\, Na^+ \overset{\Delta}{\longrightarrow} Cl-\ddot{C}-Cl + Cl^- + CO_2$

11-27

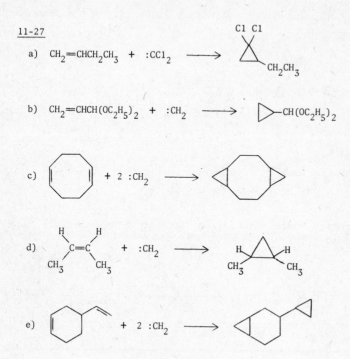

a)  $CH_2{=}CHCH_2CH_3$  +  $:CCl_2$  $\longrightarrow$

b)  $CH_2{=}CHCH(OC_2H_5)_2$  +  $:CH_2$  $\longrightarrow$  $-CH(OC_2H_5)_2$

c)  + 2 :$CH_2$  $\longrightarrow$

d)  + :$CH_2$  $\longrightarrow$

e)  + 2 :$CH_2$  $\longrightarrow$

11-28  Formation of a carbocation is a key step in the cationic polymerization process.  Ethylene would produce an energetically unfavorable primary cation.

11-29  Hydrogenation indicates that only one double bond is present, thus A must have a cyclic structure in addition to the carboxy group to account for an *IHD* = 3.  One set of reasonable structures for A and B is -

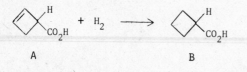

A                              B

11-30  The lead "poisons" the catalyst and destroys the effectiveness of that kind of exhaust system to reduce air polluting contaminants.  A higher percentage of branched hydrocarbons will enhance the performance of nonleaded gasoline.

11-31

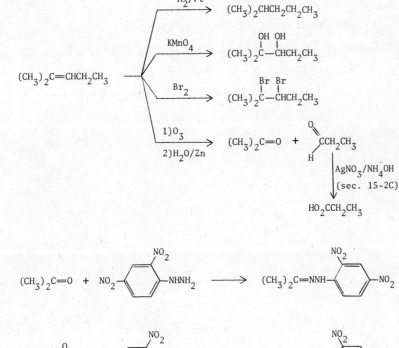

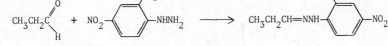

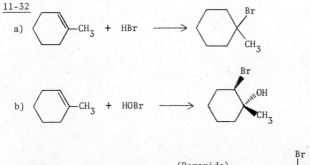

11-32

a)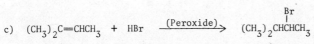

b)

c) $(CH_3)_2C=CHCH_3$ + HBr $\xrightarrow{\text{(Peroxide)}}$ $(CH_3)_2CHCHCH_3$

11-32 Contd...

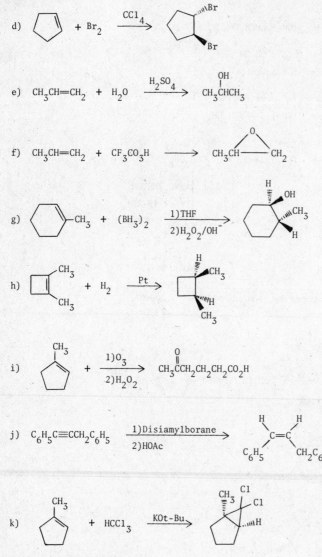

d) [cyclopentene] + Br$_2$ $\xrightarrow{CCl_4}$ [trans-1,2-dibromocyclopentane]

e) CH$_3$CH=CH$_2$ + H$_2$O $\xrightarrow{H_2SO_4}$ CH$_3$CHCH$_3$ (OH)

f) CH$_3$CH=CH$_2$ + CF$_3$CO$_3$H $\longrightarrow$ CH$_3$CH—CH$_2$ (epoxide)

g) [1-methylcyclohexene] + (BH$_3$)$_2$ $\xrightarrow{\text{1)THF} \atop \text{2)H}_2\text{O}_2/\text{OH}^-}$ [product]

h) [1,2-dimethylcyclobutene] + H$_2$ $\xrightarrow{Pt}$ [product]

i) [1-methylcyclopentene] + $\xrightarrow{\text{1)O}_3 \atop \text{2)H}_2\text{O}_2}$ CH$_3$CCH$_2$CH$_2$CH$_2$CO$_2$H

j) C$_6$H$_5$C≡CCH$_2$C$_6$H$_5$ $\xrightarrow{\text{1)Disiamylborane} \atop \text{2)HOAc}}$ [cis-alkene C$_6$H$_5$ / CH$_2$C$_6$H$_5$]

k) [1-methylcyclopentene] + HCCl$_3$ $\xrightarrow{KOt\text{-}Bu}$ [product]

11-33

a) Molecular formula = C$_4$H$_8$ ; *IHD* = 1

11-33 Contd...

a)Contd...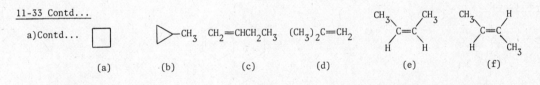

(a)        (b)        (c)        (d)        (e)        (f)

b)  c,d,e, and f

c)  only c

11-34    *IHD* = 3 for A and *IHD* = 2 for B and C.  Since B and C are diketones, this fact accounts for
their *IHD* value.  The diketones were formed by ozonolysis so that A must possess two double
bonds and a cyclic structure.    Five structures are possible.  Structures (a), (b) and (c)
are reasonable.  Cyclobutadienes such as (d) and (e) have never been isolated under normal
conditions.

(a)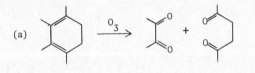

(b)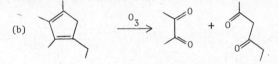

(c)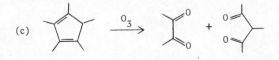

(d)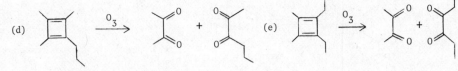

11-35

a)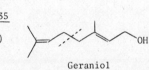

Geraniol

b)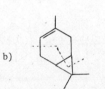

Carene

11-35 Contd...

c)

Camphor

e)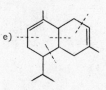

Cadinene

d)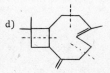

Caryophylene

f)

β-Amyrin

11-36   Acid-catalyzed  cyclization of nerol forms an intermediate carbocation which is the precursor for the three terpenes.

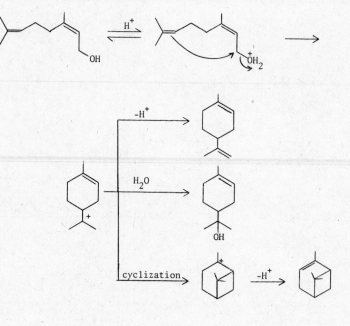

11-37

a)  $BrCH_2CH(Br)CH_2Br$

b)  $ClCH_2CH(Cl)CH_2CH_2CH=CHCO_2CH_3$

c)  $Cl_3CCO_2C(CH_3)_3$

d)  $CH_3(CH_2)_5\overset{\displaystyle O}{\overset{\displaystyle \|}{C}}CH_3$

e)  $(CH_3)_2C(Cl)CH_2I$

f)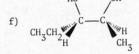

g)

h)  $(CH_3)_3CCH_2CH_2\overset{OH}{\underset{}{C}HCH_3}$

i)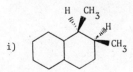

j)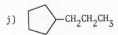

k)  $OHC(CH_2)_4CHO$

l)

m)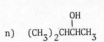

n)  $(CH_3)_2\overset{OH}{\underset{}{C}HCHCH_3}$

o)  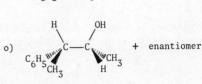    + enantiomer

erythro

p)  $(CH_3)_3CCH_2\overset{I}{\underset{}{C}}(CH_3)_2$

q)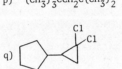

r)  $ClCH_2\overset{OH}{\underset{}{C}HCl}$ $\longrightarrow$ $ClCH_2CHO$

Unstable - this
intermediate is
an HCl adduct of
an aldehyde

s)  $p\text{-}CH_3C_6H_4CH(Cl)CH_3$

t)  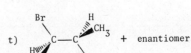    + enantiomer

threo

u)  $CH_3CH_2\overset{OH}{\underset{}{C}}(CH_3)\overset{\displaystyle O}{\overset{\displaystyle \|}{C}}CH_3$

v)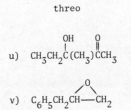

11-37 Contd...

w)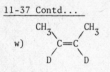

11-38

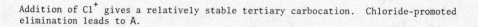
$(CH_3)_2C=\overset{*}{C}H_2$ + $Cl_2$ $\longrightarrow$ $(CH_3)_2\overset{+}{C}-\overset{*}{C}H_2Cl$ + $Cl^-$

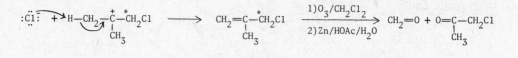
$:\overset{..}{\underset{..}{Cl}}:^-$ + $H-CH_2-\overset{+}{\underset{CH_3}{C}}-\overset{*}{C}H_2Cl$ $\longrightarrow$ $CH_2=\overset{*}{\underset{CH_3}{C}}-CH_2Cl$ $\xrightarrow{\substack{1)O_3/CH_2Cl_2 \\ 2)Zn/HOAc/H_2O}}$ $CH_2=O$ + $O=\overset{}{\underset{CH_3}{C}}-CH_2Cl$

A

Addition of $Cl^+$ gives a relatively stable tertiary carbocation. Chloride-promoted elimination leads to A.

11-39    The carbocation intermediate that forms from either alkene is essentially identical. If we make the reasonable assumption that the transition states leading to that common intermediate are very similar, then the rate difference reflects the fact that 1-butene, the thermodynamically less stable isomer, begins the reaction energetically closer to the transition state than does 2-butene.

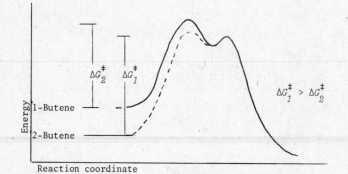

11-40

a)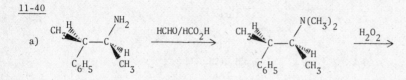

11-40 Contd...

a) Contd....

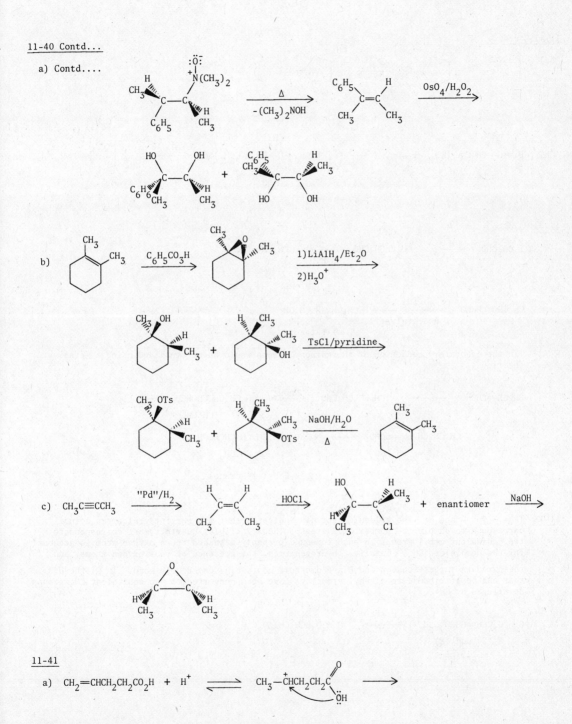

11-41

a) $CH_2=CHCH_2CH_2CO_2H$ + $H^+$ ⇌ $CH_3-\overset{+}{C}HCH_2CH_2\overset{O}{\underset{\ddot{O}H}{C}}$ ⟶

11-41 Contd...

a) Contd...

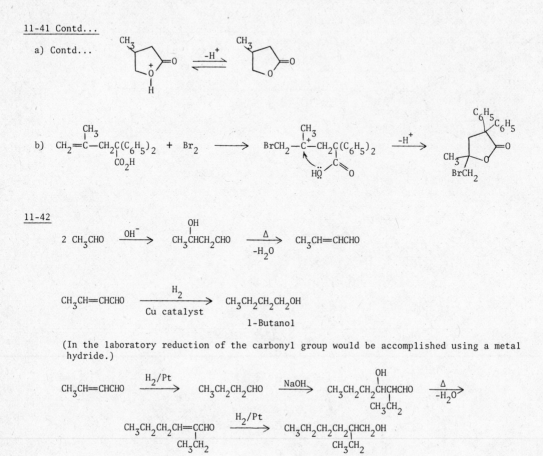

b)

11-42

$$2 \ CH_3CHO \xrightarrow{OH^-} CH_3\overset{\overset{\displaystyle OH}{|}}{C}HCH_2CHO \xrightarrow[-H_2O]{\Delta} CH_3CH{=}CHCHO$$

$$CH_3CH{=}CHCHO \xrightarrow[\text{Cu catalyst}]{H_2} CH_3CH_2CH_2CH_2OH$$
                                                    1-Butanol

(In the laboratory reduction of the carbonyl group would be accomplished using a metal
 hydride.)

$$CH_3CH{=}CHCHO \xrightarrow{H_2/Pt} CH_3CH_2CH_2CHO \xrightarrow{NaOH} CH_3CH_2CH_2\overset{\overset{\displaystyle OH}{|}}{C}H\underset{\underset{\displaystyle CH_3CH_2}{|}}{C}HCHO \xrightarrow[-H_2O]{\Delta}$$

$$CH_3CH_2CH_2CH{=}\underset{\underset{\displaystyle CH_3CH_2}{|}}{C}CHO \xrightarrow{H_2/Pt} CH_3CH_2CH_2CH_2\underset{\underset{\displaystyle CH_3CH_2}{|}}{C}HCH_2OH$$

                                2-Ethyl-1-hexanol

11-43  *IHD*= 3 for A and B.  The molecular formula indicates that the nmr integral areas actually
        correspond to double the number of H atoms.  The 3:2 triplet-quartets must correspond to
        two equivalent ethyl groups in each compound probably attached to an oxygen atom to account
        for the deshielded $CH_2$.  Catalytic hydrogenation, the presence of four oxygen atoms, and

        the nmr data suggest that A and B are diesters containing one double bond.  In C, the H's
        that can be attribtued to alkenyl groupings have been converted to two equivalent $CH_2$ groups
        deshileded by C=O.

$$C_2H_5O_2CCH{=}CHCO_2C_2H_5 \xrightarrow{H_2/Pt} C_2H_5O_2CCH_2CH_2CO_2C_2H_5$$
        (Z) and (E)

              A + B                                      C

11-44

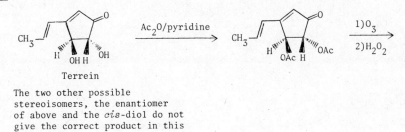

Terrein

The two other possible
stereoisomers, the enantiomer
of above and the *cis*-diol do not
give the correct product in this
sequence.

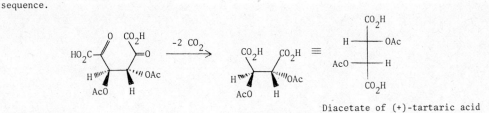

Diacetate of (+)-tartaric acid

11-45    *IHD* = 3 and the hydrogenation data indicate that the compound has three double bonds.
Four isomers can be constructed from the degradation by ozone.

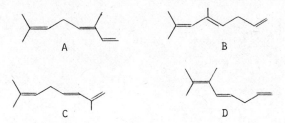

Only compound A has the head to tail isoprenoid structure typical of terpenes.

11-46

a)  $CH_3CH_2CH_2CH_2OH$ $\xrightarrow[\Delta]{H_2SO_4}$ $CH_3CH_2CH=CH_2$ $\xrightarrow{Br_2}$ $CH_3CH_2\overset{Br}{\underset{|}{CH}}CH_2Br$ $\xrightarrow[\Delta]{NaNH_2}$ $CH_3CH_2C\equiv CH$

b)  $CH_3CH_2CHO$ $\xrightarrow[2)H_3O^+]{1)NaBH_4/Et_2O}$ $CH_3CH_2CH_2OH$ $\xrightarrow[\Delta]{H_2SO_4}$ $CH_3CH=CH_2$ $\xrightarrow[2)NaNH_2/\Delta]{1)Br_2}$

$CH_3C\equiv CH$ $\xrightarrow[2)CH_3I]{1)n\text{-}BuLi/Hexane}$ $CH_3C\equiv CCH_3$ $\xrightarrow{H_2/Pt\text{-}Pb}$ $\underset{H}{\overset{CH_3}{\underset{}{}}}C=C\underset{H}{\overset{CH_3}{}}$

11-46 Contd...

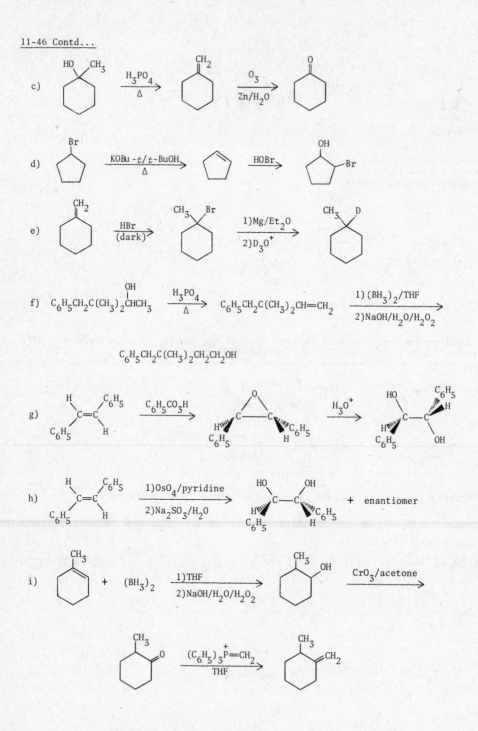

c)

d)

e)

f)   $C_6H_5CH_2C(CH_3)_2\overset{OH}{\underset{}{C}}HCH_3 \xrightarrow[\Delta]{H_3PO_4} C_6H_5CH_2C(CH_3)_2CH=CH_2 \xrightarrow[2)NaOH/H_2O/H_2O_2]{1)(BH_3)_2/THF}$

$C_6H_5CH_2C(CH_3)_2CH_2CH_2OH$

g)

h)

i)

<u>11-46 Contd...</u>

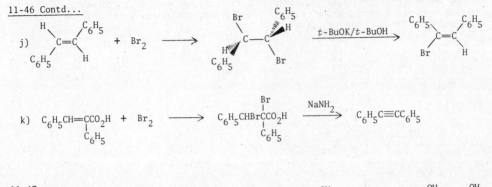

j) 

k) $C_6H_5CH=CCO_2H$ + $Br_2$ $\longrightarrow$ $C_6H_5CHBrCCO_2H$ $\xrightarrow{NaNH_2}$ $C_6H_5C{\equiv}CC_6H_5$
   with $C_6H_5$ substituent, and Br above

<u>11-47</u>

$$\underset{A}{CH_3\overset{O}{\overset{||}{C}}CH_2CH=CHCH_2\overset{OH}{\overset{|}{C}HCH_3}} \xrightarrow{LiAlH_4} \underset{B\ (opt.\ active)\ \ C\ (meso)}{CH_3\overset{OH}{\overset{|}{C}}HCH_2CH=CHCH_2\overset{OH}{\overset{|}{C}HCH_3}} \xrightarrow{H_2/Pt} \underset{D}{CH_3\overset{OH}{\overset{|}{C}}H(CH_2)_4\overset{OH}{\overset{|}{C}HCH_3}}$$

(A must have at least        (A new chiral center is produced
one chiral center.)           in the reduction step.)

$A \xrightarrow{NaOI} 2\ CH_3I + \underset{E}{HO_2CCH_2CH=CHCH_2CO_2H}$

(The haloform reaction shows the presence of a methyl ketone or methyl carbinol.)

$A \xrightarrow[2)Zn/H_2O]{1)O_3/HOAc} \underset{F}{OHCCH_2\overset{OH}{\overset{|}{C}HCH_3}} + \underset{G}{CH_3\overset{O}{\overset{||}{C}}CH_2CHO}$

(Ozonolysis cleaves a double bond and two carbonyl groups are formed at the original alkene carbon atoms.)

$F \xrightarrow{NaOI} HO_2CCH_2CO_2H + CHI_3 \xrightarrow{\Delta} CH_3CO_2H + CO_2$

(The haloform reaction cleaves the bond to methyl and oxidizes the aldehyde group.)

$G \xrightarrow{[Ox]} CH_3\overset{O}{\overset{||}{C}}CH_2CO_2H \xrightarrow{\Delta} CH_3\overset{O}{\overset{||}{C}}CH_3 + CO_2$

(Oxidation converts the aldehyde group to a carboxylic acid which readily decarboxylates. G must be a β-ketoacid or related compound.)

The sequence recorded above shows how all of the data fits together. Solving of the problem commonly begins at the end of the chemical elucidation and works backwards to construct each of the pieces in the puzzle.

11-48  *IHD* = 2 and the hydrogenation data indicates that the compound must be a cycloalkene. The nmr spectrum suggests a methyl group, slightly deshielded, one alkene proton, and a multiplet, probably due to three $CH_2$ groups.

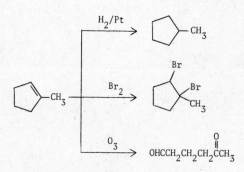

11-49  *IHD* = 6 and the hydrogenation results suggest that two triple bonds are present. The nmr peak areas actually correspond to 6:2 protons indicative of two equivalent methyl groups and a $CH_2$ or two equivalent C-H groups. The position of the $CH_3$ resonance suggests that there are two methyl ketones, a conclusion supported by the formation of oximes and the molecular formula. Only one structure (A) is consistent with these data.

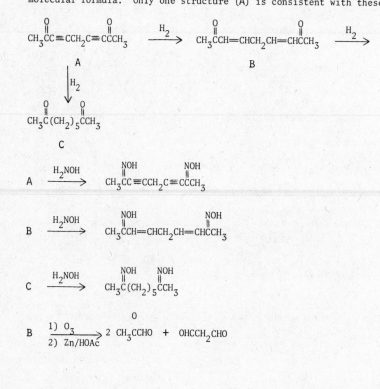

11-50  Combustion analysis provides an empirical formula of $C_7H_5$ and the mass spectrum indicates $C_{14}H_{10}$ is the molecular formula;  *IHD* = 10.  The nmr spectrum shows only aromatic H's and the IR spectrum suggests mono-substituted aromatic.  The formula would require two aromatic rings plus two carbons so that the compound is identified as $C_6H_5C{\equiv}CC_6H_5$.

11-51  The presence of a nitrogen atom, formation of a hydrochloride salt, and the Hofmann degradation show that mescaline is an amine.  The 3,4,5-trihydroxybenzaldehyde and its presumed precursor, 3,4,5-trimethoxybenzaldehyde can account for the major structural component of mescaline.  In fact, the presence of 10 carbon atoms in that compound and *IHD* = 4 for mescaline suggests that mescaline is a 3,4,5-trimethoxyaromatic connected to a two carbon alkylamine.  The nmr spectrum confirms those structural deductions.

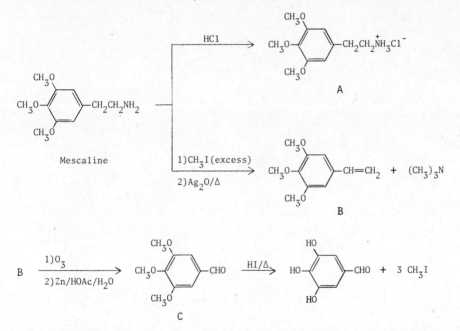

The peak areas in the nmr spectrum of gallic acid actually account for 4:2 hydrogen atoms. Two are typically aromatic and the other four could be accounted for by carboxy and hydroxy protons which rapidly exchange, thus give a single peak.  The spectral data does not provide a unique structure for gallic acid but our knowledge of the mescaline structure suggests 3,4,5-trihydroxybenzoic acid.

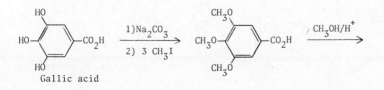

Gallic acid

11-51 Contd...

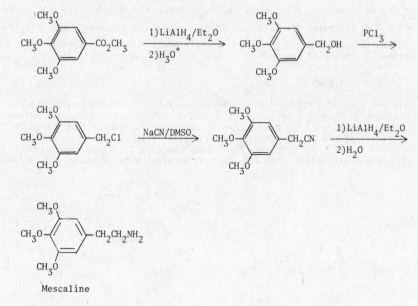

Mescaline

# 12 ADDITIONS TO CONJUGATED COMPOUNDS

12-1

12-2  A charge separated resonance structure for acrolein contributes to the larger dipole moment of that compound.

12-3

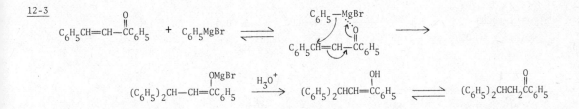

12-4  The terminal methyl group is vinylogous with a carbon atom  alpha to the carbonyl group. The methyl hydrogen atoms possess an acidity comparable to those of α-hydrogen atoms because of resonance stabilization of the conjugate base.

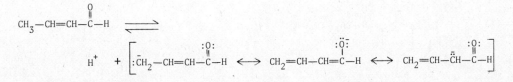

Exchange at the α-carbon atom would require formation of a carbanion which is not easily stabilized by resonance.

**12-5**  Reaction proceeds via a 1,4-addition.  The proton initially adds to the more basic carbonyl oxygen atom and promotes conjugate addition by chloride.

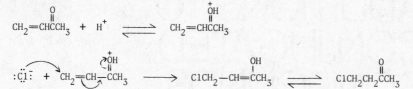

$$CH_2=CHCCH_3 \; + \; H^+ \; \rightleftharpoons \; CH_2=CHCCH_3$$

$$:\overset{..}{\underset{..}{Cl}}:^- \; + \; CH_2=CH-CCH_3 \; \longrightarrow \; ClCH_2-CH=CCH_3 \; \rightleftharpoons \; ClCH_2CH_2CCH_3$$

**12-6**  Reaction between **C** and **D** is preferred because the enolate (of diethyl malonate) is formed more easily.  Furthermore, the conjugated ketones are usually more reactive electrophiles than conjugated esters.

**12-7**

a)  $CH_2(CO_2C_2H_5)_2 \; + \; NaOC_2H_5 \; \rightleftharpoons \; Na^+ : \overset{-}{C}H(CO_2C_2H_5)_2 \; + \; C_2H_5OH$

$(H_5C_2O_2C)_2\overset{..}{C}H \; + \; CH_2=CH-C\equiv N: \; \rightleftharpoons \; (H_5C_2O_2C)_2CHCH_2CH=C=\overset{..}{\underset{..}{N}}{}^-$

$(H_5C_2O_2C)_2CHCH_2CH=C=\overset{..}{\underset{..}{N}}{}^- \; \longrightarrow \; (H_5C_2O_2C)_2CHCH_2CH_2C\equiv N \; + \; C_2H_5O^-$
    $C_2H_5O-H$

b)  $CH_3CH=CHC\overset{O}{\underset{OCH_3}{}} \; + \; H_3O^+ \; \rightleftharpoons \; CH_3CH=CHC\overset{\overset{+}{OH}}{\underset{OCH_3}{}} \; + \; H_2O$

(An enamine)

12-7 Contd...

b) Contd...

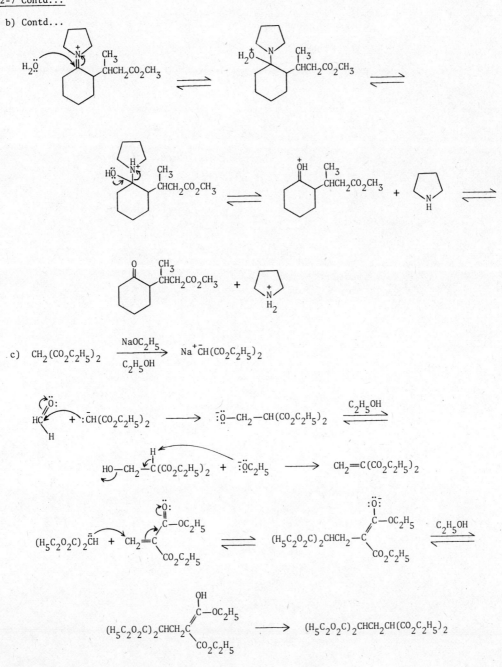

c) $CH_2(CO_2C_2H_5)_2 \xrightarrow[C_2H_5OH]{NaOC_2H_5} Na^+ \bar{C}H(CO_2C_2H_5)_2$

12-7 Contd...

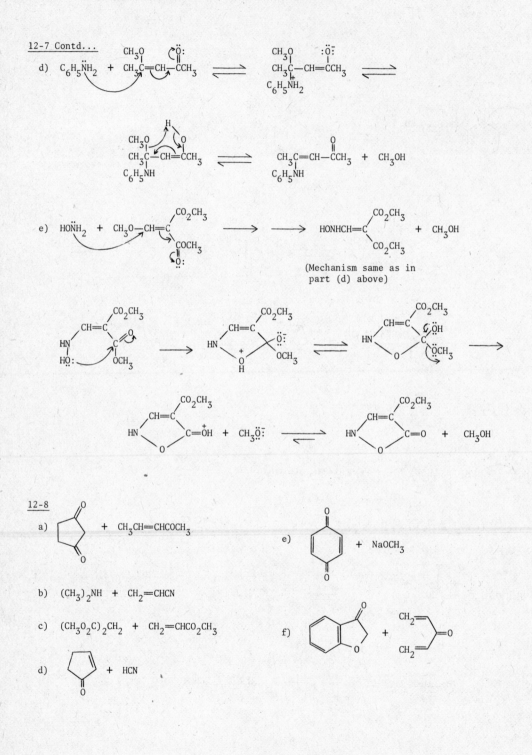

(Mechanism same as in part (d) above)

12-8

a)  + $CH_3CH=CHCOCH_3$

b) $(CH_3)_2NH$ + $CH_2=CHCN$

c) $(CH_3O_2C)_2CH_2$ + $CH_2=CHCO_2CH_3$

d) + HCN

e) + $NaOCH_3$

f) +

<u>12-9</u>
a)

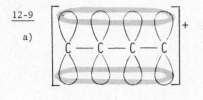

b)  $CH_2=CH-CH=CH_2$  +  $H^+$  $\rightleftharpoons$  $CH_2=CH-CH_2-\overset{+}{C}H_2$

This potential cation is primary and nonstabilized. It would be considerably less stable than the primary allylic cation depicted by resonance structure B in the text.

<u>12-10</u>

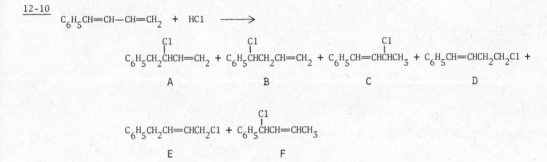

Compound D is unlikely since its carbocation precursor is primary and nonstabilized. Compound C and F come from the most favorable carbocations.

<u>12-11</u> Zinc chloride is a Lewis acid which aids removal of a $Cl^-$ to form the resonance stabilized cation. Readdition of $Cl^+$ ultimately produces the equilibrium mixture.

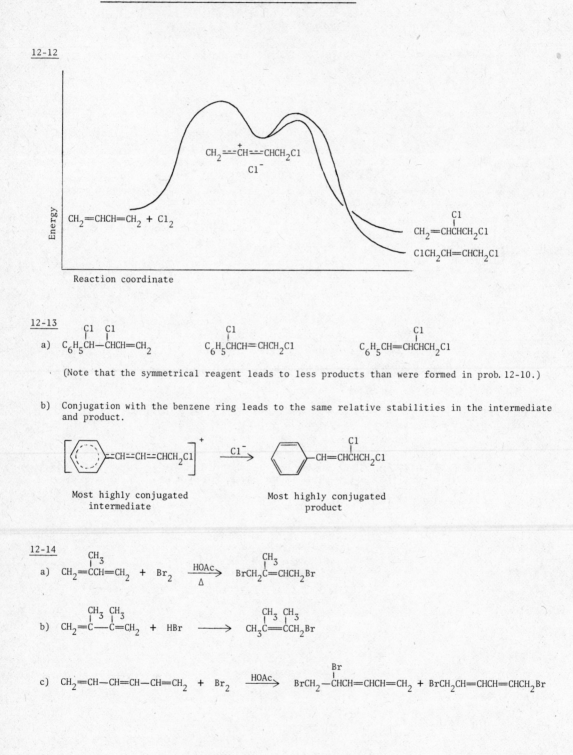

12-12

$CH_2$=CHCH=$CH_2$ + $Cl_2$

$CH_2$=$\overset{+}{CH}$==$CHCH_2Cl$
$Cl^-$

$\underset{\displaystyle Cl}{\overset{\displaystyle \quad}{CH_2=CHCHCH_2Cl}}$

$ClCH_2CH$=$CHCH_2Cl$

Energy

Reaction coordinate

12-13

a)    $C_6H_5\overset{\displaystyle Cl}{CH}-\overset{\displaystyle Cl}{CH}CH=CH_2$        $C_6H_5\overset{\displaystyle Cl}{CH}CH=CHCH_2Cl$        $C_6H_5CH=\overset{\displaystyle Cl}{CH}CHCH_2Cl$

(Note that the symmetrical reagent leads to less products than were formed in prob. 12-10.)

b)   Conjugation with the benzene ring leads to the same relative stabilities in the intermediate and product.

$$\left[ \bigcirc\!\!\!\!\!=\text{CH}==\text{CH}==\text{CHCH}_2\text{Cl} \right]^+ \xrightarrow{\ Cl^-\ } \bigcirc\!\!-\text{CH}=\overset{\displaystyle Cl}{\text{CH}}\text{CHCH}_2\text{Cl}$$

     Most highly conjugated                 Most highly conjugated
         intermediate                       product

12-14

a)    $CH_2$=$\overset{\displaystyle CH_3}{C}CH$=$CH_2$  +  $Br_2$   $\xrightarrow[\Delta]{HOAc}$   $BrCH_2\overset{\displaystyle CH_3}{C}$=$CHCH_2Br$

b)    $CH_2$=$\overset{\displaystyle CH_3}{C}$—$\overset{\displaystyle CH_3}{C}$=$CH_2$  +  HBr   $\longrightarrow$   $CH_3\overset{\displaystyle CH_3}{C}$==$\overset{\displaystyle CH_3}{C}CH_2Br$

c)    $CH_2$=CH—CH=CH—CH=$CH_2$  +  $Br_2$   $\xrightarrow{HOAc}$   $BrCH_2$—$\overset{\displaystyle Br}{CH}CH$=$CHCH$=$CH_2$ + $BrCH_2CH$=$CHCH$=$CHCH_2Br$

12-14 Contd...

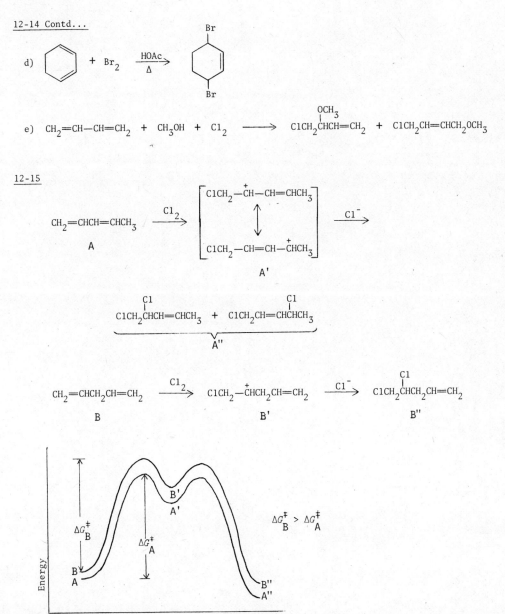

d) [cyclohexadiene] + Br$_2$ $\xrightarrow[\Delta]{\text{HOAc}}$ [4,5-dibromocyclohexene with Br substituents]

e) CH$_2$=CH—CH=CH$_2$ + CH$_3$OH + Cl$_2$ $\longrightarrow$ ClCH$_2$CHCH=CH$_2$ + ClCH$_2$CH=CHCH$_2$OCH$_3$
                                                OCH$_3$

12-15

CH$_2$=CHCH=CHCH$_3$ $\xrightarrow{Cl_2}$ $\begin{bmatrix} ClCH_2-\overset{+}{C}H-CH=CHCH_3 \\ \updownarrow \\ ClCH_2-CH=CH-\overset{+}{C}HCH_3 \end{bmatrix}$ $\xrightarrow{Cl^-}$

A                                A'

ClCH$_2$CHCH=CHCH$_3$ + ClCH$_2$CH=CHCHCH$_3$
      |Cl                               |Cl
$\underbrace{\hspace{12cm}}_{A''}$

CH$_2$=CHCH$_2$CH=CH$_2$ $\xrightarrow{Cl_2}$ ClCH$_2$-$\overset{+}{C}$HCH$_2$CH=CH$_2$ $\xrightarrow{Cl^-}$ ClCH$_2$CHCH$_2$CH=CH$_2$
                                                                |Cl

   B                                       B'                                      B''

$\Delta G^{\ddagger}_B > \Delta G^{\ddagger}_A$

The conjugated diene A is not only more stable than B but the resonance-stabilized intermediate A' is relatively more stabilized than is B'. Addition of Cl$_2$ to A is therefore more rapid than similar addition to B.

12-16

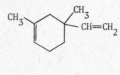 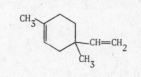 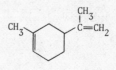

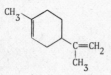 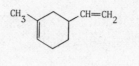 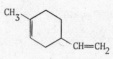

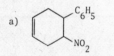 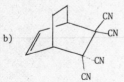 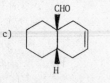

12-17

a)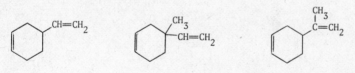

b)

c)

d)

e)

f)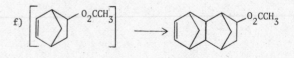

g)

12-18

a) 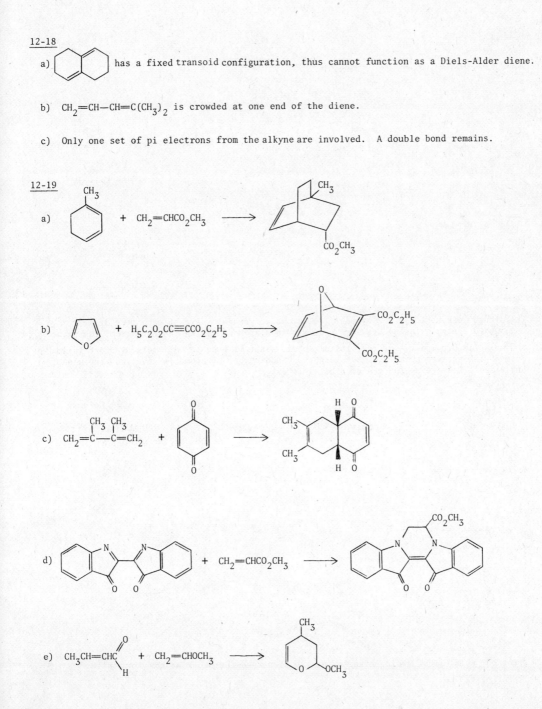 has a fixed transoid configuration, thus cannot function as a Diels-Alder diene.

b) $CH_2{=}CH{-}CH{=}C(CH_3)_2$ is crowded at one end of the diene.

c) Only one set of pi electrons from the alkyne are involved.  A double bond remains.

12-19

a)

b)

c)

d)

e)

12-19 Contd...

f)   $CH_2{=}CHCH{=}CH_2$  +  $CH_2{=}C(CN)_2$  $\longrightarrow$

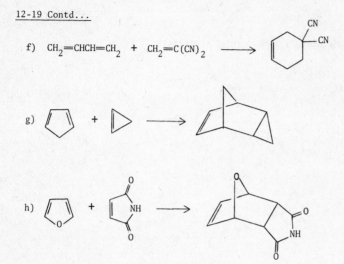

g)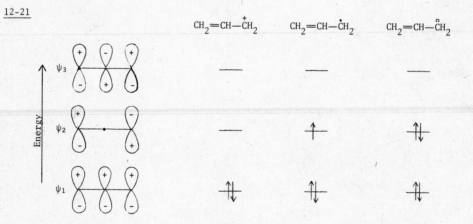

h)

12-20  The student can best see the symmetry relations between orbitals at each atom of a conjugated system by using drawings and/or molecular models.  In the $C_6$ system, the plane and axis lie between two of the orbital lobes.  That is true for all molecular orbitals formed with an even number of atoms.  When an odd number of atoms is involved, the plane and axis is located at the center orbital lobe.

12-21

$$CH_2{=}CH{-}\overset{+}{C}H_2 \qquad CH_2{=}CH{-}\overset{\bullet}{C}H_2 \qquad CH_2{=}CH{-}\overset{\bar{\phantom{C}}}{C}H_2$$

12-22  Treat one molecule of cyclopentadiene as the diene and the other as the dienophile.

12-22 Contd...

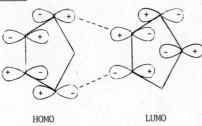

HOMO              LUMO

12-23

a)  An allowed [4 + 2] cycloaddition in which one molecule of the α,β-unsaturated  aldehyde is the diene and another is the dienophile.

b)  An allowed [4 + 2] cycloaddition in which one double bond of allene is the dienophile.

c)  A forbidden [2 + 2] cycloaddition.

d)  An allowed [6 + 4] cycloaddition.

e)  A forbidden [4 + 4] cycloaddition.

f)  In problem 12-23 (d) the product represents a [6 + 4] cycloaddition.  A suprafacial-suprafacial process between a butadiene and hexatriene system is symmetry allowed.

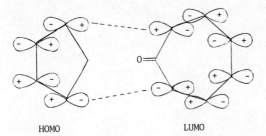

HOMO                      LUMO

In problem 12-23 (e) the product represents a [4 + 4] cycloaddition.  A suprafacial-suprafacial process between two butadiene systems is not symmetry allowed.

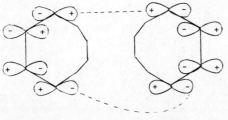

HOMO                      LUMO

12-24   In order for the two ethylene molecules to combine in a geometrically feasible manner, the
[2 + 2] cycloaddition must be suprafacial-suprafacial.  A plane of symmetry is maintained.
Thus we consider a symmetry plane for the bonding and antibonding orbitals of the two
ethylene molecules as well as for the new sigma bonds of cyclobutane.  The two ethylene
molecules provide a total of four molecular orbitals, two bonding and two antibonding.
Four molecular orbitals are developed for the two new sigma bonds of the potential
cyclobutane product.  Two are bonding and two are antibonding.

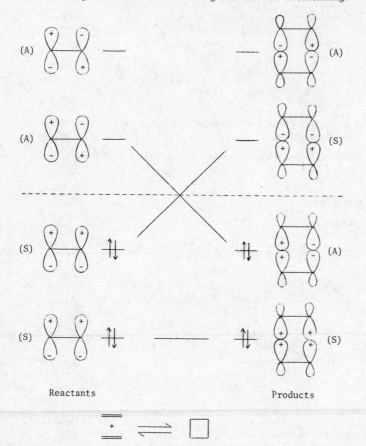

Reactants                          Products

In order to maintain orbital symmetry correlation in the above diagram, correlation must
occur between a bonding orbital of reactant and an antibonding orbital of product.  The
[2 + 2] cycloaddition is therefor energetically unfavorable and symmetry forbidden.

12-25

a) Parent = 215 nm
   $\alpha$ - C   =  10 nm
   $\beta$ - C   =  12 nm
   1 exo  =   5 nm
   _____
   $\lambda_{max}$  = 242 nm

b) Parent = 215 nm
   3 C    =  15 nm
   1 exo  =   5 nm
   _____
   $\lambda_{max}$  = 235 nm

c) Parent = 215 nm
   $\beta$ - C   =  12 nm
   $\beta$ - Cl  =  12 nm
   _____
   $\lambda_{max}$  = 239 nm

d) Parent = 250 nm
   $m$ - R    =   3 nm
   $o$ - NR$_2$ =  20 nm
   _____
   $\lambda_{max}$  = 273 nm

e) Parent = 246 nm
   $o$ - OH =   7 nm
   $p$ - OH =  25 nm
   $2m$ - R  =   6 nm
   _____
   $\lambda_{max}$  = 284 nm

12-26  Protonation of the carbonyl oxygen atom enhances the electrophilicity of the carbon-carbon double bond in the $\alpha,\beta$-unsaturated carbonyl compound.

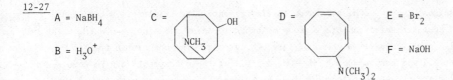

12-27
A = NaBH$_4$          C = [structure with OH and NCH$_3$]          D = [cyclooctadiene with N(CH$_3$)$_2$]          E = Br$_2$

B = H$_3$O$^+$                                                                                 F = NaOH

12-28

a) [Cl, OCH$_3$] CH$_3$CH—CCH$_2$CH=CHCH$_3$ [Cl]

b) [Cl, C$_2$H$_5$] CH$_3$CH—CCH$_2$CH=CHCH$_3$ [Cl]

c) [Cl] CH$_3$CHCHCH$_2$CH$_2$CH=CHCO$_2$H [Cl]

d) [Cl] CH$_2$=CHCO$_2$CH$_2$CHCH$_2$Cl

12-28 Contd...

e) 

\+ 

g) $CH_3CH_2CH_2CH{=}CHC\overset{\displaystyle O}{\diagdown}$ 

$\diagdown NHCH_2\overset{\textstyle Cl}{\underset{}{C}}HCH_2Cl$

f) 

[The more strained double bond is the
more reactive. In this example angle
strain is relieved in going from $sp^2$ (120°)
to $sp^3$ (109°)]

12-29   $IHD$ = 3. Catalytic hydrogenation indicates only one carbon-carbon double bond. The IR
spectrum suggests an ether (C-O-C stretching at 1100 cm$^{-1}$) and the peaks at 1667 and
1620 cm$^{-1}$ are indicative of a conjugated carbonyl and double bond since they are shifted to
lower frequencies. The UV absorption is consistent with and α,β-unsaturated carbonyl
compound that has a substituent on the α and β positions (calc. $\lambda_{max}$ 237 nm). Those data
would account for the two oxygen atoms and two of the $IHD$. The nmr spectrum shows a singlet
(3) at 2.4 ppm typical of $CH_3\overset{\displaystyle O}{\overset{\|}{C}}-$ and only a single proton in the alkene region (6.2 ppm).

Those data suggest $\overset{H}{\diagdown}C{=}C-\overset{\displaystyle O}{\overset{\|}{C}}CH_3$ as a structural fragment. The triplet (1.0 ppm) and
quartet (3.2 ppm) are surely an ethyl group attached to an oxygen atom; —OCH$_2$CH$_3$. The
multiplet (1-2 ppm) would fit a chain of three CH$_2$ groups. The one proton triplet
deshielded to 4.8 ppm can be due to CH$_2$—CH—O-. All of these fragments can be combined to
form a cyclic structure (that accounts for the third $IHD$) consistent with all of the data.

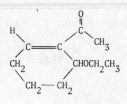

12-30   $IHD$ = 2. The UV absorption suggests a substituted α,β-unsaturated carbonyl group since a
$C_6$ diene could not give the high $\lambda_{max}$ value. Two possible structure are:

12-30 Contd...

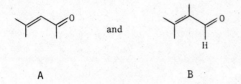

A                    B

The nmr spectrum is consistent with A.

12-31

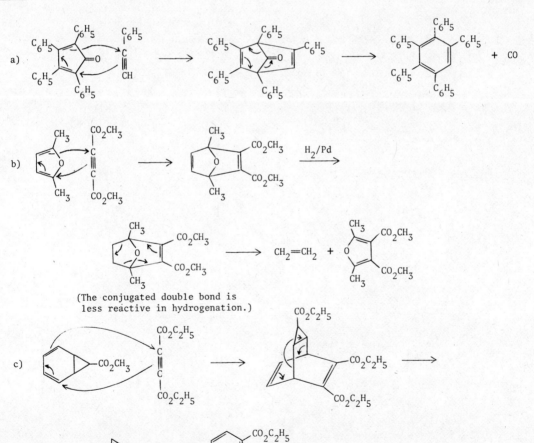

12-32

a)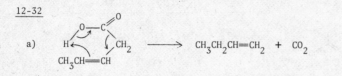

$$CH_3CH_2CH=CH_2 \ + \ CO_2$$

b)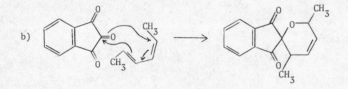

c)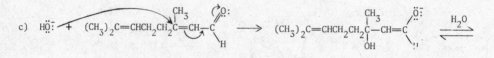

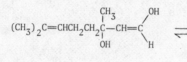

(This is an aldol)

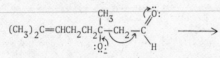

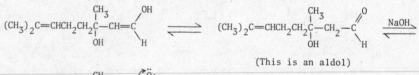

(The final step is a reverse aldol reaction.)

d) $Br-CH_2-C\equiv C-CH_2-Br \ + \ Zn \ \longrightarrow \ Br-CH_2-C\equiv C-CH_2-ZnBr \ \longrightarrow$

$$CH_2=C=C=CH_2 \ + \ ZnBr_2$$

e) $CH_3CH=CHCH=CHCO_2C_2H_5 \xrightarrow{\text{KOEt/EtOH}} K^+ \ :\bar{C}H_2CH=CHCH=CHCO_2C_2H_5$

$$H_5C_2O_2C-C\overset{\ddot{O}:}{\underset{OC_2H_5}{\big|}} \ + \ :\bar{C}H_2CH=CHCH=CHCO_2C_2H_5 \ \longrightarrow$$

12-32 Contd...

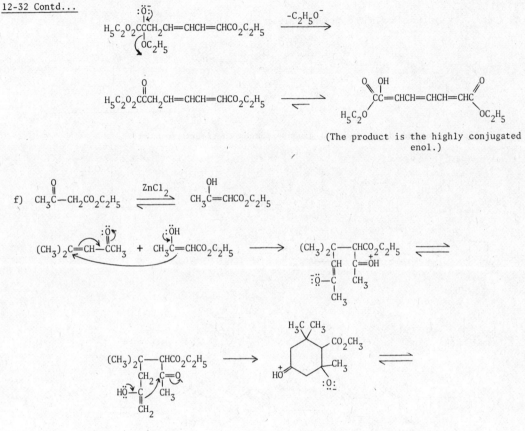

$$H_5C_2O_2CCH_2CH=CHCH=CHCO_2C_2H_5 \xrightarrow{-C_2H_5O^-}$$

$$H_5C_2O_2CCCH_2CH=CHCH=CHCO_2C_2H_5 \rightleftharpoons$$

(The product is the highly conjugated enol.)

f)   $CH_3C-CH_2CO_2C_2H_5 \overset{ZnCl_2}{\rightleftharpoons} CH_3C=CHCO_2C_2H_5$

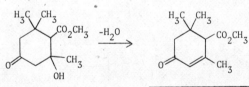

$(CH_3)_2C=CH-CCH_3$ + $CH_3C=CHCO_2C_2H_5 \longrightarrow (CH_3)_2C-CHCO_2C_2H_5 \rightleftharpoons$

$(CH_3)_2C-CHCO_2C_2H_5 \longrightarrow$

The Lewis acid promotes decarboxylation of the vinylogous β-keto ester.

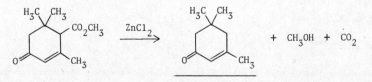

$\xrightarrow{ZnCl_2}$ + $CH_3OH$ + $CO_2$

12-32 Contd...

f) Contd...    Cyclization in the opposite direction produces the third product.

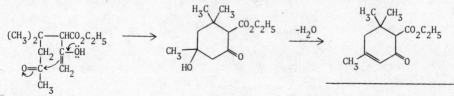

Cyclization to the ester carbonyl group produces the fourth product.

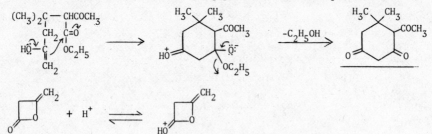

g)

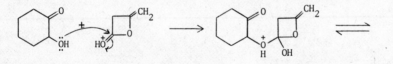

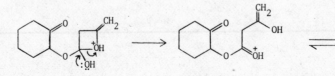

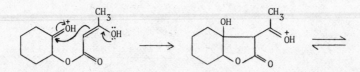

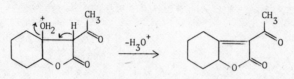

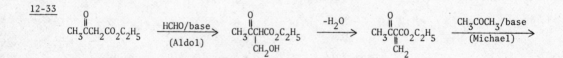

12-33

$CH_3CCH_2CO_2C_2H_5$  $\xrightarrow[\text{(Aldol)}]{\text{HCHO/base}}$  $CH_3CCHCO_2C_2H_5$  $\xrightarrow{-H_2O}$  $CH_3CCCO_2C_2H_5$  $\xrightarrow[\text{(Michael)}]{CH_3COCH_3/base}$

12-33 Contd...

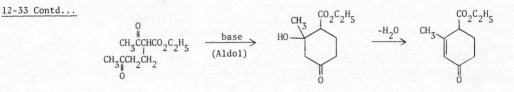

12-34

a) The problem is treated as a [6 + 2] cycloaddition.  In the HOMO-LUMO method $\Psi_1$ of the $C_2$ portion can be the HOMO and $\Psi_4$ of the $C_6$ portion can be the LUMO.  The cycloaddition would be a symmetry allowed suprafacial-antarafacial process.  The actual reaction is forbidden since the geometry would require a suprafacial-suprafacial process.

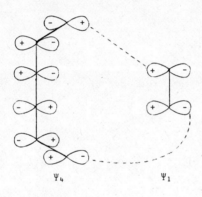

b) The azide group can be treated as a $C_3$ system with four electrons, that is, as an allyl group $(-\ddot{\underset{\cdot\cdot}{N}}-\ddot{N}=\ddot{N}^+)$.  We can thus use the allyl $\Psi_3$ as our LUMO and $\Psi_1$ of a $C_2$ system as the HOMO.  The reaction is an allowed suprafacial-suprafacial process.

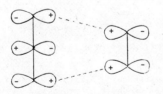

12-35

a) The IR spectrum of C is consistent with an α,β-unsaturated carbonyl compound and the UV spectrum suggests that one substituent is located on that chromophore.  The nmr spectrum shows two alkene protons and possibly a methyl ketone (2.2 ppm, s, 3).  The *IHD* of 3 suggests

12-35 Contd...

a) Contd...   a cyclic structure in addition to the α,β-unsaturated carbonyl.  The broad nmr
peak at 1.7 ppm would fit $-(CH_2)_4-$ and the single proton multiplet at 2.5 ppm would be
consistent with a ring position at which a substituent group is located.  A cyclopentane with
a $C_4$-α,β-unsaturated carbonyl side chain will fit the data.

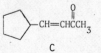

C

b) Compound C can be readily prepared by an aldol-dehydration sequence between the following
reactants.

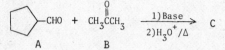

12-36  The following sequence is expected for the reactions indicated.

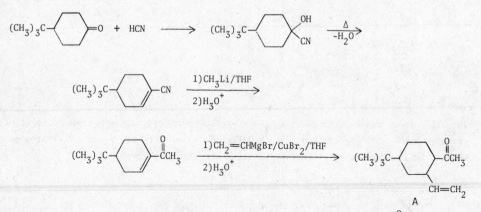

A has MW = 208.  The two major peaks in the mass spectrum are due to $CH_3\overset{O}{\overset{||}{C}}-$ (43) and
$(CH_3)_3C-$ (57).  The IR absorption is normal for a ketone as is the unsymmetrical alkene
absorption.  The nmr chemical shift values are consistent with A with the methyl and
*tert*-butyl peaks both overlapping the broad multiplet of the ring protons.

12-37

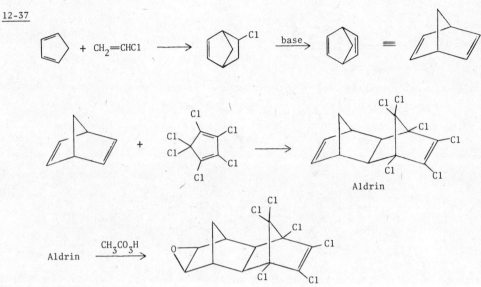

Aldrin

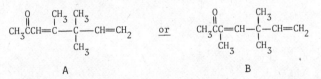

12-38   Elemental analysis gives an empirical formula of $C_{10}H_{16}O$ and mass spectral analysis confirms this as the molecular formula. The nmr multiplet at 4.9 - 6.2 ppm for 4 protons suggests that at least two double bonds are present. The IR spectrum is consistent with an $\alpha,\beta$-unsaturated carbonyl structure. Two double bonds and a carbonyl group would account for the *IHD* of 3. No aldehydic proton is present in the nmr spectrum so the carbonyl group must be a ketone. The groups of singlets in the nmr spectrum of 6,3, and 3 protons indicates two equivalent and two different methyl groups. The two equivalent methyl groups are not deshielded while the two nonequivalent methyl groups are consistent with a methyl ketone and a methyl attached to a carbon-carbon double bond. Two reasonable structural formulas, A and B, should be considered (no differentiation is made between geometrical isomers).

$$CH_3CCH=C\overset{\overset{\displaystyle CH_3}{|}}{\underset{\underset{\displaystyle CH_3}{|}}{C}}-CH=CH_2$$

A

<u>or</u>

$$CH_3CC=CH-\overset{\overset{\displaystyle CH_3}{|}}{\underset{\underset{\displaystyle CH_3}{|}}{C}}-CH=CH_2$$

B

Structure A is the more probable since the alkene C-H beta to the carbonyl group on an $\alpha,\beta$-unsaturated carbonyl compound is typically deshielded into the aromatic region ($\sim$7 ppm) in the nmr spectrum.

12-39

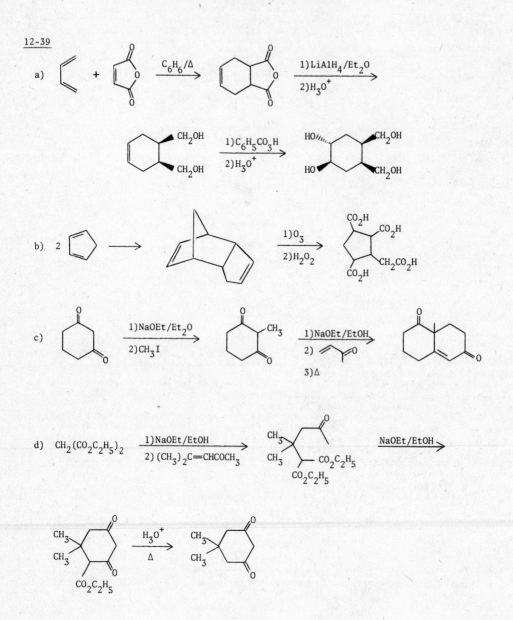

# 13 SUBSTITUTIONS AT UNSATURATED CARBON- AROMATIC COMPOUNDS

13-1

Ortho

Meta

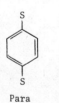 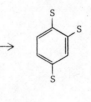

Para

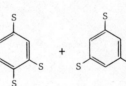

13-2

Substituents adjacaent
on a triangle face

Substituents adjacent
on a square face

Substituents nonadjacent
(only possible on a
square face)

13-3

a)  827 - 789 = 38 kcal/mol
    (3460 - 3300 = 160 kJ/mol), which is relatively close to the resonance energy calculated
    from hydrogenation data.

b)

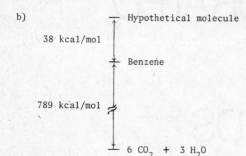

            — Hypothetical molecule

38 kcal/mol

          Benzene

789 kcal/mol

      6 $CO_2$  +  3 $H_2O$

13-4

13-5  Conjugated cyclic compounds with $4n + 2$ electrons,
      $\therefore$ Aromatic: a, c, d, f, g


      Conjugated cyclic compounds with $4n$ electrons,
      $\therefore$ Nonaromatic: b, h


      Compounds with $4n + 2$ conjugated electrons, but not having cyclic conjugation,
      $\therefore$ Nonaromatic: e, j


      Compounds with $4n$ electrons and noncyclic conjugation,
      $\therefore$ Nonaromatic: i


13-6

a + b)  If we assume that four cyclooctene double bonds are equivalent to a hypothetical
        nonstabilized cyclooctatetraene, then 4 x (-23 kcal/mol) = -92 kcal/mol [4 x (-97 kJ/mol) =
        -388 kJ/mol] is the energy released on hydrogenation of that species.  Since -101 kcal/mol
        (-422 kJ/mol) is released on hydrogenation of cyclooctatetraene, the actual compound is less
        stable (by 9 kcal/mol; 34 kJ/mol) than the hypothetical model.  The apparent destabilization
        is consistent with the antiaromatic properties predicted for cyclooctatetraene.

13-7

a) If cyclooctatetraene were planar, the adjacent p-orbitals of the double bonds would be expected to interact.  This would give an unfavorable $4n$ $\pi$-electron system.

b) The dianion is a $4n + 2$ electron system, thus favors a planar aromatic configuration.

c) Cyclooctatetraene has typical single and double bonds.  The dianion is aromatic and all of the carbon-carbon bonds are equivalent.


13-8

a) Azulene is a cyclic conjugated compound with $4n + 2$ ($n = 2$) electrons.

b)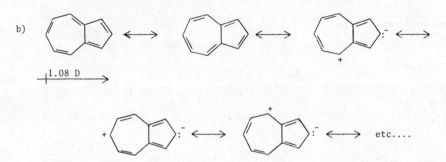

The dipole is directed toward the five membered ring.  Structures with a delocalized negative charge in a five membered ring and a delocalized positive charge in a seven membered ring resemble the cyclopentadiene anion and tropylium cation, both of which show some aromatic stability.


13-9   The [14]-annulene is a $4n + 2$ electron system and is found to be aromatic.   [16]-Annulene is a $4n$ electron system and is nonaromatic.


13-10   The difference, 32 kcal/mol (134 kJ/mol), is approximately equal to the loss of resonance energy going from benzene to a 1,3-cyclohexadiene.

13-11

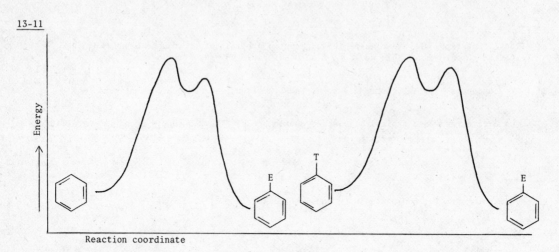

Reaction coordinate

The first steps are essentially the same.  The second is slower (higher energy) for tritiated benzene.

13-12

a)  Rate = $k(E^+)(ArH)$

b)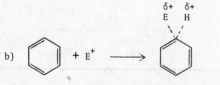

Transition state

The transtition state for a one-step reaction depicts breaking of the bond to the hydrogen atom in the rate-controlling step, thus would lead to a significant kinetic isotope effect.

13-13

a)  The intermediates leading to ortho and para substitution have more resonance structures and are energetically more favorable than the intermediate of meta substitution.

Ortho: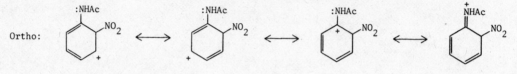

13-13 Contd...

a) Contd...

Para:

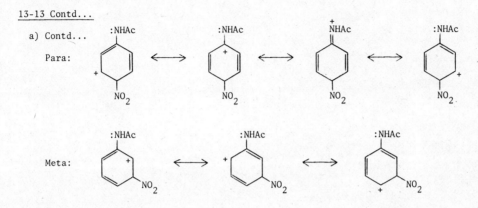

Meta:

b)   The amide substituent is sufficiently large to inhibit substitution at the ortho position.

13-14

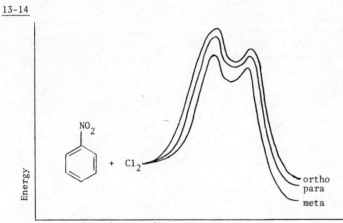

13-15   Toluene is 61 times more reactive than benzene in this reaction.   $\dfrac{98.4}{1.6}$ = 61

13-16   The electron donating resonance effect by the nitrogen and oxygen containing substituents is much greater than the electron withdrawing inductive effect, even in the ground state of the molecules.

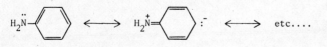

13-16 Contd...

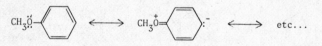

$CH_3\ddot{\ddot{O}}$ ⟷ $CH_3\overset{+}{O}$ :⁻ ⟷ etc...

13-17

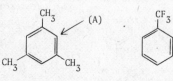

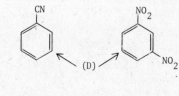

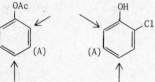

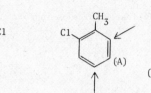

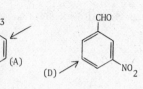

13-18

$o_f{}^{CH_3} = 3 \times .329 \times 605 = 597$

$m_f{}^{CH_3} = 3 \times .003 \times 605 = 5.4$

$p_f{}^{CH_3} = 6 \times .668 \times 605 = 2,425$

13-19   The two positions ortho to one methyl group and para to the other will have a relative
reactivity of 2 x 4.5 x 749 = 6740, the one position meta to each substituent
4.8 x 4.8 = 23, and the one orhto to both 4.5 x 4.5 = 20.  The calculated percentage of
substitution is:

$\dfrac{6740}{6783}$ x 100 = 99.4%        $\dfrac{23}{6783}$ x 100 = 0.3%        $\dfrac{20}{6783}$ x 100 = 0.3%

Predicted

Observed

13-20  For substituted phenylacetic and benzoic acids    $\Delta G^{\circ}{}_{PA} = \rho\,\Delta G^{\circ}{}_B + C$

Similarly for the unsubstituted case    $\Delta G^{\circ}_{O_{PA}} = \rho\,\Delta G^{\circ}_{O_B} + C$

Subtracting one equation for the other gives    $\Delta G^{\circ}{}_{PA} - \Delta G^{\circ}_{O_{PA}} = \rho\,(\Delta G^{\circ}{}_B - \Delta G^{\circ}_{O_B})$

Since    $\Delta G^{\circ} = -2.3\ RT\ \log K$

Then    $\Delta G^{\circ}{}_{PA} - \Delta G^{\circ}_{O_{PA}} = \rho\,(-2.3\ RT)(\log K_B - \log K_{O_B}) = \rho\,(-2.3\ RT)\ \log \dfrac{K_B}{K_{O_B}}$

But    $\Delta G^{\circ}{}_{PA} - \Delta G^{\circ}_{O_{PA}} = -2.3\ RT\ \log \dfrac{K_{PA}}{K_{O_{PA}}}$

Thus    $\log \dfrac{K_{PA}}{K_{O_{PA}}} = \rho\,\log \dfrac{K_B}{K_{O_B}} = \rho\sigma$

13-21  Electron donating substituents have negative sigma values since they decrease the stability of the conjugate base of the substituted acid.  The greater the electron donating effect, the greater the magnitude of the negative sigma constant.  Similarly, electron withdrawing substituents stabilize the negative charge on the conjugate base and enhance acidity, thus they have positive values for sigma.  The $\sigma_m$ and $\sigma_p$ values are expected to differ significantly when direct conjugation between the substituent and conjugate base anion can occur.  The para, but not the meta relationship of groups can lead to direct conjugation.

13-22

a)  The $pK_a$ value for $C_6H_5CO_2H$ is 4.2 .

Since $\rho = 1.0$ for ionization of benzoic acids;

$\log K(p\text{-}CH_3C_6H_4CO_2H) = (-0.17 \times 1.0) + \log K(C_6H_5CO_2H)$

$= -0.17 - 4.2 = -4.37$

$\therefore pK_a\ (p\text{-}CH_3C_6H_4CO_2H) = 4.37.$

b)  $\log K(m\text{-}NO_2C_6H_4CO_2H) = (0.71 \times 1.0) - 4.2 = -3.49$

$\therefore pK_a(m\text{-}NO_2C_6H_4CO_2H) = 3.49.$

c)  The Hammett linear free energy relationship can be extended to reaction rates by using the sigma substituent values determined from acidities.

$\log k(p\text{-}ClC_6H_4CO_2C_2H_5) = \rho\sigma + \log 82$

$= (2.43 \times 0.23) + 1.91$

$= 0.56 + 1.91 = 2.47$

$\therefore k(p\text{-}ClC_6H_4CO_2C_2H_5) = 295\ 1/mol\text{-}sec$

<u>13-22 Contd...</u>

d)  A positive value of $\rho$ indicates that reaction is favored by electron withdrawal by a substituent.  This is consistent with addition of a nucleophile in the rate-controlling step.

<u>13-23</u>  Mononitration is readily accomplished on the activated phenol.  But each nitro group deactivates the ring so that polynitration requires more extreme conditions.

<u>13-24</u>

a)
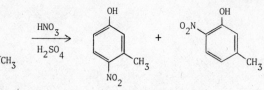

Ortho and para to the directing groups. Ortho substitution takes place at the less hindered position.

b)
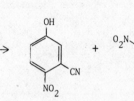

Ortho and para to the directing OH group.  Ortho substitution takes place at the less hindered position.

c)
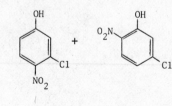

As (a)

d)
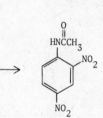

The amide nitrogen atom directs ortho and para.

e)
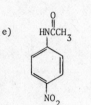
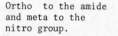

Ortho  to the amide and meta to the nitro group.

13-25  In aqueous base the very reactive phenoxide anion is formed.  The electron withdrawing
effect as each bromine atom substitutes favors formation of the anion even more.  The
partially substituted material reacts more readily than phenol so that only tribromophenol
is recovered.

13-26  The second Br$_2$ molecule acts as a catalyst to enhance the displacement of Br$^-$.

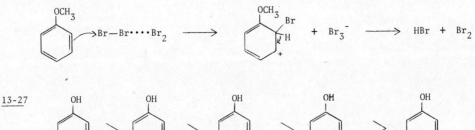

13-27

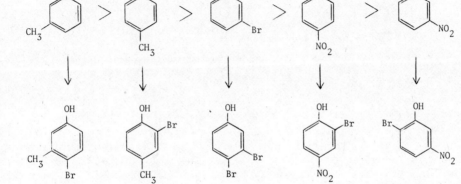

13-28  Base forms the phenoxide, a much more nucleophilic species than phenol.

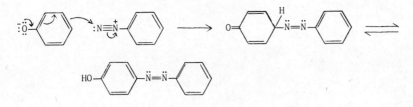

13-29  In cymene, a relatively good cationic leaving group - the 2-propyl cation - can be formed.

13-30

a)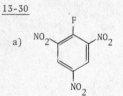

1-Fluoro-2,4,6-trinitrobenzene

b)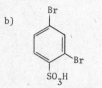

2,4-Dibromobenzenesulfonic acid

c)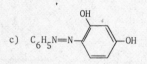

2,4-Dihydroxyazobenzene

d)

p-t-Butylnitrobenzene

e)

2,5-
Dichloronitrobenzene

3,4-
Dichloronitrobenzene

f) 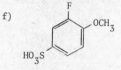 +

3-Fluoro-4-
methoxybenzenesulfonic
acid

3-Fluoro-2-
methoxybenzenesulfonic
acid

g)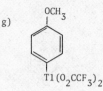

Tl(O₂CCF₃)₂

$p$-Methoxyphenylthallium ditrifluoroacetate

h)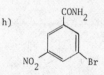

5-Bromo-3-nitrobenzamide

i)

$o$-Iodoacetanilide      $p$-Iodoacetanilide

13-31  A *tert*-butyl cation is formed in each case.

$$(CH_3)_3C-Cl \ + \ FeCl_3 \ \rightleftharpoons \ (CH_3)_3C^+ \ FeCl_4^-$$

$$(CH_3)_2C=CH_2 \ + \ HF/BF_3 \ \rightleftharpoons \ (CH_3)_3C^+ \ BF_4^-$$

$$(CH_3)_3C-\ddot{O}H \ + \ H_2SO_4 \ \rightleftharpoons \ (CH_3)_3C-\overset{+}{O}H_2 \ HSO_4^- \ \rightleftharpoons \ (CH_3)_3C^+ \ HSO_4^- \ + \ H_2O$$

$$\text{[benzene]} \ + \ \overset{+}{C}(CH_3)_3 \ \longrightarrow \ \text{[arenium]} \ \longrightarrow \ \text{[} t\text{-butylbenzene]} \ + \ H^+$$

13-32

$$CH_3CH_2CH_2Br \ + \ AlBr_3 \ \rightleftharpoons \ CH_3\overset{H}{\underset{|}{C}}H-CH_2-Br\cdots AlBr_3 \ \longrightarrow \ CH_3CH=CH_2 \ + \ \overset{+}{H}\cdots Br\text{-}\bar{A}lBr_3$$

$$(CH_3)_2\overset{+}{C}H \ \ Br\bar{A}lBr_3 \ \longrightarrow \ (CH_3)_2CHBr \ + \ AlBr_3$$

Formation of a secondary carbocation favors rearrangement.

13-33  The rate of rearrangement of 1-chloropropane to 2-chloropropane depends on the reaction temperature.  At lower temperature the Friedel-Crafts reaction is slightly more rapid than rearrangement and nonrearranged product predominates.

13-34  Racemization demonstrates that the intermediate is sufficiently free to become planar.  This is consistent with a carbocation intermediate.  An $S_N2$ process would lead to inversion stereochemistry.

13-35

[toluene] $+ \ CH_3Cl \ \xrightarrow{AlCl_3} \ $ [o-xylene] $+$ [m-xylene] $+$ [p-xylene] $+$

o-Xylene     m-Xylene     p-Xylene

13-35 Contd...

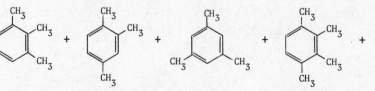

Hemitylene     Pseudocumene     Mesitylene     Prehnitene

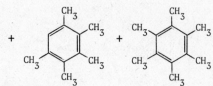

Isodurene        Durene        Pentamethylbenzene   Hexamethylbenzene

13-36   The result is consistent with the cationic character of the migrating group since a tertiary carbocation is formed more readily than a primary carbocation.

13-37

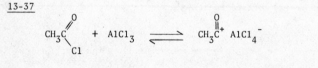

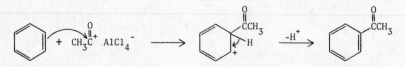

13-38   The exchange of chlorine atoms is consistent with formation of an acyl cation and supports the suggestion that such an intermediate is also involved in the Friedel-Crafts acylation.

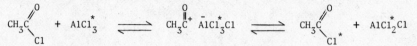

13-39  The two carbonyl groups of the anhydride complex the catalyst.

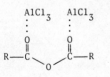

13-40

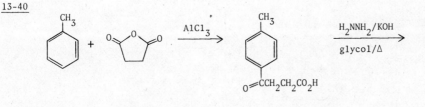

 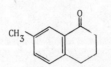

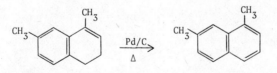

13-41

$Cl_3CCHO$ + $H^+$ ⇌ $Cl_3C\overset{+}{C}HOH$

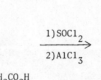

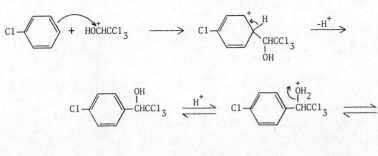

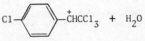

13-41 Contd...

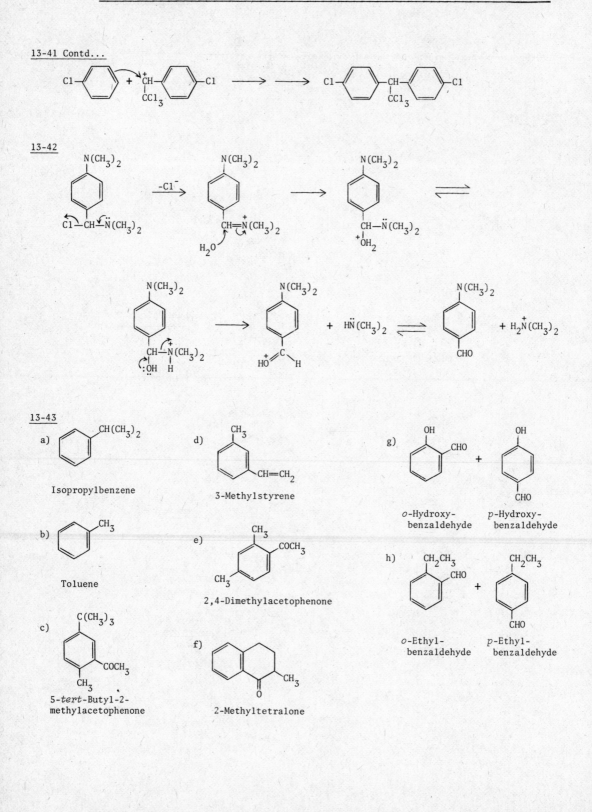

13-42

13-43

a) Isopropylbenzene

d) 3-Methylstyrene

g) o-Hydroxy-benzaldehyde   p-Hydroxy-benzaldehyde

b) Toluene

e) 2,4-Dimethylacetophenone

h) o-Ethyl-benzaldehyde   p-Ethyl-benzaldehyde

c) 5-tert-Butyl-2-methylacetophenone

f) 2-Methyltetralone

13-44
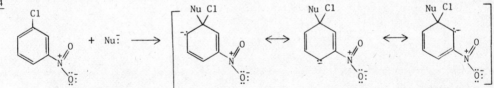

No direct conjugation between the aromatic ring and the nitro group is possible so as to stabilize the negative charge of the anionic intermediate. Anion stabilization is almost always required for nucleophilic aromatic substitution to take place.

13-45   The 2,6-dimethyl groups force the nitro group out of the plane of the aromatic ring. Resonance stabilization of the negative charge formed in the addition step is markedly decreased.

13-46   The electron withdrawing nitro groups stabilize the negative charge of the conjugate base by resonance, therefore the protonated form (the phenol) is very acidic ($pK_a \approx 0$).

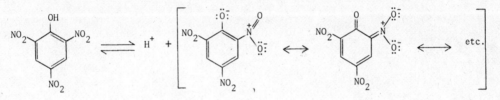

13-47   The three nitro groups stabilize the negative charge of the Meisenheimer complex through resonance.

13-48   The data suggest that halogen does not leave in the rate controlling step but does have an influence on this step. That is, two steps are involved. The more electronegative fluorine enhances attack of the nucleophile by inductive stabilization of the forming negative charge, thus increasing the speed of the rate controlling step.

13-49   Nucleophilic substitution on a haloalkane is considerably more favorable than on a haloaromatic since aromaticity is disrupted in the addition step with the latter substrates.

13-50   The isomerization is consistent with (though doesn't necessarily require) a phenyl cation intermediate.

$$C_6H_5-\overset{*+}{N}\equiv N: \quad \rightleftarrows \quad C_6H_5-\overset{+}{N}\overset{*\ddot{N}}{\underset{N}{\parallel}} \quad \rightleftarrows \quad C_6H_5-\overset{+}{N}\equiv\overset{*}{N}:$$

13-51   The phenyl cation ion is very unstable relative to *tert*-butyl.  It reacts very quickly, thus is much less selective than *tert*-butyl.

13-52

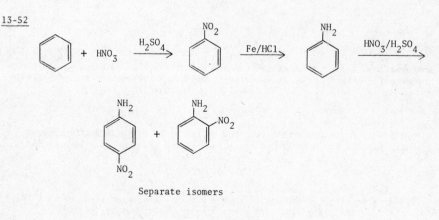

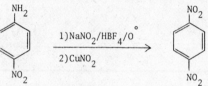

Separate isomers

13-53  Delocalization of the positive charge on the nitrogen atom by the aromatic ring enhances stability relative to that observed with an alkyl substrate.

13-54  The addition-elimination pathway normally occurs only when electron withdrawing groups are available to stabilize the intermediate anion (Meisenheimer complex).

13-55

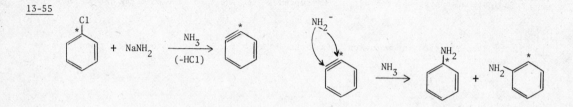

13-56  Reaction of phenoxide (formed from the phenol product plus base) with unreacted
chlorobenzene produces the ether.  At the high temperature of this process both
addition-elimination and benzyne pathways are probably involved.

13-57

a)

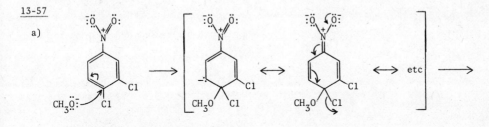

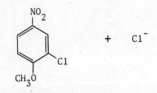

2-Chloro-4-nitroanisole

b)

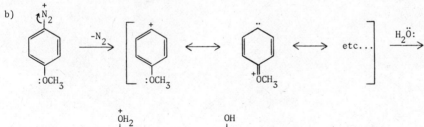

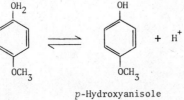

p-Hydroxyanisole

c)

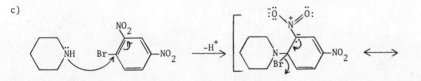

13-57 Contd...

c) Contd...

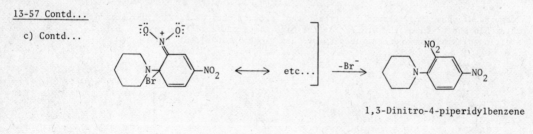

1,3-Dinitro-4-piperidylbenzene

d)

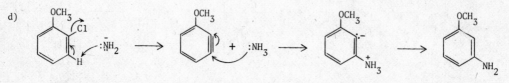

*m*-Methoxyaniline

(The ortho position is sufficiently hindered so that meta substitution predominates.)

13-58

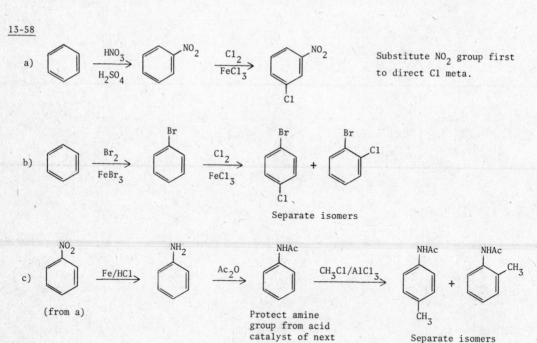

a) Substitute NO₂ group first to direct Cl meta.

$$\text{Substitute NO}_2 \text{ group first to direct Cl meta.}$$

b) Separate isomers

c) (from a)    Protect amine group from acid catalyst of next two steps.    Separate isomers

13-58 Contd...

c) Contd...

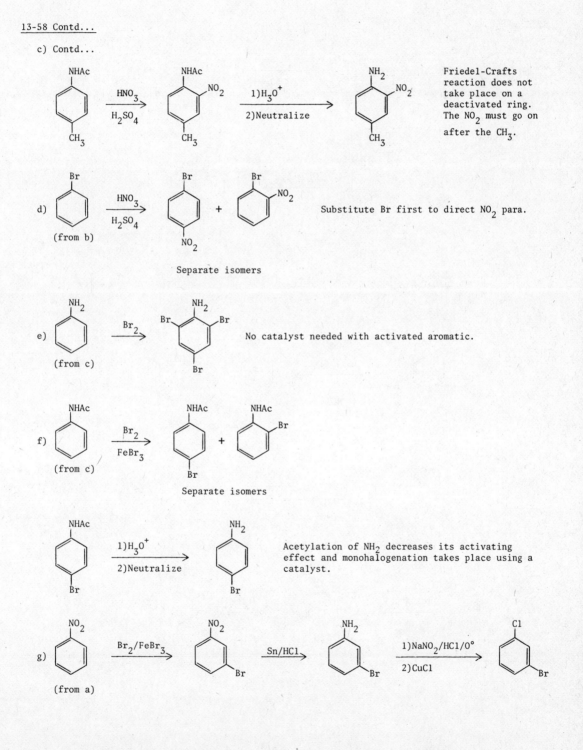

d)

(from b)

Separate isomers

Substitute Br first to direct NO$_2$ para.

e)

(from c)

No catalyst needed with activated aromatic.

f)

(from c)

Separate isomers

Acetylation of NH$_2$ decreases its activating effect and monohalogenation takes place using a catalyst.

g)

(from a)

13-58 Contd...

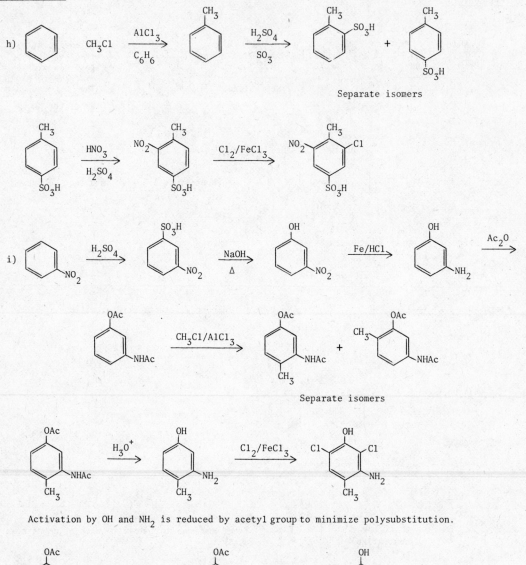

Separate isomers

Separate isomers

Activation by OH and $NH_2$ is reduced by acetyl group to minimize polysubstitution.

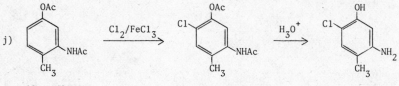

(from i)

13-58 Contd...

k) (from c)

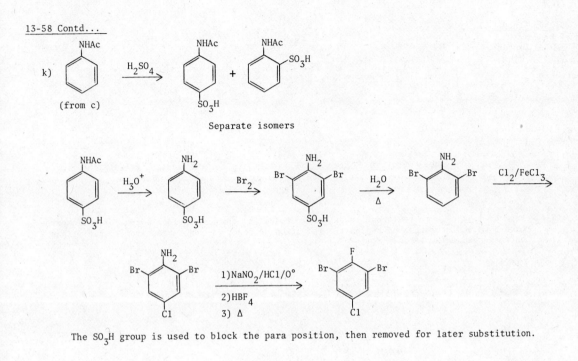

Separate isomers

The SO₃H group is used to block the para position, then removed for later substitution.

13-59

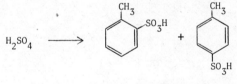

Separate isomers

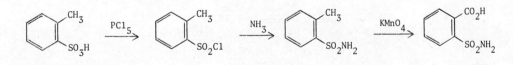

13-60

a)

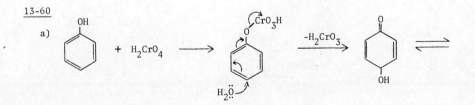

13-60 Contd...

a) Contd...

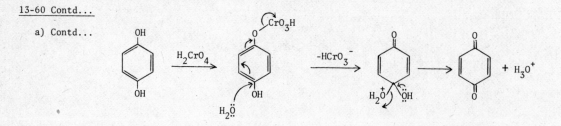

b) A *meta*-quinone does not exist. There is no possibility for conjugation between the two potential carbonyl groups so that all the initial stability would be lost.

13-61 Benzene is much more resistant to catalytic reduction than is cyclohexadiene or cyclohexene. Once a molecule of benzene begins the reduction sequence it reacts much more rapidly than an unchanged molecule.

13-62

a)

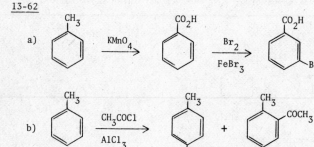

b)

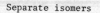

Separate isomers

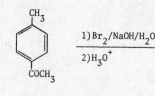 

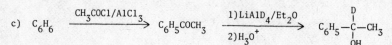

13-62 Contd...

d) $C_6H_6$ $\xrightarrow{Br_2/FeBr_3}$ $C_6H_5Br$ $\xrightarrow{Mg/Et_2O}$ $C_6H_5MgBr$ $\xrightarrow[2)H_3O^+]{1)CH_2-CH_2/Et_2O}$ $C_6H_5CH_2CH_2OH$

13-63

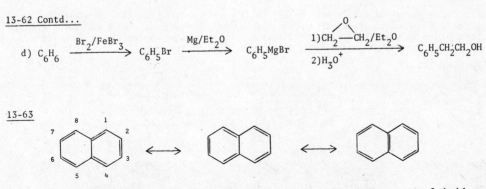

We can account for the trend in bond lengths by considering the amount of double or single bond character as represented by the resonance structures. Thus the 2-3 and identical 6-7 bonds are designated twice as double bonds and four times as single bonds. They therefore have more single bond character and are relatively longer. A similar analysis can be applied to the other bonds.

13-64 An α-substituent is close to the hydrogen atom on the 8-position (a *peri* relationship). There is less steric hindrance between the β-substituent and the adjacent hydrogen atoms since the groups point away from each other.

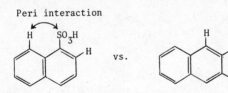

13-65

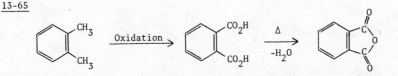

13-66 Reaction at the 9,10-positions disrupts aromaticity the least. The two benzenoid structures of the intermediates possess more resonance stabilization than one naphthalene structure.

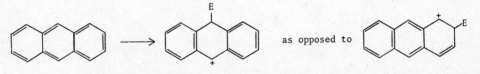

13-67  When reaction occurs at the 2- or 4-positions, the intermediate benefits from conjugation
with the 1-substituent without disrupting the second aromatic ring.  With a 2-substituent,
1-substitution is stabilized by resonance within the same ring whereas 3-substitution
would require disruption of the total naphthalene aromaticity.

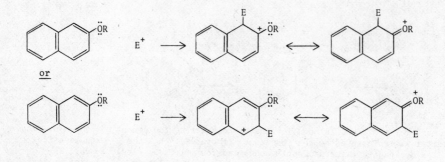

13-68

a)

b)

Separate isomers

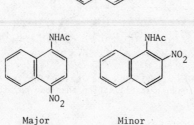

Major                Minor

Separate isomers

13-68 Contd...

b) Contd...

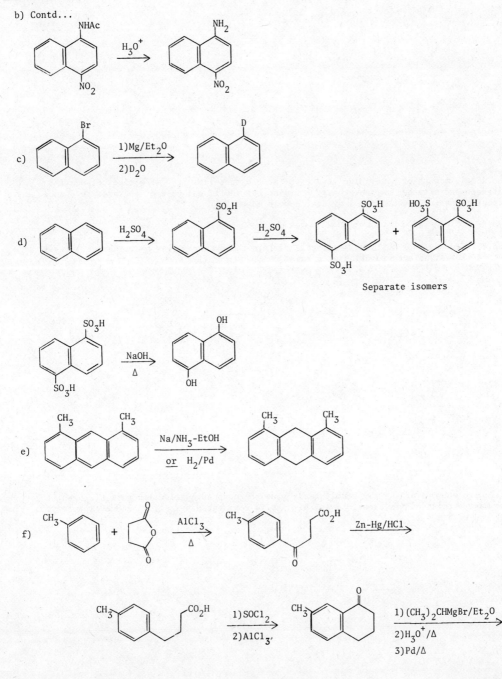

Separate isomers

13-68 Contd....

f) Contd...

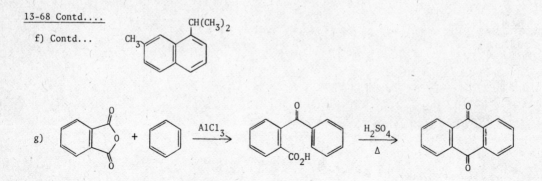

g)

13-69    The dipole moment of piperidine is due to the electronegativity difference between the nitrogen and attached carbon atoms.  Pyridine has additional charge separated resonance structures which account for a greater dipole moment.

13-70    The electron pair of aniline is delocalized into the aromatic ring by resonance.  It is much less available to function as a base.

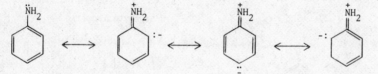

13-71

a)

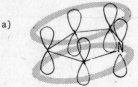

b)    The four electrons of the two double bonds plus the nonbonding electron pair of the nitrogen atom make a total of six electrons in this cyclic conjugated system.  The Hückel rule is followed with $n = 1$.

13-72

$$CH_3\overset{O}{\overset{\|}{C}}CH_2CO_2Et \ + \ H^+ \ \rightleftharpoons \ CH_3\overset{\overset{+}{O}H}{\overset{\|}{C}}CH_2CO_2Et$$

13-72 Contd...

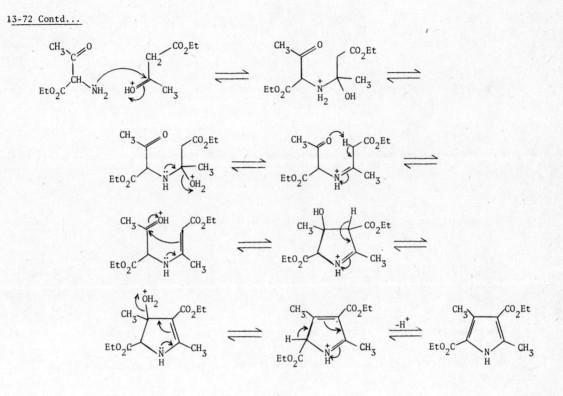

13-73

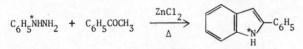

The experiment confirmed that the β-nitrogen atom of phenylhydrazine is lost as ammonia.

13-74   The cyclohexanone structure is retained and leads to a tricyclic heterocycle known as a carbazole.

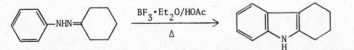

1,2,3,4-Tetrahydrocarbazole

13-75

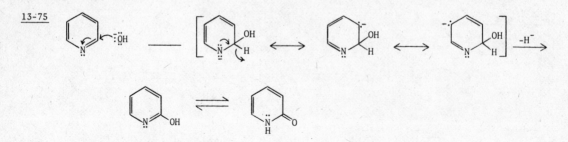

2-Pyridone is a resonance stabilized tautomer of 2-hydroxypyridine.

13-76

a)  The conjugate base of γ-picoline is stabilized by delocalization of charge by the nitrogen atom.

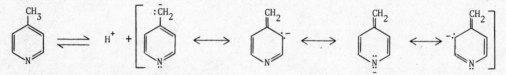

Direct conjugation of the negative charge with the nitrogen atom of β-picoline is not possible.

b)  The intermediate formed from decarboxylation of A is stabilized by interaction with the pyridine ring.

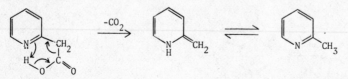

13-77  Pyridine oxide is more reactive than pyridine in both electrophilic and nucleophilic substitution.  The oxygen anion can function as an electron donor while the positive nitrogen is an electron acceptor.

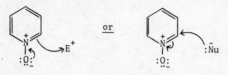

13-78

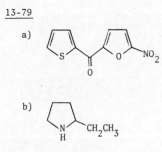

13-79

a)

f)

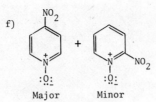

Major        Minor

b)

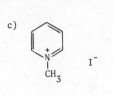

c)

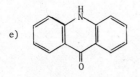    I⁻

g)

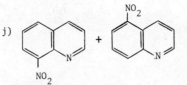

d)

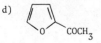

h)

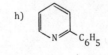

e)

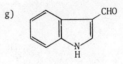

i)

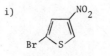

j)

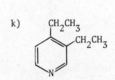

k)

13-80

a)

b) 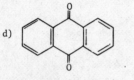 + polyalkylation

c)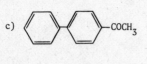

d)

e)

f)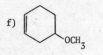

g)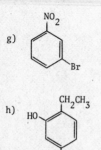

h)

i)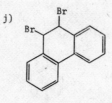

j)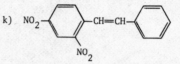

k)

l)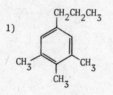

m)

n)

o)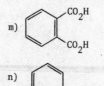

13-80 Contd...

p)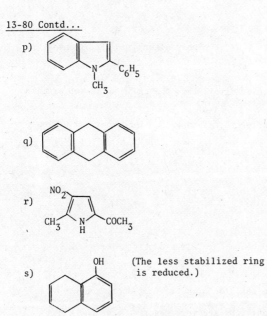

t)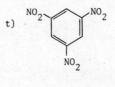

q)

u)

r)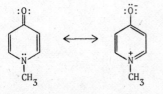

s)      (The less stabilized ring
                             is reduced.)

13-81

a) Aromatic with $4n + 2$ electrons

b) A $4n$ electron system; not aromatic

c) A resonance structure illustrates some degree of aromatic character.

d) A resonance structure shows that each ring has some aromatic character.

13-81 Contd...

e) The structure is seen to have $4n + 2$ electrons ($n = 2$) when only alternate multiple bonds are involved in the cyclic conjugated system.

f) Six electrons are in conjugation but not in a cyclic array, thus the compound is not aromatic.

g) Cyclic conjugation of 6 electrons through the empty orbital on each boron atom provides an aromatic system.

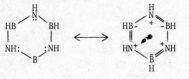

h) An electron pair on oxygen participates in conjugation for this aromatic heterocycle.

13-82  Substitution of an electronegative halogen atom onto the aromatic ring decreases the basicity of aniline. HX formed in the substitution protonates aniline more effectively than it protonates the haloanilines. The haloanilines are more reactive than the anilinium ion, thus react further.

13-83

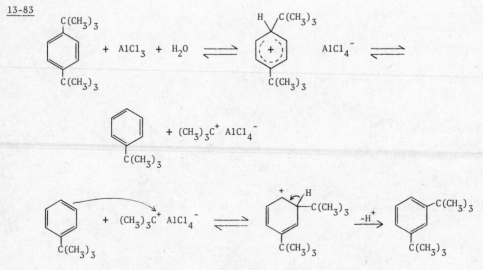

The o-di-*tert*-butylbenzene would be very crowded.

13-84. Benzyne is the dienophile which adds across the 9,10 position of anthracene (the diene).

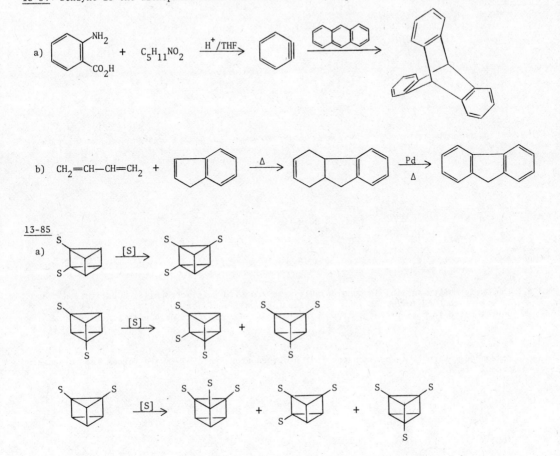

a)

b)  $CH_2{=}CH{-}CH{=}CH_2$ +

13-85

a)

b)  The Kekulé structure that gives two trisubstituted products is ortho disubstituted and leads to a 1,2-disubstituted cyclohexane.  The disubstituted Ladenberg isomer that gives two trisubstituted products does not have the substituents on adjacent carbon atoms, thus does not lead to a 1,2-disubstituted cyclohexane.

13-86 *IHD* = 5.  Reaction with phenylhydrazine suggests an aldehyde or ketone and the positive haloform test indicates a methyl ketone.  Compound B is a carboxylic acid produced from the haloform reaction.  Compound C is an alcohol derived from the ketone A and can also undergo the haloform reaction.  The acid D with mp of 121-122° is benzoic acid, an observation consistent with the *IHD* of 5 for A.

13-86 Contd...

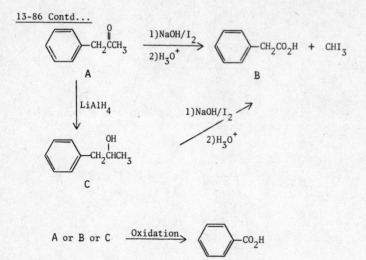

 A or B or C $\xrightarrow{\text{Oxidation}}$

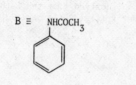

D

13-87 The unprotonated aniline is considerably more reactive in electrophilic substitution than is the protonated form. As long as at least a small equilibrium concentration of the unprotonated form is present, it will nitrate in the ortho and para positions.

13-88 Nonbonded interactions between the four hydrogen atoms pointed inward forces the molecule out of planarity.

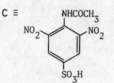

13-89 The fluorine atom is sufficiently electronegative to enhance the acidity of the α-deuterium atoms and base-promoted exchange with the solvent takes place. Fluoride is a poor leaving group in this reaction so that elimination to form benzyne or direct nucleophilic substitution does not occur.

13-90

A ≡ $(CH_3CO)_2O$     B ≡ NHCOCH₃     C ≡

13-90 Contd...

D ≡ C₂H₅O₂CCHCH₂CO₂C₂H₅  (with CHO substituent)
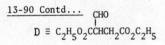

E ≡ NH₃

F ≡
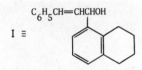

G ≡ CH₃COCl/AlCl₃

H ≡
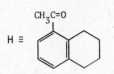

I ≡
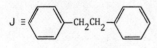

J ≡
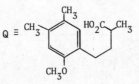

K ≡ CNCH₂—⬡—CH₂CH₂—⬡—CH₂CN
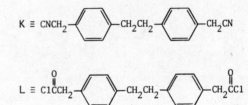

L ≡ ClCCH₂—⬡—CH₂CH₂—⬡—CH₂CCl
(with O double bonds)

M ≡

N ≡

O ≡ NaOH, (CH₃)₂SO₄

P ≡
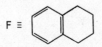

Q ≡

13-91  The data suggest that the mechanism is changing with temperature.  The 50:50 mixture at
       higher temperature is consistent with the benzyne mechanism.  At the lower temperature
       direct nucleophilic substitution accounts for 71% of the reaction.

13-92

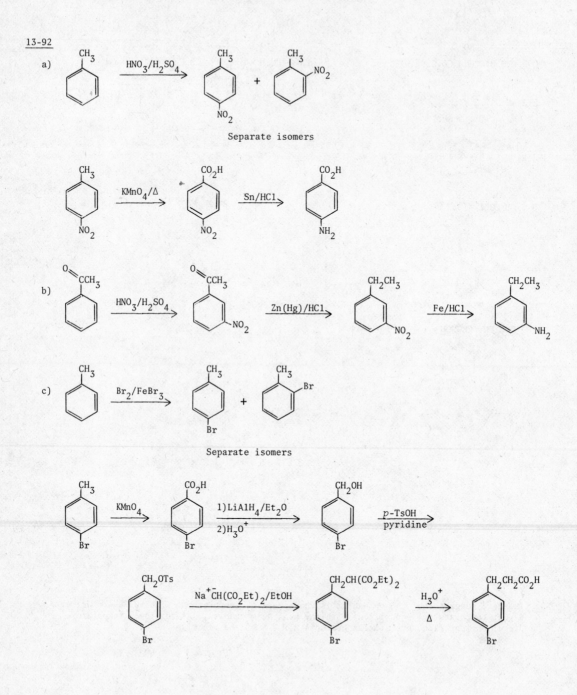

13-92 Contd...

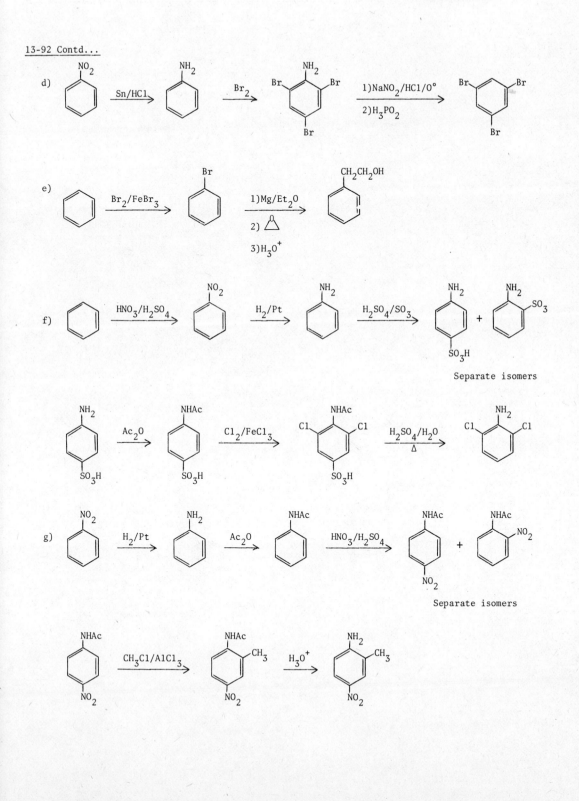

13-92 Contd...

h)

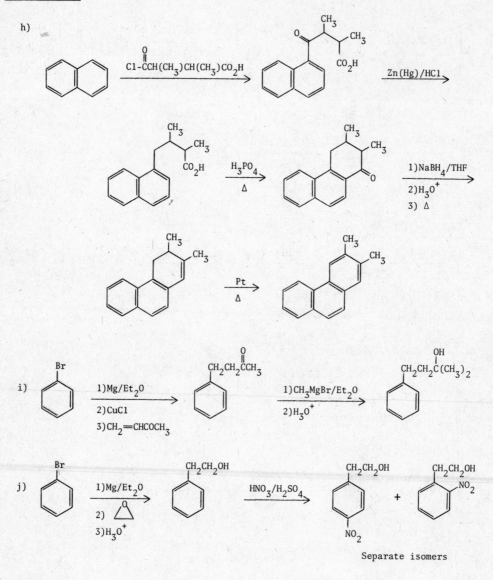

Separate isomers

13-92 Contd...

j) Contd...

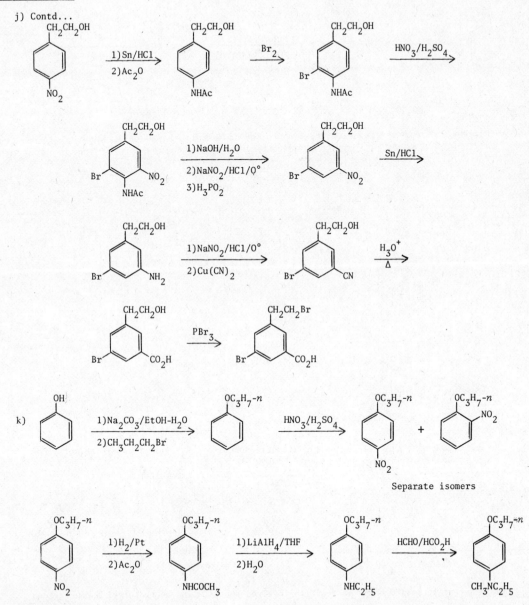

k)

Separate isomers

13-92 Contd...

1)

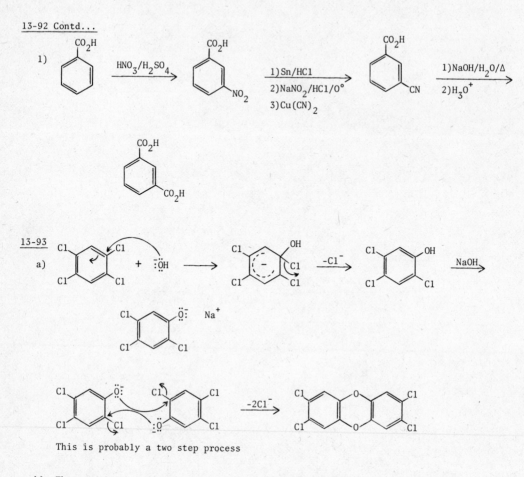

13-93

a)

This is probably a two step process

b)  The reaction is a double electrophilic aromatic substitution.  Formation of the methylene
    bridge probably takes place one step at a time.

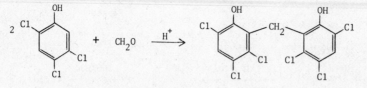

13-94  *IHD* = 4.  If we assume that the reaction involves substitution by the ethyl formoyl group

$(CH_3CH_2O\overset{\overset{O}{\|}}{C}-)$, then the original heterocycle must have a molecular formula of $C_5H_6O$.  The
ethyl ester is consistent with the triplet (1.2 ppm) and quartet (3.8 ppm) in the nmr.  The

13-94 Contd... nmr spectrum shows that the heterocycle has a methyl group (s, 2.4 ppm) and two single protons (6.1 and 7.1 ppm) on adjacent carbon atoms (J = 5 Hz). The only compound consistent with these data is

13-95 The 3-hydroxythiophene exists as a mixture of the keto and enol tautomers. The carbonyl group is shifted to a low frequency because it is conjugated with the double bond and sulfur atom.

13-96

a) Normal position for alkene protons.

b) Normal position for alkene protons. Resonance between adjacent double bonds is minimal since the molecule is nonplanar.

c) The two methyl groups are in the center of an aromatic ring current and are strongly shielded.

d) The indicated $CH_2$ groups lie over the central part of the aromatic ring and are slightly shielded by the aromatic ring current.

13-97 The UV model compound is

The *IHD* = 8 requires that the unknown have one more ring or double bond than the model and the molecular formula requires two additional carbon atoms compared to the model. The nmr spectrum shows three aromatic protons and the methoxy singlet (3.8 ppm). The two triplets indicate adjacent, deshielded methylene groups ($-CH_2-CH_2-$). The singlet at 2.3 ppm is a methyl group attached to a nitrogen atom or an aromatic ring carbon atom.
Possible structures are

13-97 Contd...

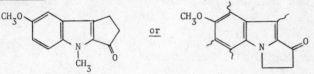

or    (With a $CH_3$ group at one
of the wavy bond lines.)

13-98  *IHD* = 5, and the UV spectral model accounts for all of this.

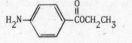

Formation of a hydrochloride salt is consistent with one or both of the nitrogen atoms
existing as amines.  The nmr spectrum, the broad peak at 4.15 ppm which exchanges two
hydrogen atoms for deuterium is probably due to an $-NH_2$ group.  The multiplet between 6.5
and 8.0 is due to the *para*-disubstituted aromatic ring.  The data to this point suggests
that the remaining atoms of novocaine are connected to the ethyl group of the ester in the
UV model.  The nmr absorption at 4.3 ppm is probably the $-OCH_2$ group and must be adjacent
to a $CH_2$ group to account for the triplet.  These data suggest that the rest of the molecule,
$C_4H_{10}N$, is attached to that end atom of the model.  The nmr triplet at 1.0 suggests two
identical methyl groups split by adjacent $CH_2$ groups.  That is surely two ethyl groups and
the requisite $CH_2$ quartets are deshielded to 2.6.  The five peak pattern can originate from
the overlap of that quartet and the triplet for the $CH_2$ group beta to the ester oxygen atom
and deshielded by attachment to a nitrogen atom.

triplet at 2.8 ppm

quartet at 2.6 ppm

Combine to give these five peaks.

The structure of novocaine is:

$H_2N-$⟨ring⟩$-CCH_2CH_2N(CH_2CH_3)_2$
         ‖
         O

13-99  The IR spectrum suggests the presence of a carbonyl group (1670 cm$^{-1}$) possibly an amide and
the nmr shows an aromatic group, probably *para*-disubstituted.  Those account for the *IHD*
of 5.  The nmr spectrum shows an ethyl group (1.4 and 4.0 ppm) with the $CH_2$ group deshielded,

13-99 Contd...   probably because of attachment to an oxygen atom.  (Attachment to a nitrogen atom or an aromatic ring would not deshield that much.)  The nmr peak at 2.1 ppm is consistent with a methyl next to the carbonyl group.  The disappearance, on treatment with $D_2O$, of the nmr peak at 8 ppm and the IR peak at $3350^{-1}$ is typical of an N—H or O—H group.  (The N—D or O—D stretching frequencies are near 2400 $cm^{-1}$ in the IR.)  We have evidence for the following groups:

$$\text{—} \bigcirc \text{—} \quad ; \quad \text{—OCH}_2\text{CH}_3; \quad \overset{\overset{\displaystyle O}{\|}}{\text{CH}_3\text{C}}\text{—NH—}$$

These fragments account for all of the atoms of phenacetin.

$$\overset{\overset{\displaystyle O}{\|}}{\text{CH}_3\text{C}}\text{—NH} \text{—} \bigcirc \text{—OCH}_2\text{CH}_3$$

Phenacetin

# 14 ORGANIC SYNTHESIS

<u>14-1</u>

a) $CH_3Li$ + $CH_2O$ $\xrightarrow[\text{2)}H_3O^+]{\text{1)Hexane}}$ $CH_3CH_2OH$ $\xrightarrow[\substack{\text{(Distill volatile}\\\text{gaseous product)}}]{CrO_3/H_2SO_4}$

$CH_3CHO$ $\xrightarrow[\substack{\text{2)}H_3O^+\\\text{3)}CrO_3/H_2SO_4}]{\text{1)}CH_3Li/\text{Hexane}}$ $CH_3COCH_3$

2 $\overset{.}{C}H_3MgBr$ + 2 $CO_2$ $\xrightarrow[\text{2)}H_3O^+]{\text{1)Et}_2O}$ 2 $CH_3CO_2H$ $\xrightarrow[\Delta]{Ba(OH)_2}$ $CH_3COCH_3$

b-1) *$CH_3CH_2OH$ + $PBr_3$ $\longrightarrow$ $CH_3CH_2Br$ $\xrightarrow[\substack{\text{2)}*CH_3CHO\\\text{3)}H_3O^+}]{\text{1)Mg/Et}_2O}$ $CH_3CH_2\overset{\overset{OH}{|}}{C}HCH_3$ $\xrightarrow{CrO_3/H_2SO_4}$ $CH_3CH_2COCH_3$

$CH_3I$ $\xrightarrow{NaCN/DMSO}$ $CH_3CN$ $\xrightarrow[\text{2)}H_3O^+]{\text{1)}*CH_3CH_2MgBr/Et_2O}$ $CH_3CH_2COCH_3$

b-2) *$CH_3COCH_3$ $\xrightarrow[\text{2)}H_3O^+]{\text{1)}CH_3MgBr/Et_2O}$ $(CH_3)_3COH$

*$CH_3CO_2H$ $\xrightarrow{CH_3OH/H^+}$ $CH_3CO_2CH_3$ $\xrightarrow[\text{2)}H_3O^+]{\text{1)2 }CH_3MgBr/Et_2O}$ $(CH_3)_3COH$

b-3) *$CH_3CH_2MgBr$ + $CH_2O$ $\xrightarrow[\text{2)}H_3O^+]{\text{1)Et}_2O}$ $CH_3CH_2CH_2OH$ $\xrightarrow{HI}$ $CH_3CH_2CH_2I$

*Prepared in an earlier part of problem 14-1.

14-2
|          | (For 100% yield)                                              | (For calculated yield) |
| a) | 32%;                          2.6g                             |         8.2g          |
| b) | 12%; 1.2 g of $CH_2(CO_2C_2H_5)$; 1.3 g of $C_6H_5CH_2Br$      | 10.0g and 10.8g       |
| c) | 3,4%;                         0.47g                            |        13.8g          |

14-3 Only those steps not expected to proceed with a reasonable yield are discussed below.

a) The second step would give predominant addition to the carbonyl group rather than conjugate addition.

b) The preferred enolate is formed by removal of the benzylic proton and would lead to reaction at the benzylic carbon atom.

c) Significant self condensation of acetaldehyde is expected. The regiospecificity of the HOBr addition is reversed.

d) The cyano group may be reduced by the $LiAlH_4$, though at a slower rate than the carbonyl.

14-4

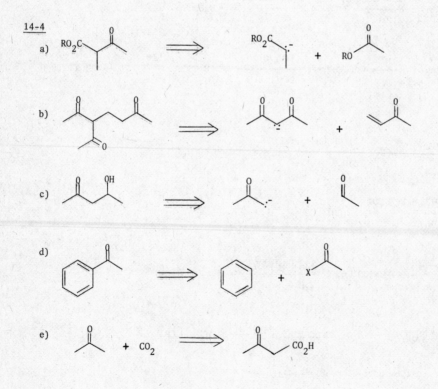

14-5

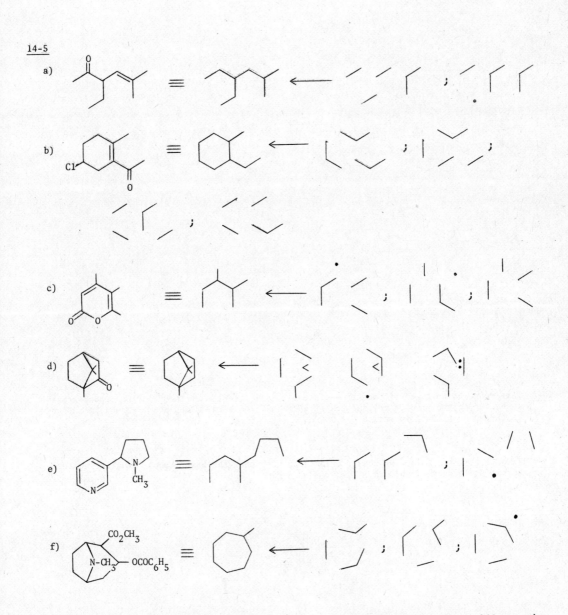

a)

b)

c)

d)

e)

f)

14-6  See answer to problem 14-4.  The nucleophiles are on the left and the electrophiles on the right of each equation.  Problem e), as written, is not a construction reaction.

14-7

i)

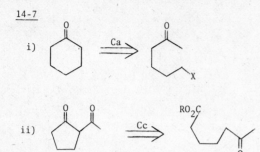

ii)

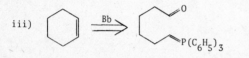

iii)

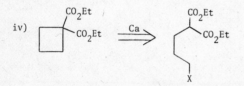

iv)

CO$_2$Et

CO$_2$Et

14-8    This reaction would correspond to Aa in table 14-1 except that the "leaving group" remains connected to the product molecule. In table 14-2 the epoxide would correspond to a span of three for product formation.

14-9    In outlining the following construction sequences only the major steps for altering the carbon skeleton are included.

a)

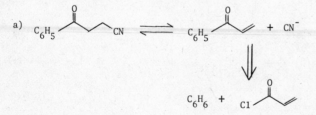

14-9 Contd...

b)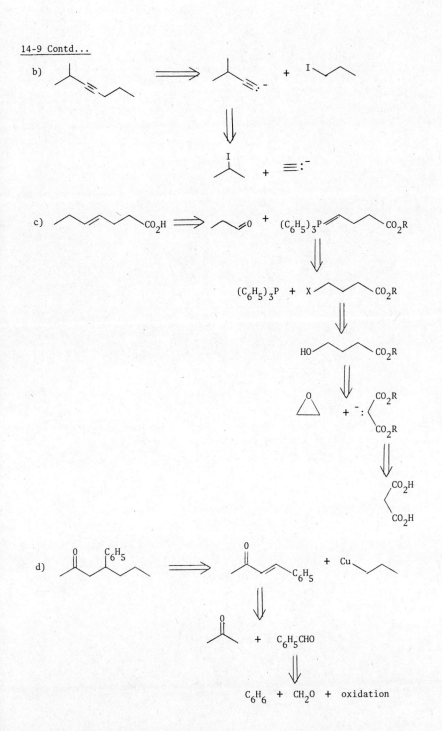

c)

d)

14-9 Contd....

e)

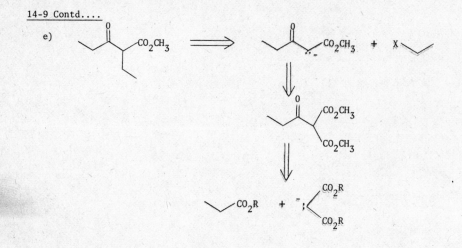

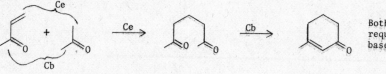

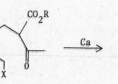

14-10  Two examples are;

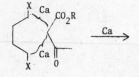

Both steps
require a
base.

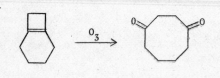

Both steps
require a
base.

14-11

a)

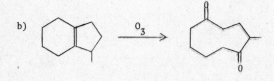

b)

14-12

a)  $C_6H_5COCH_2CH_3$ $\xrightarrow[2)H_3O^+]{1)NaBH_4/THF}$ $C_6H_5\overset{OH}{\underset{|}{CH}}CH_2CH_3$ $\xrightarrow[\Delta]{H_3PO_4}$ $C_6H_5CH=CHCH_3$

$C_6H_5CH=CHCH_3 + H_2O$ $\xrightarrow[\textit{•}]{H_2SO_4}$ $C_6H_5\overset{OH}{\underset{|}{CH}}CH_2CH_3$ $\xrightarrow[2)\Delta]{1)CrO_3/pyridine}$ $C_6H_5COCH_2CH_3$

b)  As in part (a).  Conjugated double bond forms.

$C_6H_5CH=CHCH_3$ $\xrightarrow[2)H_2O_2/H_2O/OH^-]{1)(BH_3)_2/THF}$ $C_6H_5CH_2\overset{OH}{\underset{|}{CH}}CH_3$ $\xrightarrow[2)\Delta]{1)CrO_3/pyridine}$ $C_6H_5CH_2COCH_3$

c)  $C_6H_5CH_2COCH_3$ $\xrightarrow{NH_3}$ $C_6H_5CH_2\overset{NH}{\underset{\|}{C}}CH_3$ $\xrightarrow[2)H_2O]{1)NaBH_4/THF}$ $C_6H_5CH_2\overset{NH_2}{\underset{|}{CH}}CH_3$

d)  $C_6H_5\overset{O}{\underset{\|}{C}}\!\!\!\diagdown\!\!\!\diagup\!\!\!CO_2H$ $\xrightarrow[2)H_3O^+]{1)LiAlH_4/Et_2O}$ $C_6H_5\overset{OH}{\diagup}\!\!\!\diagdown\!\!\!\diagup\!\!\!\diagdown OH$ $\xrightarrow{PCl_5}$

$C_6H_5\overset{Cl}{\diagup}\!\!\!\diagdown\!\!\!\diagup\!\!\!\diagdown^{Cl}$

$C_6H_5\overset{Cl}{\diagup}\!\!\!\diagdown\!\!\!\diagup\!\!\!\diagdown^{Cl}$ $\xrightarrow[EtOH]{NaOAc}$ $C_6H_5\overset{OAc}{\diagup}\!\!\!\diagdown\!\!\!\diagup\!\!\!\diagdown^{OAc}$ $\xrightarrow{H_3O^+}$

$C_6H_5\overset{OH}{\diagup}\!\!\!\diagdown\!\!\!\diagup\!\!\!\diagdown^{OH}$ $\xrightarrow[\Delta]{CrO_3/H_2SO_4}$ $C_6H_5\overset{O}{\underset{\|}{C}}\!\!\!\diagdown\!\!\!\diagup\!\!\!CO_2H$

e)  $\overset{OH}{\diagup}\!\!\!\diagdown\!\!\!\diagup\!\!\!\diagdown^{OH}$ $\xrightarrow[\Delta]{CrO_3/H_2SO_4}$ $\overset{O}{\underset{\|}{C}}\!\!\!\diagdown\!\!\!\diagup\!\!\!CO_2H$ $\xrightarrow[2)NH_3]{1)SOCl_2}$

$\overset{O}{\underset{\|}{C}}\!\!\!\diagdown\!\!\!\diagup\!\!\!CO_2NH_2$ $\xrightarrow[2)H_2O]{1)LiAlH_4/Et_2O}$ $\overset{OH}{\diagup}\!\!\!\diagdown\!\!\!\diagup\!\!\!\diagdown^{NH_2}$

f)  (cyclohexene ring) $CO_2H$ $\xrightarrow[2)H_3O^+]{1)LiAlH_4/Et_2O}$ (cyclohexene ring) $CH_2OH$ $\xrightarrow[2)HBr]{1)Br_2}$ (cyclohexane ring with $Br$, $Br$, $CH_2Br$)

14-12 Contd....

f) Contd.....

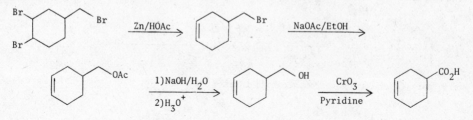

14-13

a)  $HC\equiv C^-Na^+$  +  $CH_3CH_2CH_3Br$  $\xrightarrow{THF}$  $CH_3CH_2CH_2C\equiv CH$  $\xrightarrow[\text{2)}CH_3CH_2CH_2Br]{\text{1)}NaNH_2/THF}$

$CH_3CH_2CH_2C\equiv CCH_2CH_2CH_3$  $\xrightarrow[\text{HOAc}]{H_2/Pt}$  $CH_3(CH_2)_6CH_3$

b)  3 $C_2H_5MgBr$  +  $(MeO)_2C=O$  $\xrightarrow[\text{2)}H_3O^+/\Delta]{\text{1)}Et_2O}$  $[(C_2H_5)_3COH]$  $\xrightarrow{H^+}$

$(C_2H_5)_2C=CHCH_3$  $\xrightarrow[\text{HOAc}]{H_2/Pt}$  $(C_2H_5)_3CH$

c)  $CH_3COCH_3$  $\xrightarrow[\text{2)}CH_3CO_2Me]{\text{1)}NaOMe/MeOH}$  $CH_3COCH_2COCH_3$  $\xrightarrow[\text{2)}2\ CH_3I]{\text{1)}NaOMe/MeOH}$

$CH_3COC(CH_3)_2COCH_3$  $\xrightarrow[\text{DMSO}]{H_2NNH_2/NaOH}$  $(CH_3CH_2)_2C(CH_3)_2$

d)  $(CH_3)_2CHCuCl$  +  $CH_2=CHCN$  $\xrightarrow{Et_2O}$  $(CH_3)_2CHCH_2CH_2CN$  $\xrightarrow[\text{2)}H_3O^+]{\text{1)}(CH_3)_2CHMgBr/Et_2O}$

$(CH_3)_2CHCH_2CH_2COCH(CH_3)_2$  $\xrightarrow[\text{DMSO}]{H_2NNH_2/t\text{-BuOK}}$  $(CH_3)_2CH(CH_2)_3CH(CH_3)_2$

14-14  Only those steps not expected to proceed with a reasonable yield are discussed below.

a)  Intramolecular cyclization (lactone formation) more favorable.

b)  OK

14-14 Contd...

c) Addition of HCN to aldehyde is more rapid.

d) OK

e) Substitution more rapid at primary carbon atom.

f) OK

g) Reaction by more nucleophilic nitrogen atom faster.

h) As the Grignard reagent forms in one reactant molecule, it will react with the carbonyl group of another.


14-15

a) Protection of the hydroxy group as a tetrahydropyranyl ether or as a ketal is possible, but would then require a nonacidic esterification such as $SOCl_2$/NaOH/$CH_3OH$. A simpler approach to the desired esterification would be to form the carboxylate salt, then add a methylating agent such as $CH_3I$.

b) OK

c) Protect    the aldehyde as an acetal, then add HCN under neutral or slightly basic conditions.

d) OK

e) Substitution at the primary carbon atom by $AcO^-$ would protect that position. After cyanide substitution at the secondary carbon, hydrolysis to an alcohol, under mild conditions so as not to hydrolyze the nitrile, then conversion to the chloride accomplishes the synthesis.

f) OK

g) In chapter 16 we will learn that many methods are available for protecting amino groups in the presence of most other functional groups.

h) Protect the carbonyl group as ketal.


14-16  The carboxylate groups can be converted to esters, then the product allowed to equilibrate in dilute acid or base to give the more stable diequatorial esters. (They are in a 1,3-relationship, thus will be cis.) Subsequent reduction of the carbonyl group by approach of $H^-$ from the less hindered equatorial side gives the axial OH, cis to the ester groups. Hydrolysis provides the desired product.

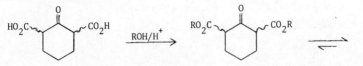

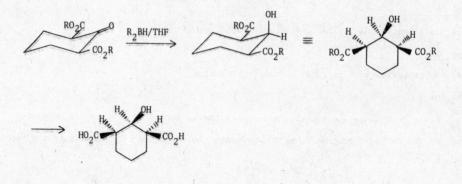

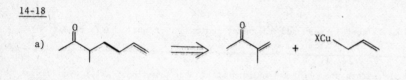

<u>14-17</u>  For the convergent pathway each two step sequence proceeds in 56% yield (0.75 x 0.75 x 100).
The final convergent step therefore results in a 42% (0.56 x 0.75 x 100) overall yield.
It would require 1.2 kg of starting material to produce 1 kg of product (0.5 x 1/0.42).
For the linear pathway the yield is 24% (0.75 x 0.75 x 0.75 x 0.75 x 0.75).  It would
require 2.1 kg to produce 1 kg of product (0.5 x 1/0.24).

<u>14-18</u>

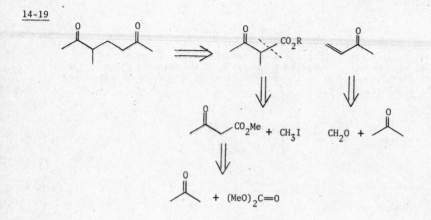

a)

b)

(Aldehydes react preferentially with Wittig reagents.)

<u>14-19</u>

14-19 Contd...    The final step involves a conjugate addition and removal of the ester group which is present to ensure regiospecificity in the addition.    All of the other construction steps involve small available synthons and relatively simple reactions. However as a route to 3-methyl-6-hepten-2-one this approach would not be preferred since selective reduction of the 2,6-diketone would be quite difficult.

14-20

a)  Chirality at that carbon atom is destroyed in the next step so it isn't important.

b)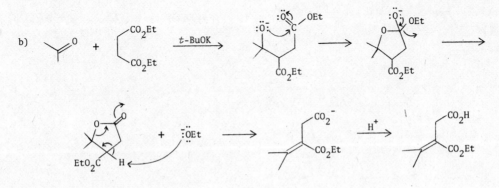

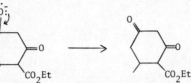

c)  See fifth entry, table 14-3.

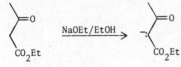

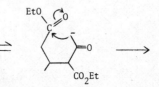

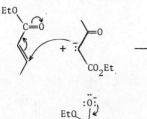

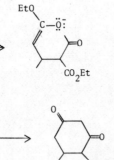

14-20 Contd...

d)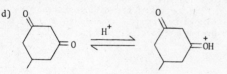

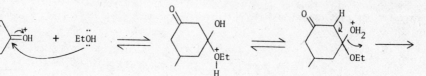

e)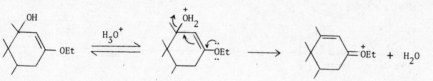

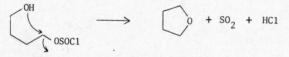

f) Formation of the intermediate thio ester immediately results in an intramolecular cyclization.

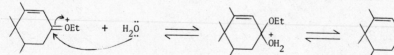

14-20 Contd...

f)Contd....

However, conversion of the diol to a dianion with methyllithium keeps the two ends apart and inhibits ring formation as a sulfonate diester rapidly forms. Then substitution by chloride gives the desired product.

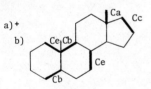

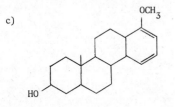

14-21

a)+
b)

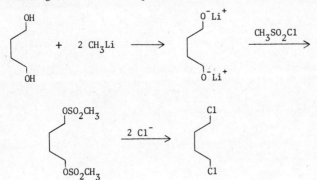

d)

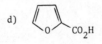

c)

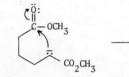

e)

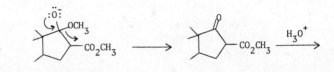

14-21 Contd...

e) Contd...

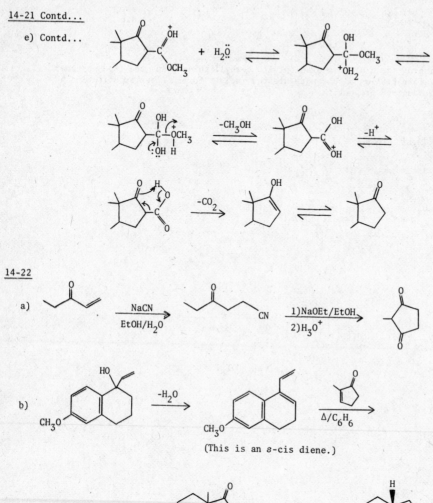

14-22

a)

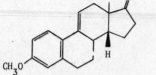

b)

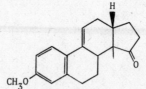

(This is an *s*-cis diene.)

Stereochemistry at *C-D* ring
junction is wrong

or

Regiochemistry is wrong

14-22 Contd...

c)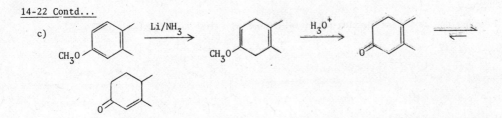

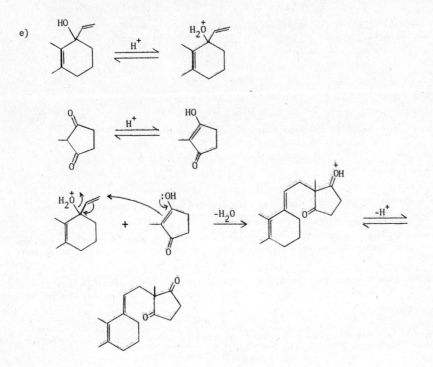

d) When resolution is required to give optically active product, it is best to carry this
operation out as late as possible in the synthesis.  Both estrone and the last
intermediate to β-vetivone are alcohols.  They can be resolved using an optically active
amine salt of their phthalate esters.  (See sec. 8-4.)

e)

14-23

a) Following the sequence from citral to intermediate A we have: an aldol (Cb), an acid
catalyzed cyclization, and aldol (Cb), and a substitution (Aa).  From 3-buten-2-one
to intermediate B we have: an addition (Db).  From A plus B to vitamin A we have: an
addition (Db).

14-23 Contd....

b) It functions as a base forming potential anions at O and the acetylenic carbon.

c)

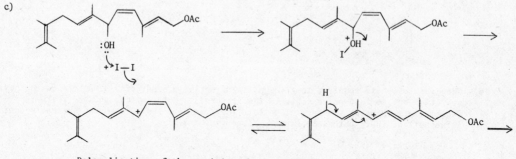

Delocalization of the positive charge results in isomerization of the Z double bond.

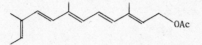

d) Acetylation is more rapid at the less hindered primary hydroxy group.


14-24

a) Would give a mixture of products resulting from the two potential enolates.

b) Would give mono plus polyalkylation. Formation of the mono enolate anion with a strong base such as LDA, then addition of 1 CH$_3$I or alkylation of the enamine would be better.

c) Steric hindrance might inhibit substitution by the isopropyl group. If feasible it would have been better to alkylate acetophenone with the isopropyl first, then add the two methyl groups.

d) This Claisen product has no acidic hydrogen to remove and shift equilibrium. Reaction must be carried out using strong base (LDA, NaH, etc.).

e) OK

f) A would give cyclization to form a six-membered ring.

g) We would expect the less hindered ester enolate to form. The desired product is best made by alkylation of methyl acetoacetate.

14-25

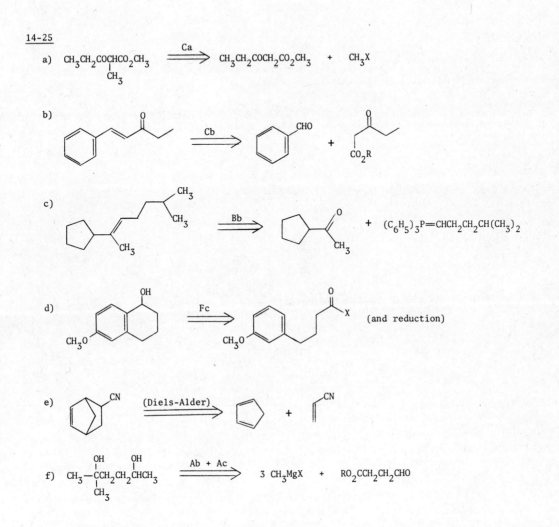

a)   $CH_3CH_2COCHCO_2CH_3$ $\xrightarrow{Ca}$ $CH_3CH_2COCH_2CO_2CH_3$ + $CH_3X$
     ┃
     $CH_3$

b)   ⟶ $\xrightarrow{Cb}$ ⟶ CHO + (ketone with $CO_2R$)

c)   $\xrightarrow{Bb}$ + $(C_6H_5)_3P=CHCH_2CH_2CH(CH_3)_2$

d)   $\xrightarrow{Fc}$      (and reduction)

e)   $\xrightarrow{(Diels-Alder)}$ + 

f)   $CH_3-CCH_2CH_2CHCH_3$ $\xrightarrow{Ab\ +\ Ac}$ 3 $CH_3MgX$ + $RO_2CCH_2CH_2CHO$
        ┃          ┃
        OH        OH
        ┃
        $CH_3$

14-26

a) No; both carbonyl groups would reduce.  One must protect the aldehyde carbonyl as an acetal.

b) No; would give mixture of potential Claisen products.  No direct method for using the given starting materials is obvious.

c) Unlikely; would result principally in elimination of HCl.  It is best to substitute OAC for Cl, then to hydrolyze the ester.

14-26 Contd...

d)  Not as written; two moles of Grignard reagent are required.  The first would form a carboxylate salt and the second would add to the carbonyl.  Subsequent formation of the lactone would require acid catalysis.

e)  No; catalytic hydrogenation would also reduce the carbon-carbon double bond.  The use of $LiAlH_4$ would be selective for reduction of the cyano group.

14-27

a)  $R_2C=O$  +  $XZnCH_2CO_2CH_3$  $\longrightarrow$  $R_2C(OH)CH_2CO_2CH_3$

b)  ROH  $\xrightarrow{PBr_3}$  RBr  $\xrightarrow[2)CH_2O]{1)Mg/Et_2O}$  $RCH_2OH$

c)  RCHO  +  $(C_6H_5)_3P=CH_2$  $\longrightarrow$  $RCH=CH_2$  $\xrightarrow[2)H_2O/H_2O_2/NaOH]{1)(BH_3)_2/THF}$

$RCH_2CH_2OH$  $\xrightarrow[Pyridine]{CrO_3}$  $RCH_2CHO$

d)  ROH  $\xrightarrow{PBr_3}$  RBr  $\xrightarrow[2)\triangle_O]{1)Mg/Et_2O}$  $RCH_2CH_2OH$

e)  ArBr  $\xrightarrow[2)CH_2O]{1)Mg/Et_2O}$  $ArCH_2OH$  $\xrightarrow{PBr_3}$  $ArCH_2Br$  $\xrightarrow[DMSO]{NaCN}$  $ArCH_2CN$  $\xrightarrow[\Delta]{H_3O^+}$  $ArCH_2CO_2H$

f)  ROH  $\xrightarrow[2)Mg/Et_2O]{1)PBr_3}$  RMgBr  $\xrightarrow[CuCl_2]{CH_2=CHCO_2R}$  $RCH_2CH_2CO_2R$  $\xrightarrow{LiAlH_4}$  $RCH_2CH_2CH_2OH$

g)  $RCOCH_3$  $\xrightarrow[2)BrCH_2CO_2R']{1)LDA/THF}$  $RCOCH_2CH_2CO_2R'$  $\xrightarrow{H_3O^+/\Delta}$  $RCOCH_2CH_2CO_2H$

h)  $RCH_2OH$  $\xrightarrow[2)NaCN/DMSO]{1)PBr_3}$  $RCH_2CN$  $\xrightarrow{LiAlH_4}$  $RCH_2CH_2NH_2$

14-27 Contd...

i) $R_2CHOH$ $\xrightarrow[H_2SO_4]{CrO_3}$ $R_2C{=}O$ $\xrightarrow{(C_6H_5)_3P{=}CHCH_3}$ $R_2C{=}CHCH_3$

j) $RCO_2H$ $\xrightarrow[2)(CH_3)_2NH]{1)SOCl_2}$ $RC\overset{O}{\underset{N(CH_3)_2}{\diagdown}}$ $\xrightarrow{LiAlH_4}$ $RCH_2N(CH_3)_2$

14-28

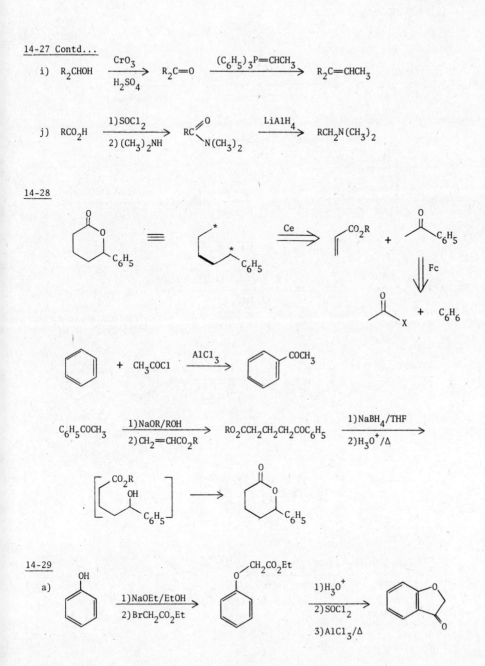

14-29 Contd...

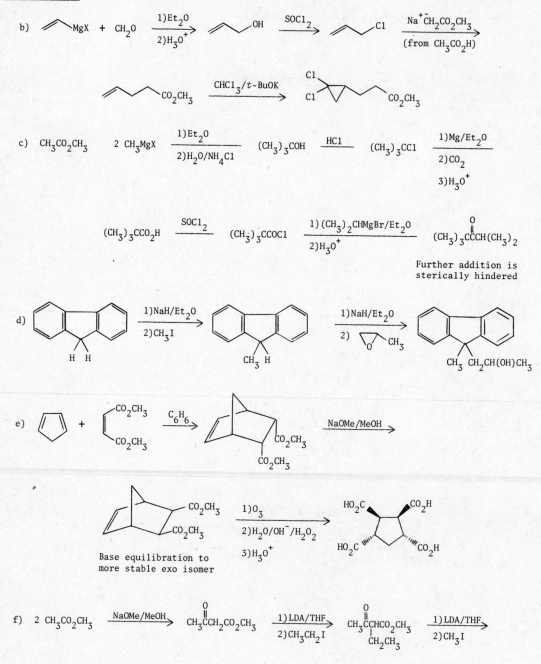

b)

c)

Further addition is
sterically hindered

d)

e)

Base equilibration to
more stable exo isomer

f)

14-29 Contd...

f) Contd...    $CH_3\overset{O}{\overset{\|}{C}}-\overset{CO_2CH_3}{\underset{CH_3}{\overset{|}{\underset{|}{C}}}}-CH_2CH_3$  $\xrightarrow[\text{2)}H_3O^+]{\text{1)LiAlH}_4/\text{Et}_2O}$  $CH_3\overset{OH}{\overset{|}{CH}}-\overset{CH_2OH}{\underset{CH_3}{\overset{|}{\underset{|}{C}}}}-CH_2CH_3$

14-30

A ≡ (structure: methyl vinyl ketone)

B ≡ NaOEt/EtOH

C ≡ HO⌣OH/TsOH

D ≡ $(BH_3)_2$/THF

E ≡ $H_2O$/NaOH/$H_2O_2$

F ≡ (decalin structure with dioxolane and OH)

G ≡ $CrO_3$/Acetone

H ≡ $(C_6H_5)_3P{=}CH_2$

I ≡ (decalin structure with dioxolane and $CH_2$)

J ≡ (decalin structure with OH and $CH_2$)

K ≡ $PBr_3$

L ≡ Mg/$Et_2O$

M ≡ $CO_2$

N ≡ $CH_2N_2$

O ≡ $CH_3MgBr/Et_2O$

P ≡ $H_3O^+$

14-31

a) (acetone structure) $\xrightarrow[\text{2)} \text{isopropyl-Br}]{\text{1)LDA/THF}}$ (ketone structure) $\xrightarrow{\text{HCN}}$ (cyanohydrin structure with OH, CN) $\xrightarrow[\Delta]{H_3O^+}$ (hydroxy acid structure with OH, $CO_2H$)

b) (structure)$CO_2H$ $\xrightarrow{\text{MeOH/H}^+}$ (structure)$CO_2Me$

(structure)Br $\xrightarrow[\text{2)} \text{(structure)}CO_2Me]{\text{1)Mg/THF/CuCl}_2}$ (structure)$CO_2Me$ $\xrightarrow[\text{2)}H_3O^+]{\text{1)}H_2O/OH^-}$ (structure)$CO_2H$

c) $CH_3CH_2CHO$ + $XZnCH_2CO_2Me$ $\xrightarrow[\text{2)}H_3O^+]{\text{1)Et}_2O}$ $CH_3CH_2\overset{OH}{\overset{|}{CH}}CH_2CO_2Me$ $\xrightarrow[\text{Pyridine}]{CrO_3}$

14-31 Contd...

c) Contd...

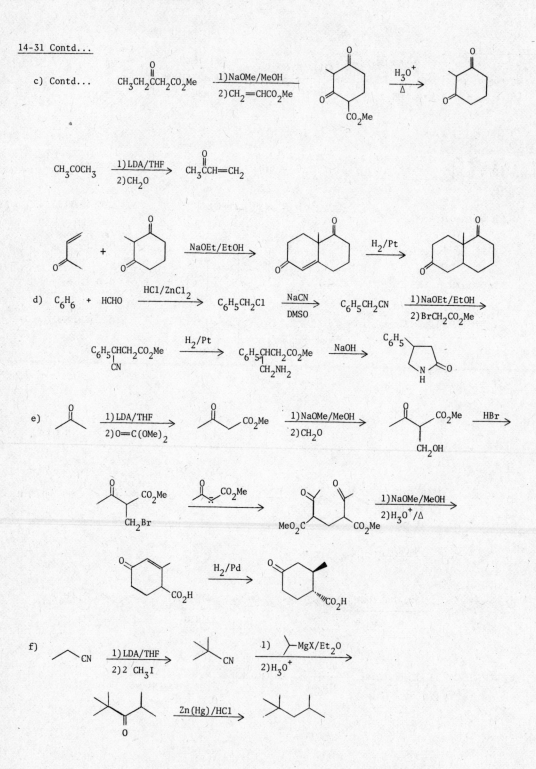

14-31 Contd...

g)  $CH_2(CO_2H)_2$  $\xrightarrow{MeOH/H^+}$  $CH_2(CO_2Me)_2$  $\xrightarrow[\text{2) 2 } CH_2=CHCOCH_3]{\text{1) LDA/THF}}$

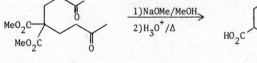

$\xrightarrow[\text{2)}H_3O^+/\Delta]{\text{1)NaOMe/MeOH}}$

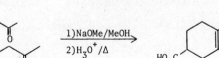

h)  2 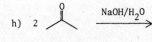  $\xrightarrow{NaOH/H_2O}$  [CH_2=C(CH_3)COCH_3 structure]  $\xrightarrow{H_2/Pd}$  [structure]  $\xrightarrow[\text{2)}O=C(OMe)_2]{\text{1)NaOMe/MeOH}}$

$MeO_2C$-[structure]  $\xrightarrow[\text{2)}CH_3I]{\text{1)NaOMe/MeOH}}$  $MeO_2C$-[structure]  $\xrightarrow[\text{2)}CH_2=CHCOCH_3^*]{\text{1)NaOMe/MeOH}}$

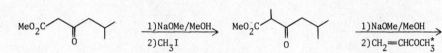

$\xrightarrow{H_3O^+/\Delta}$  [structure]  $\xrightarrow{H_2/Pt}$  [structure]

i)  $CH_3COCH_2CO_2Me^*$  $\xrightarrow[\text{2) 2 } C_2H_5I]{\text{1)NaOMe/MeOH}}$  $(C_2H_5)_2\overset{CO_2Me}{\underset{}{C}}COCH_3$  $\xrightarrow[\Delta]{H_3O^+}$  $(C_2H_5)_2CHCOCH_3$

$C_6H_5CH_2Cl^* + (C_6H_5)_3P$  $\longrightarrow$  $(C_6H_5)_3\overset{+}{P}CH_2C_6H_5$  $Cl^-$  $\xrightarrow{NaH/THF}$  $(C_6H_5)_3P=CHC_6H_5$

$(C_2H_5)_2CHCOCH_3 + (C_6H_5)_3P=CHC_6H_5$  $\longrightarrow$  $(C_2H_5)_2CH\overset{CH_3}{\underset{}{C}}=CHC_6H_5$  $\xrightarrow{H_3O^+}$

$(C_2H_5)_2CH\overset{CH_3}{\underset{}{C}}HCHC_6H_5$
$\underset{OH}{}$

*Prepared in previous part of prob. 14-31.

# 15 CARBOHYDRATES AND NUCLEOSIDES

15-1

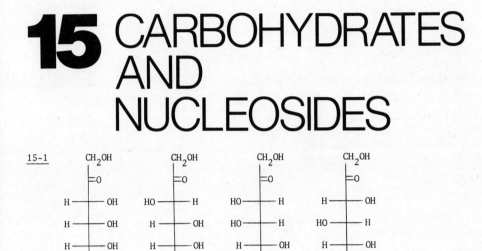

15-2   D-Glucose ≡   2R,3S,4R,5R-2,3,4,5,6-Pentahydroxyhexanal
       L-Glucose ≡   2S,3R,4S,5S-2,3,4,5,6-Pentahydroxyhexanal

15-3   Common names are included.  Students may find the plane or axis of symmetry in each
       meso form more obvious by using Haworth structures (se. 14-2B).

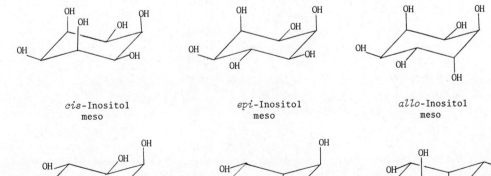

*cis*-Inositol
meso

*epi*-Inositol
meso

*allo*-Inositol
meso

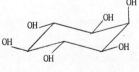

*myo*-Inositol
meso

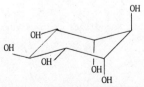

*muco*-Inositol
meso

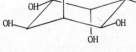

*neo*-Inositol
meso

15-3 Contd....

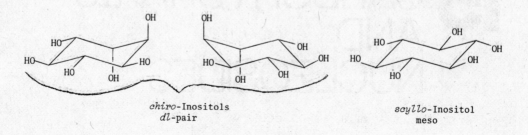

chiro-Inositols          scyllo-Inositol
dl-pair                      meso

15-4

1) Conversion of glucose to a poly-iodide then reduction to *n*-hexane shows that glucose has a straight chain structure.

2) Typical reactions of aldehydes and ketones.

3) Mild oxidation to a carboxylic acid is typical of aldehydes.

4) Reduction is consistent with an aldehyde and acetylation confirms six (5 + 1) hydroxy groups after reduction of the carbonyl group.

15-5

1) The hemiacetal exists in equilibrium with the aldehyde form. Typical aldehyde reactions require conversion of the hemiacetal to the aldehyde, a process which is slow in many cases.

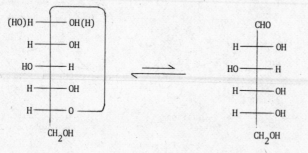

2) The pentacetates are epimers and differ in configuration at the anomeric carbon atom.

15-5 Contd....

2) Contd....

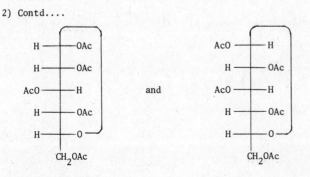

and

3) The α- and β-hemiacetals are converted to acetals thus only one mol of alcohol is required.

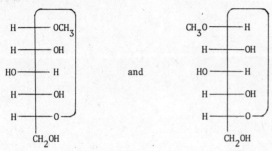

and

4) These are the two hemiacetals.

5) Both hemiacetals interconvert through the open chain structure. The same position of equilibrium is reached starting from either anomer.

15-6

a)

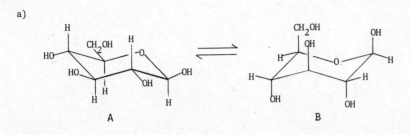

15-6 Contd...

b)  Conformation A is expected to represent glucose because all large groups are equatorial.

15-7

a)  β-D-Glucose

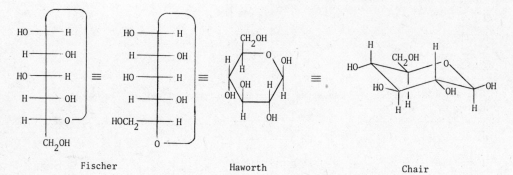

Fischer                      Haworth                              Chair

β-L-Glucose

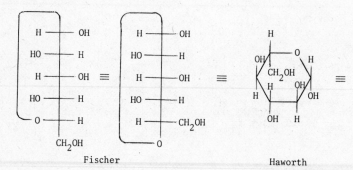

Fischer                              Haworth

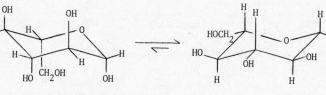

Chair

Note that transformation of the Haworth formula to a chair conformational formula leads to the conformation with most hydroxy groups axial.  Ring  flip gives the expected conformation which must be the enantiomer of β-D-glucose shown above.

15-7 Contd...

b)  Let  X = fraction of isomers with 18.7° rotation;

then 1 - X = fraction of isomers with 112° rotation.

$$18.7°X  +  112°(1 - X) = 52.7°$$

$$X = 0.636$$

$$1 - X = 0.364$$

The more abundant isomer (63.6%) is the β-anomer with all large groups equatorial in the chair form.  The α-isomer (36.4%) has the anomeric hydroxy group axial.

15-8    Galactaric acid has a plane of symmetry.  It is a meso compound.  Note also that meso sugars will not have a D or L designation since they can be drawn either way by rotation of 180° in the plane of the paper.

15-9

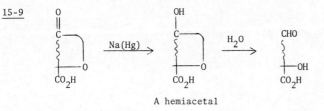

A hemiacetal

15-10

a)  1 HCHO  +  5 $HCO_2H$

b)  1 HCHO  +  4 $HCO_2H$

c)  2 HCHO  +  4 $HCO_2H$

Note that oxidative cleavage on both sides of a carbon atom gives $HCO_2H$ and cleavage on only one side gives R—CHO.  Cleavage of an aldehyde or carboxylic acid gives $RCO_2H$.

15-11    The α-anomer possesses an axial hydroxy group which is less accessible for reaction with bromine during the initial formation of a hypobromite.  It has been proposed that the α-anomer actually isomerizes to the β form before oxidation.  One mechanism proposed for the process also includes the anti stereoelectronic requirements favorable for the β-anomer intermediate.

15-11 Contd....

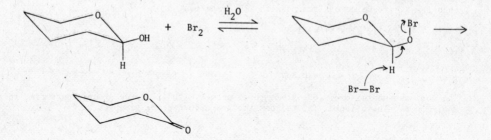

15-12   Products differ in configuration at the original anomeric carbon atom.

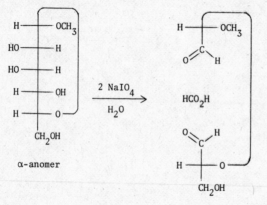

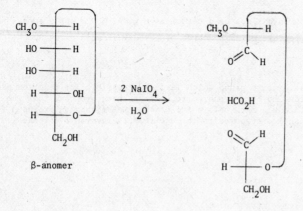

15-13

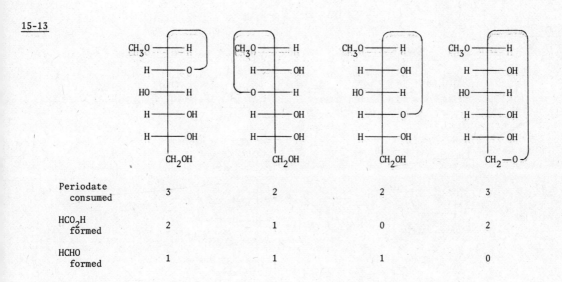

| | | | | |
|---|---|---|---|---|
| Periodate consumed | 3 | 2 | 2 | 3 |
| HCO$_2$H formed | 2 | 1 | 0 | 2 |
| HCHO formed | 1 | 1 | 1 | 0 |

15-14

a)

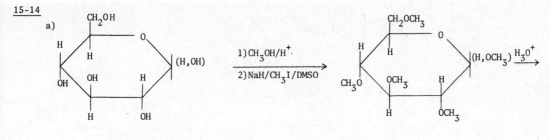

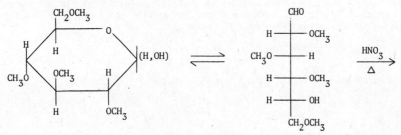

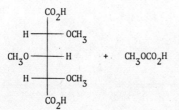

15-14 Contd....

b)

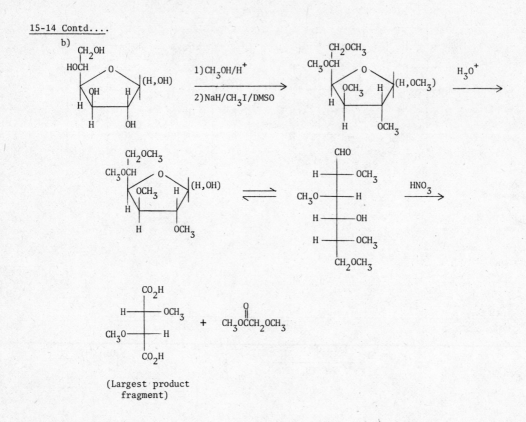

(Largest product
fragment)

15-15   The products are diastereomers, thus differ in physical properties and in the thermodynamics
for their formation.  In this example one epimer has greater nonbonded repulsion between
the C-2 and C-4 hydroxy groups than does the other.

15-16

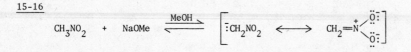

15-16 Contd....

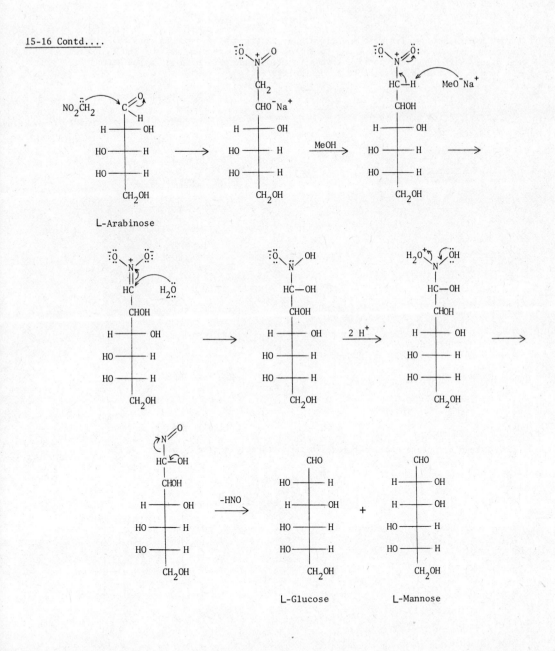

L-Arabinose

L-Glucose     +     L-Mannose

15-17   Allose and galactose give meso aldaric acids, thus are eliminated as possibilities.
Since glucose and mannose are known to differ only at carbon 2, altrose and talose,
the sugars with identical configurations to allose and galactose at carbon atoms
3,4, and 5, must also be rejected as possibilities.

15-18   Both aldaric acids are meso.

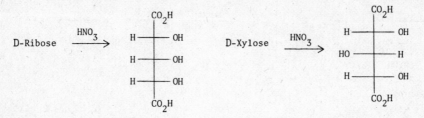

15-19

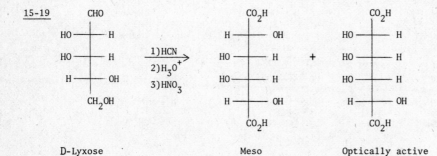

D-Lyxose              Meso              Optically active

The D-Lyxose structure would not lead to two optically active $C_6$ aldaric acids.

15-20

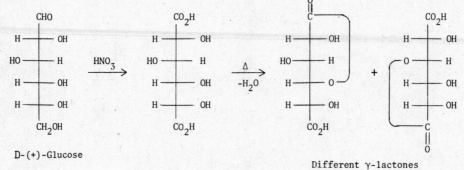

D-(+)-Glucose

Different γ-lactones

15-20 Contd...

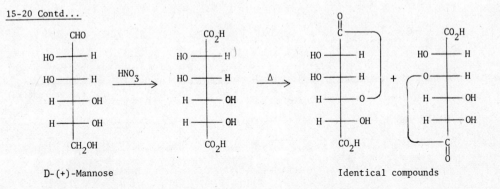

D-(+)-Mannose                                    Identical compounds

15-21  Only D isomer shown though Fischer actually carried through a DL mixture until the
mannonic acid was resolved.

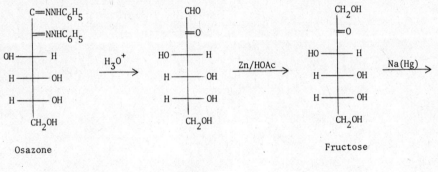

Osazone                                          Fructose

Mannitol              Mannose                    Mannonic acid
(This epimer was                                 (DL isomers separated
major product.)                                  here)

15-21 Contd...

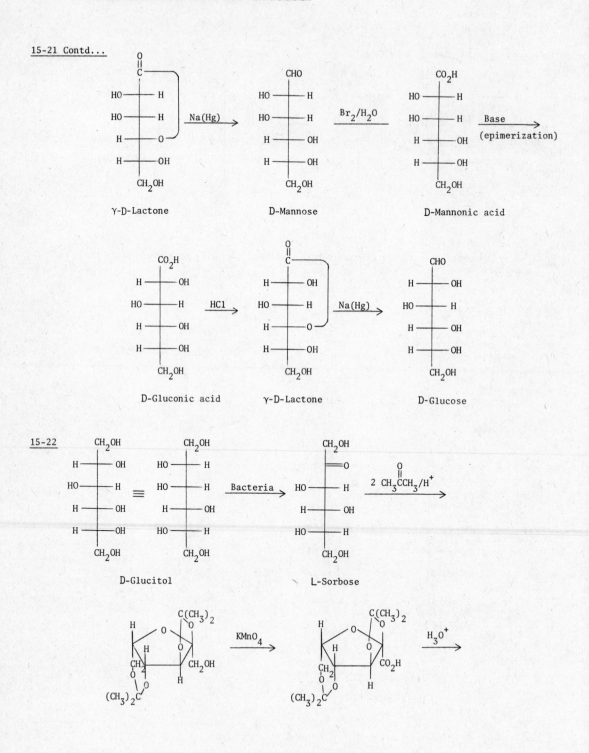

γ-D-Lactone

D-Mannose

D-Mannonic acid

D-Gluconic acid

γ-D-Lactone

D-Glucose

15-22

D-Glucitol

L-Sorbose

15-22 Contd...

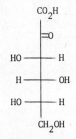

2-Keto-L-Gulonic acid

15-23

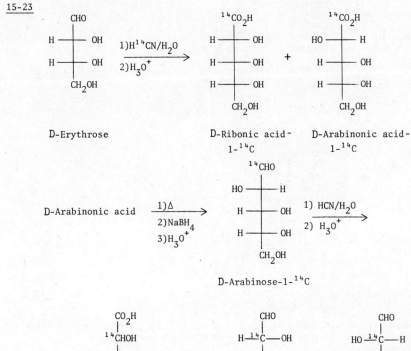

D-Erythrose

$^{14}CO_2H$

D-Ribonic acid-
1-$^{14}C$    +

D-Arabinonic acid-
1-$^{14}C$

D-Arabinonic acid   1)Δ
                    2)NaBH₄
                    3)H₃O⁺

$^{14}CHO$

D-Arabinose-1-$^{14}C$

1) HCN/H₂O
2) H₃O⁺

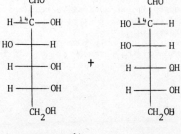

D-Glucose-2-$^{14}C$      D-Mannose-2-$^{14}C$

15-24

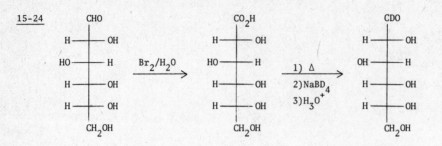

15-25

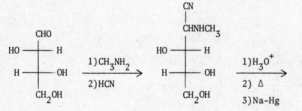

D-Threose

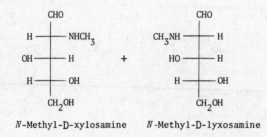

N-Methyl-D-xylosamine    N-Methyl-D-lyxosamine

Separate epimers

15-26 Formation of an isopropylidene derivative requires that two hydroxy groups be relatively close together. Acetone typically gives a cyclic five-membered ring ketal when functioning as a protecting group.
The pyranose ring glucose can only form one 1,2-O-isopropylidene derivative. As the very low concentration of the furanose is derivatized with two moles of acetone, equilibrium shifts to form more furanose, etc.

15-27

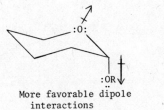 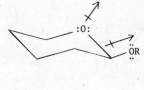

More favorable dipole
interactions

b) More favorable solvation of the less hindered equatorial methoxy group stabilizes the
β-anomer.

15-28

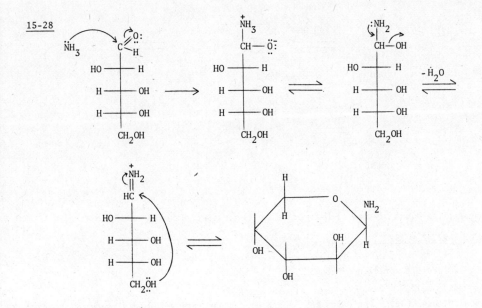

15-29  Interaction between the cyclic oxygen atom and C—Cl bond favors an  axial chlorine
atom so as to move negative ends of the dipoles as far apart as possible (the anomeric
effect; prob. 15-27).

15-30

a)  The result  demonstrates that the oxygen atom at the anomeric carbon must have come from
the water, thus the aglycone departs from this carbon atom with the initial anomeric
oxygen.

b)  The relatively stable *tert*-butyl cation departs and produces $t\text{-Bu}^{18}\text{OH}$.  Both of the
results above are similar to those observed during ester hydrolysis (sec. 8-3).

15-31

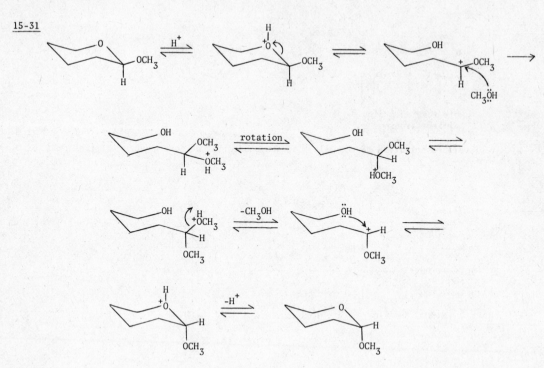

15-32

a)  Invert sugar is an equal mixture of D-fructose and D-glucose.  It will have an optical
    rotation of

$$\frac{-92.4° + 52.7°}{2} = -19.9°$$

Sucrose has a specific rotation of +66.5°.

b)  The absence of mutarotation incidates that sucrose does not eacily form a mixture of anomers.
    It is often easier to obtain crystals from a solution of one component rather than from a
    mixture of closely related isomers because identical molecules can form a more ordered
    crystal.

15-33

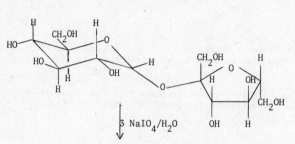

3 NaIO$_4$/H$_2$O

15-33 Contd...

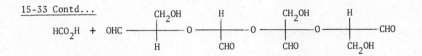

$$HCO_2H \; + \; OHC \underset{H}{\overset{CH_2OH}{\rule{0pt}{0pt}}} O \underset{CHO}{\overset{H}{\rule{0pt}{0pt}}} O \underset{CHO}{\overset{CH_2OH}{\rule{0pt}{0pt}}} O \underset{CH_2OH}{\overset{H}{\rule{0pt}{0pt}}} CHO$$

15-34

i)   D-Glucose and D-galactose, the components of lactose, are connected by a β-glycoside linkage.

ii)  Either glucose or galactose must have a hemiacetal group in the lactose structure.

iii) The tetramethylgalactose fragment shows that galactose is present as a pyranose ring. Furthermore, the only remaining hydroxy group is at the anomeric carbon atom. Since this is the only hydroxy available to form a glycoside linkage to the glucose, galactose cannot be the reducing portion of lactose. The trimethylglucose fragment does not differentiate between a furanose and pyranose structure. Since glucose must be the reducing portion of lactose the anomeric hydroxy must be free. Thus the hydroxy groups at 4 and 5 will form the cyclic structure and the glycoside linkage.

iv)  The tetramethylgluconic acid fragment shows that the 4-hydroxy group of glucose forms the glycoside bond to galactose. The 5-hydroxy group must therefore be involved in a pyranose ring. The chemistry of this structural elucidation is:

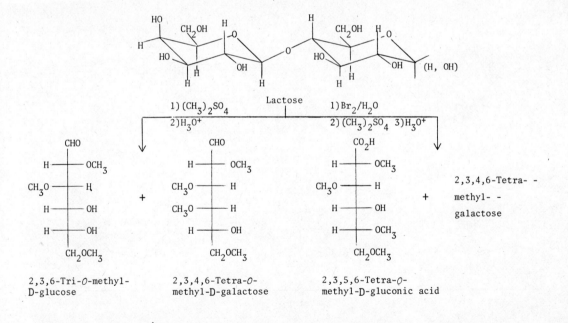

2,3,6-Tri-O-methyl-
D-glucose

2,3,4,6-Tetra-O-
methyl-D-galactose

2,3,5,6-Tetra-O-
methyl-D-gluconic acid

15-35 Maltose and cellobiose are reducing sugars. α,α-Trehalose and raffinose do not have hemiacetal or hemiketal groups, therefore are nonreducing.

15-36

a)  The 2,3,6-trimethyl derivative is characteristic of the 1,4-linked polyglucose.

The 2,3-dimethyl derivative is derived from glucose fragments 1,4-linked in a straight chain but also containing a branch at carbon 6.

The 2,3,4,6-tetramethyl derivatives are from the ends of the polysaccharide chains.

b)  Amylose has no branches thus would give principally the 2,3,6-trimethyl derivative along with a small quantity of the 2,3,4,6-tetramethyl derivative from the terminal groups.

15-37  The tight linear helix of amylose favors intramolecular hydrogen bonding and inhibits solvation.  The more open branched structure of amylopectin more readily interacts with solvent.

15-38  Pulping is carried out in strongly basic media.  The glucoside (acetal) bonds are relatively stable toward base.

15-39

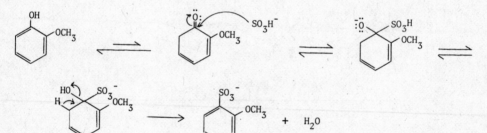

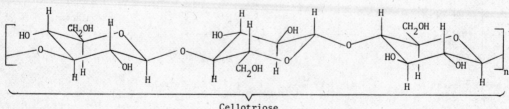

15-40

Cellotriose

15-41  They exist as mono- or dianions (or an equilibrium mixture of the two) since the $pK_a$ values of phosphoric acid are:

$$pK_{a^1} = 2.12 \; ; \;\; pK_{a^2} = 7.21.$$

15-42

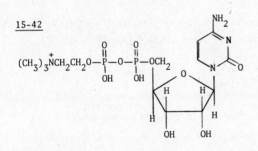

15-43

Nucleosides are sugar glycosides.  The isoalloxazine group is not connected to ribose by a glycoside bond but is an *N*-alkyl substituent.

15-44

a)

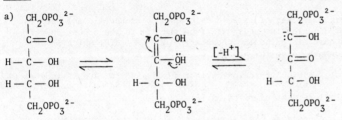

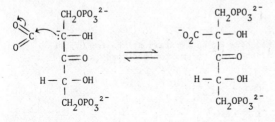

b)

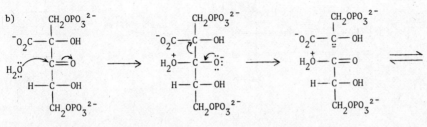

15-45   In one experiment a plant was fed $C^{18}O_2$ and in the other $H_2{}^{18}O$. In the first experiment no $^{18}O$ was found in the oxygen formed while the second experiment yielded labeled oxygen.

15-46   The 10 reaction of the Krebs cycle are summarized below:

1)   The thioester acetyl-CoA enolizes and adds to the α-ketoacid in an aldol reaction. Subsequent hydrolysis of the thioester leads to a more stable carboxylate anion.

2)   Elimination of water to give the conjugated double bond.

3)   Readdition of water in a conjugate addition to produce a different isomer.

4)   Dehydrogenation (oxidation) of the alcohol serves to reduce $NAD^+$ to NADH.

5)   Decarboxylation of a β-ketoacid releases the first molecule of carbon dioxide.

6)   An oxidative decarboxylation releases the second carbon dioxide molecule. This is a complex step in which $NAD^+$ is also reduced to NADH.

7)   The hydrolysis of the thioester, like that of an acid chloride, is exothermic and here is coupled with phosphorylation of a nucleotide phosphate from the di- to the higher-energy triphosphate. The nucleotides here are guanosine phosphates (GDP ⟶ GTP) which serve the same function as the more common adenosine phosphates, ADP and ATP.

8)   Dehydrogenation is accomplished by another reaction which reduces $NAD^+$ to NADH as in step (4).

9)   Conjugate addition of water parallels that of reaction (3).

10)   In the final oxidation, $NAD^+$ dehydrogenates the secondary alcohol to the ketone of oxaloacetate [like step (4)], preparing it for condensation with a new thio- activated acetate molecule in reaction (1).

15-47   In order to follow the convention that the aldehyde group is drawn at the top of the structural formula, some of the original D-aldohexoses become L-aldohexoses in these proposed transformations.

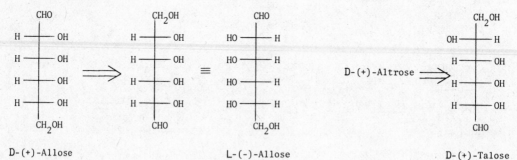

D-(+)-Allose              L-(-)-Allose                              D-(+)-Talose

15-47 Contd....

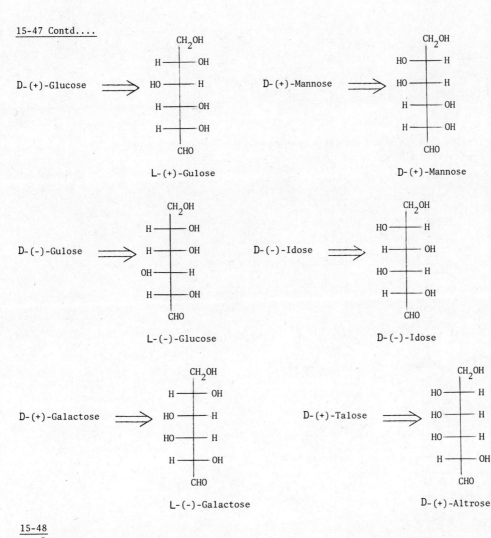

D-(+)-Glucose ⟹

CH₂OH
H —— OH
HO —— H
H —— OH
H —— OH
CHO

L-(+)-Gulose

D-(+)-Mannose ⟹

CH₂OH
HO —— H
HO —— H
H —— OH
H —— OH
CHO

D-(+)-Mannose

D-(-)-Gulose ⟹

CH₂OH
H —— OH
H —— OH
OH —— H
H —— OH
CHO

L-(-)-Glucose

D-(-)-Idose ⟹

CH₂OH
HO —— H
H —— OH
HO —— H
H —— OH
CHO

D-(-)-Idose

D-(+)-Galactose ⟹

CH₂OH
H —— OH
HO —— H
HO —— H
H —— OH
CHO

L-(-)-Galactose

D-(+)-Talose ⟹

CH₂OH
HO —— H
HO —— H
HO —— H
H —— OH
CHO

D-(+)-Altrose

15-48

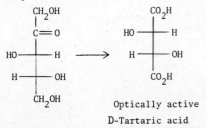

CH₂OH
C=O
HO —— H
H —— OH
CH₂OH

→

CO₂H
HO —— H
H —— OH
CO₂H

Optically active
D-Tartaric acid

15-49

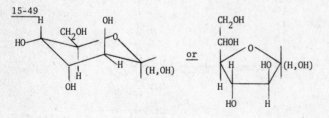

The furanose ring has the preferred all trans configuration.  The pyranose ring has two unfavorable axial hydroxy groups.

15-50

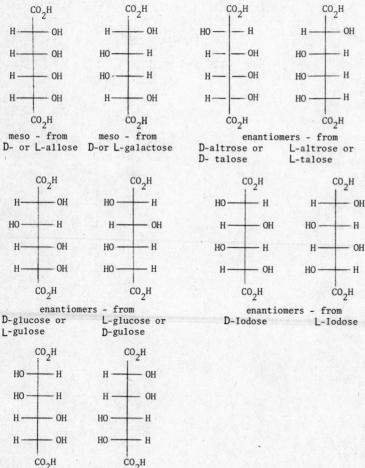

meso - from
D- or L-allose

meso - from
D-or L-galactose

enantiomers - from
D-altrose or          L-altrose or
D- talose             L-talose

enantiomers - from
D-glucose or          L-glucose or
L-gulose              D-gulose

enantiomers - from
D-Iodose              L-Iodose

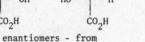

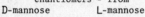

enantiomers - from
D-mannose             L-mannose

15-51

Benzaldehyde normally forms 6-ring acetals with carbohydrates.  In D-glucose only the hydroxy
groups at the 2- and 4- positions are cis to each other.

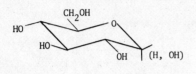

15-52

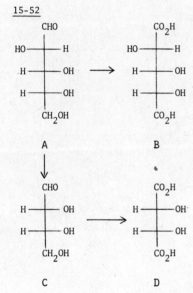

A          B

CHO                    CO$_2$H

H ────── OH        H ────── OH

H ────── OH        H ────── OH

CH$_2$OH                   CO$_2$H

C          D

15-53

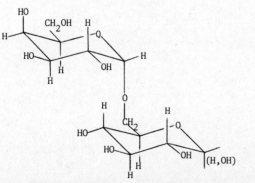

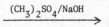
(CH$_3$)$_2$SO$_4$/NaOH

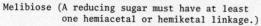
Melibiose (A reducing sugar must have at least
one hemiacetal or hemiketal linkage.)

15-53 Contd....

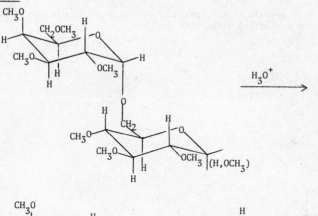

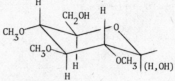

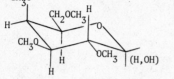

2,3,4,6-Tetramethyl-D-galactose   +   2,3,4-Trimethyl-D-glucose

These data do not define configuration at the anomeric carbon atom or of the linkage between the monosaccharides.

15-54

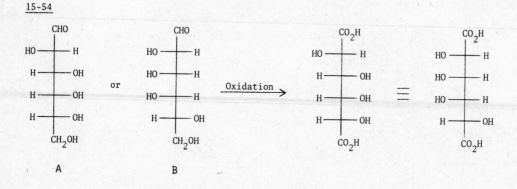

15-54 Contd....

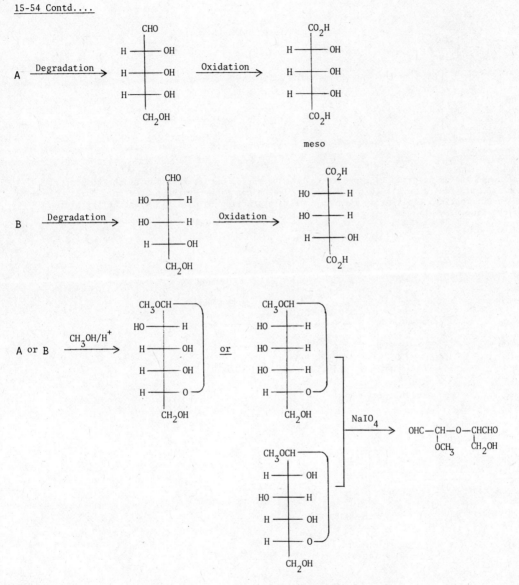

OHC—CH—O—CHCHO
     |            |
    OCH₃    CH₂OH

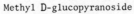

Methyl D-glucopyranoside

15-55

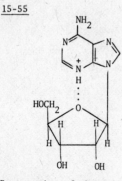

Protonation of the amino group is expected to be more rapid, but protonation of the heterocyclic nitrogen atom provides a more acidic intermediate which can transfer the proton in a more favorable conformation. No similar intramolecular interaction is possible with the pyrimidine base of cytidine.

15-56

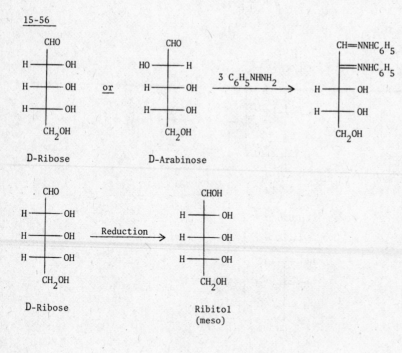

15-56 Contd....

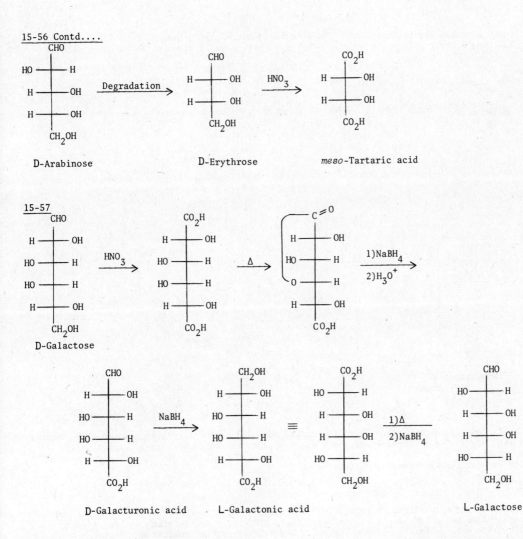

D-Arabinose                  D-Erythrose              *meso*-Tartaric acid

15-57

D-Galactose

D-Galacturonic acid   .   L-Galactonic acid                          L-Galactose

15-58   Hydrogen bonding between cis hydroxy groups is an energetically favorable contribution to
the axial conformation.

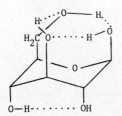

15-59  If the ring had opened first, then the aldehyde oxidized to a carboxylic acid, the resulting aldaric acid would be meso, thus cyclization would produce the racemic lactone.

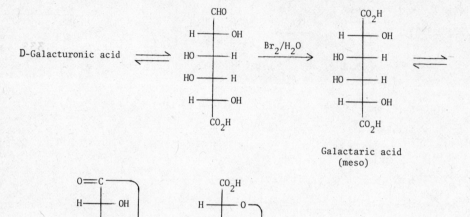

Galactaric acid
(meso)

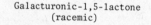

Galacturonic-1,5-lactone
(racemic)

15-60  The cyclodextrins are optically active chiral compounds since they are composed of D-glucose units.  Inclusion of racemic sulfinate ester results in two diastereomers, one with (R) sulfinate and one with (S) sulfinate.  Separation of the diastereomers and regeneration of the free sulfinate accomplishes resolution.

15-61  A positive benedicts test, mutarotation, and reaction with phenylhydrazine indicates that gentiobiose has a hemiacetal or hemiketal group.  Cleavage by emulsion confirms a β-linkage between the two glucose units.  (See also structure proof of melibiose; prob. 15-53.)

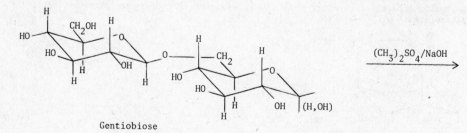

Gentiobiose

15-61 Contd.....

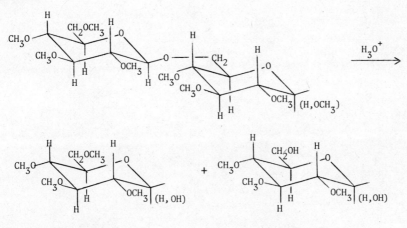

2,3,4,6-Tetramethyl-D-glucose          2,3,4-Trimethyl-D-glucose

15-62

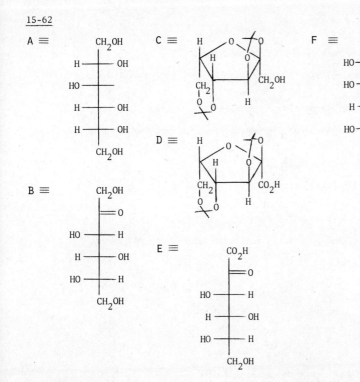

15-63

A ≡ CH₃OH/H⁺

E ≡ CrO₃/pyridine

B ≡ C₆H₅CHO/H⁺

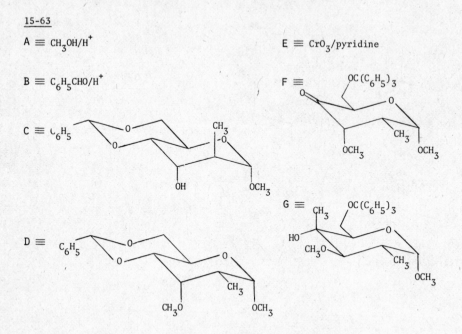

(1) Methyl ketal gives principally α-anomer (see problem 15-27).

(2) Benzaldehyde acetal forms six-membered ring in protecting hydroxy groups at the 4 and 6 positions.

(3) Reagent adds methyl group to less-hindered side of epoxide to give trans-diaxial product.

(4) Epimerization takes place alpha to the carbonyl group to give the more stable equatorial methyl.

(5) Hydrogenolysis of the benzylic protecting group.

(6) Protection of hydroxy as triphenylmethyl (trityl) ether. The bulky reagent is selective for the primary alcohol.

(7) Epimerization alpha to the carbonyl to give the equatorial methoxy group.

(8) Actually obtain a mixture of axial and equatorial addition, but the desired isomer crystallizes from the mixture.

# 16 AMINO ACIDS, PEPTIDES, AND PROTEINS

16-1

a)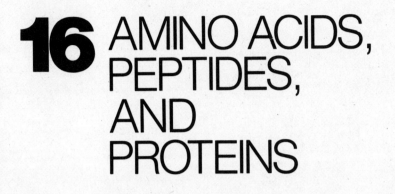

L-Valine

L-Leucine

L-Isoleucine

b) Only one L-stereoisomer of valine and leucine are possible. Isoleucine can exist as two L-stereoisomers because the β-carbon is chiral also.

c) (2)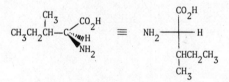

The thiomethylene group has priority over the carboxy group since the sulfur atom has a higher atomic number than the oxygen atom.

16-2

A ≡        CH(SC_2H_5)_2

        H ——|—— NH_2
                                2 C_2H_5SH/H^+
        HO ——|—— H

        H ——|—— OH

        H ——|—— OH

            CH_2OH

C ≡        CH_3

        H ——|—— NHAc

        HO ——|—— H

        H ——|—— OH

        H ——|—— OH

            CH_2OH

B ≡        CH(SC_2H_5)_2

        H ——|—— NHAc

        AcO ——|—— H

        H ——|—— OAc

        H ——|—— OAc

            CH_2OAc

D ≡        CH_3

        H ——|—— NHAc

            CO_2H

16-3

a)  $K_{a1} = \dfrac{[H^+][H_3\overset{+}{N}CH_2CO_2^-]}{[H_3\overset{+}{N}CH_2CO_2H]}$

$K_{a2} = \dfrac{[H^+][H_2NCH_2CO_2^-]}{[H_3\overset{+}{N}CH_2CO_2^-]}$

b) At pH = 4   $[H^+] = 10^{-4}$

$\dfrac{K_{a1}}{[H^+]} = \dfrac{[H_3\overset{+}{N}CH_2CO_2^-]}{[H_3\overset{+}{N}CH_2CO_2H]} = \dfrac{10^{-2.35}}{10^{-4}} = 10^{1.65} = 45$

16-4 The observation indicates that the carboxylic acid group is a relatively stronger acid than the amino group is a base.

16-5 At pH values other than the isoelectric point most of the amino acid molecules in solution are of the same charge. They repel each other and are solvated by the water. At the electrically neutral p*I* value, charge repulsion is minimized. Molecules come together and precipitate (proteins coagulate). Solvation is less favorable because a solvent molecule must accommodate two different charges in the same amino acid molecule.

16-6

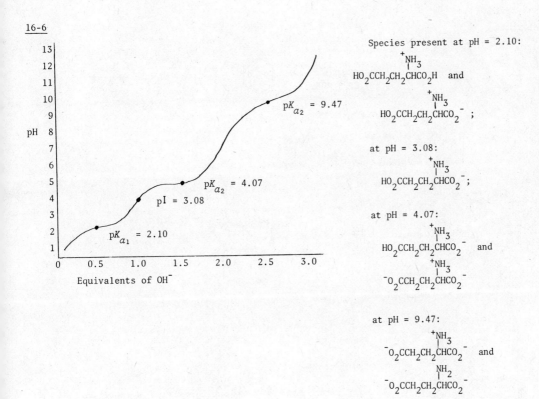

pH

pK_{a_1} = 2.10

pI = 3.08

pK_{a_2} = 4.07

pK_{a_2} = 9.47

Equivalents of OH⁻

Species present at pH = 2.10:

$$\underset{\underset{\displaystyle HO_2CCH_2CH_2CHCO_2H}{|}}{\overset{+NH_3}{}} \quad and$$

$$\underset{\underset{\displaystyle HO_2CCH_2CH_2CHCO_2^-}{|}}{\overset{+NH_3}{}} \quad ;$$

at pH = 3.08:

$$\underset{\underset{\displaystyle HO_2CCH_2CH_2CHCO_2^-}{|}}{\overset{+NH_3}{}} \quad ;$$

at pH = 4.07:

$$\underset{\underset{\displaystyle HO_2CCH_2CH_2CHCO_2^-}{|}}{\overset{+NH_3}{}} \quad and$$

$$\underset{\underset{\displaystyle ^-O_2CCH_2CH_2CHCO_2^-}{|}}{\overset{+NH_3}{}}$$

at pH = 9.47:

$$\underset{\underset{\displaystyle ^-O_2CCH_2CH_2CHCO_2^-}{|}}{\overset{+NH_3}{}} \quad and$$

$$\underset{\underset{\displaystyle ^-O_2CCH_2CH_2CHCO_2^-}{|}}{\overset{NH_2}{}}$$

16-7  The diethyl acetamidomalonate approach can also be used for each of the following.

$$CH_2(CO_2C_2H_5)_2 \; + \; Br_2 \; \xrightarrow{CCl_4} \; BrCH(CO_2C_2H_5)_2$$

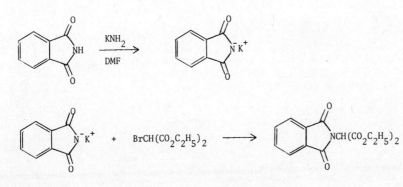

16-7 Contd....

a)

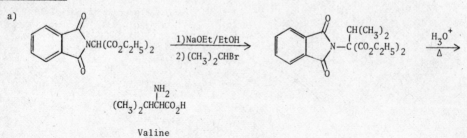

$$(CH_3)_2CHCHCO_2H$$ with $NH_2$

Valine

b)

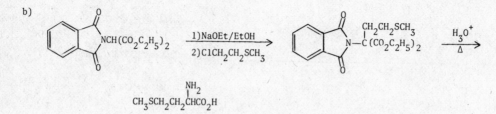

$$CH_3SCH_2CH_2CHCO_2H$$ with $NH_2$

Methionine

c)

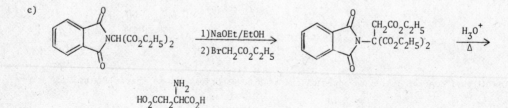

$$HO_2CCH_2CHCO_2H$$ with $NH_2$

Apartic acid

16-8

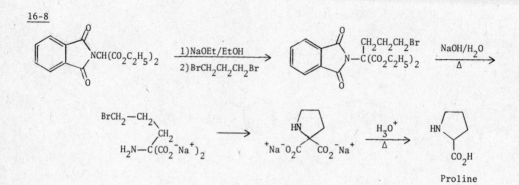

Proline

16-9

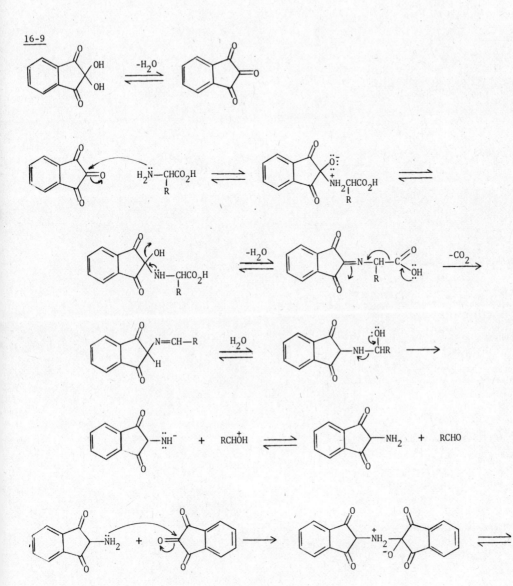

16-9 Contd....

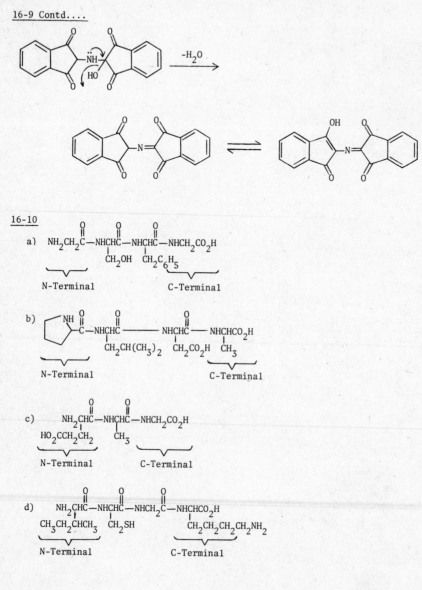

16-10

a)

$$NH_2CH_2\overset{O}{\overset{\|}{C}}-NHCH\overset{O}{\overset{\|}{C}}-NHCH\overset{O}{\overset{\|}{C}}-NHCH_2CO_2H$$
$$\quad\qquad\qquad\;\; CH_2OH \;\; CH_2C_6H_5$$

N-Terminal          C-Terminal

b)

$$\overset{NH}{\underset{}{}}\overset{O}{\overset{\|}{C}}-NHCHC \longrightarrow NHCH\overset{O}{\overset{\|}{C}}- NHCHCO_2H$$
$$\qquad\qquad CH_2CH(CH_3)_2 \;\; CH_2CO_2H \;\; CH_3$$

N-Terminal                    C-Terminal

c)

$$NH_2CH\overset{O}{\overset{\|}{C}}-NHCH\overset{O}{\overset{\|}{C}}-NHCH_2CO_2H$$
$$HO_2CCH_2CH_2 \quad CH_3$$

N-Terminal          C-Terminal

d)

$$NH_2CH\overset{O}{\overset{\|}{C}}-NHCH\overset{O}{\overset{\|}{C}}-NHCH_2\overset{O}{\overset{\|}{C}}-NHCHCO_2H$$
$$CH_3CH_2CHCH_3 \;\; CH_2SH \qquad\qquad CH_2CH_2CH_2CH_2NH_2$$

N-Terminal                    C-Terminal

16-11

a)  The terminal amino and carboxylic acid groups are so far from each other that they do not
    interact.  Deviations in p$K_a$ values of peptides from those of alkylamines and carboxylic
    acids are due principally to the influence of other adjacent groups in the peptide.

b)  $pI = 3.42 + (\frac{7.94-3.42}{2}) = 5.68$

16-12
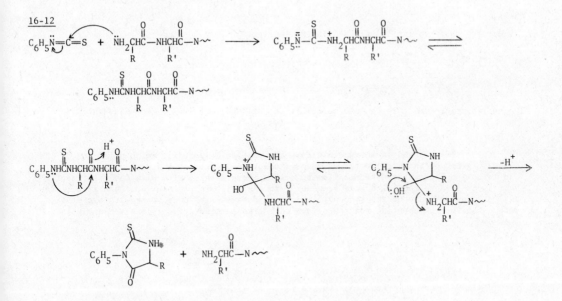

16-13 Formation of the Sanger derivative requires a nucleophilic aromatic substitution reaction. Even with the electron withdrawing nitro groups these reactions tend to be poor. By contrast nucleophilic substitution on a sulfonyl chloride is usually a rapid, high yield process.

16-14 The sulfide group reacts with the cyanogen bromide to form a sulfonium salt, but subsequent cleavage as occurs with methionine would require a strained, 4-atom cyclic intermediate.

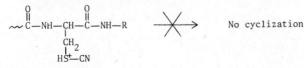

No cyclization

16-15 Since one valine is the N-terminal amino acid either fragment *3* or *5* must be at that end. The cyanogen bromide reaction indicates that methionine must be connected to glycine or valine by the methionine carboxylic acid group. Fragment *1* shows that it is the glycine that is connected to methionine and fragment *5* indicates that valine and glycine are connected. One valine thus is the C-terminal amino acid. The composition of *1* also shows that phenylalanine must be connected to methionine.

—Phe—Met—Gly—Val

The other valine - the N-terminal amino acid - must be connected to leucine while fragment

<u>16-15 Contd...</u>

    *2* indicates that proline is attached to the leucine.

$$\text{Val—Leu—Pro—}$$

    The heptapeptide structure can now be completed: Val—Leu—Pro—Phe—Met—Gly—Val.

<u>16-16</u>   The enzymes trypsin and chymotrypsin cleave the peptide at specific amino acids and at the carboxy group of those amino acids. Dansyl chloride identifies the N-terminal amino acid and carboxypeptidase the C-terminal amino acid. These data coupled with the results of hydrolysis lead to the amino acid sequence. In the following we show how each step in the analysis reveals more of the sequence. Each new data must be consistent with previous data. The two pentapeptide fragments from chymotrypsin cleavage complete the analysis.

Terminal
analysis    : Ala—                                      —Thr

Trypsin    : Ala—$\begin{pmatrix} \text{Lys—Gly} \\ \text{or} \\ \text{Gly—Lys} \end{pmatrix}$(Phe, Ile, Arg, Val)$\begin{pmatrix} \text{Leu—Trp} \\ \text{or} \\ \text{Trp—Leu} \end{pmatrix}$—Thr

Hydrolysis   :             Lys——Ile       Arg——Leu

Chymotrypsin : Ala—Gly—Lys—Ile—Phe—Val—Arg——Leu——Trp——Thr

                                 Cleaved by
                               chymotrypsin

                    Cleaved by trypsin

<u>16-17</u>    $(0.90)^{40} \times 100 = 1.5\%$

<u>16-18</u>

  a) $(CH_3)_3COH + Cl\overset{O}{\overset{\|}{C}}Cl \xrightarrow{\text{Et}_2O} (CH_3)_3CO\overset{O}{\overset{\|}{C}}Cl$

    This reagent is unstable and is usually prepared and used at low temperatures as needed.

  b) $(CH_3)_3CO\overset{O}{\overset{\|}{C}}NHCH_2\overset{O}{\overset{\|}{C}}-N\sim + H^+ \rightleftharpoons (CH_3)_3C\overset{+}{\underset{H}{\overset{O}{\overset{\|}{O}}}}CNHCH_2\overset{O}{\overset{\|}{C}}-N\sim \longrightarrow$

16-18 Contd....

b) Contd...

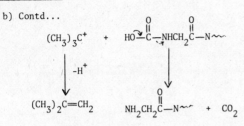

16-19  Four dipeptides would be expected to form: Ala—Ala;  Gly—Gly;  Ala—Gly;  Gly—Ala.


16-20  Other protecting and activating groups can also be used in the following sequences.
Abbreviations are:

Z $\equiv$ Benzoxycarbonyl

Boc $\equiv$ $t$-Butoxycarbonyl

If $\equiv$ Isobutyl formate

NCA $\equiv$ $N$-carboxyanhydride

a) Phe $\xrightarrow{Z—Cl}$ Z—Phe $\xrightarrow[DCC]{Ala—OCH_3}$ Z—Phe—Ala—OCH$_3$ $\xrightarrow{H_3O^+}$

with Ala $\xrightarrow{CH_3OH/H^+}$ Ala—OCH$_3$

Z—Phe—Ala $\xrightarrow[DCC]{Val—OCH_3}$ Z—Phe—Ala—Val—OCH$_3$ $\xrightarrow{HBr/HOAc}$ Phe—Ala—Val

with Val $\xrightarrow{CH_3OH/H^+}$ Val—OCH$_3$

b) Ile $\xrightarrow{Boc—Cl}$ Boc—Ile $\xrightarrow{If—Cl}$ Boc—Ile—If $\xrightarrow{Met—OEt}$

with Met $\xrightarrow{EtOH/H^+}$ Met—OEt

Boc—Ile—Met—OEt $\xrightarrow{H_3O^+}$ Boc—Ile—Met $\xrightarrow{Asp—(O-t-Bu)_2}$

with Asp $\xrightarrow{t-BuOH/H^+}$ Asp—(O-$t$-Bu)$_2$

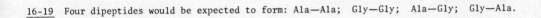

16-20 Contd.....

   b)Contd....

$$Boc - Ile - Met - Asp - (O\text{-}t\text{-}Bu)_2 \xrightarrow{\text{HBr/HOAc}} Ile - Met - Asp$$

   c)  $Leu \xrightarrow{\text{ClCOCl}} Leu - NCA \xrightarrow{\text{Phe}} Leu - Phe \xrightarrow{\text{MeOH/H}^+}$

           Ala

            $\downarrow$ ClCOCl

$$Leu - Phe - OMe \xrightarrow{\text{Ala} - \text{NCA}} Ala - Leu - Phe - OMe \xrightarrow[\text{DCC}]{\text{Boc}_2\text{Lys}}$$

$$Boc_2Lys - Ala - Leu - Phe - OMe \xrightarrow{\text{HBr/HOAc}} Lys - Ala - Leu - Phe$$

16-21  One step at a time:  $(0.90)^5 \times 100 = 59\%$

       Each tripeptide formed, then coupled:  $(0.90)^2 \times 0.90 \times 100 = 73\%$

16-22

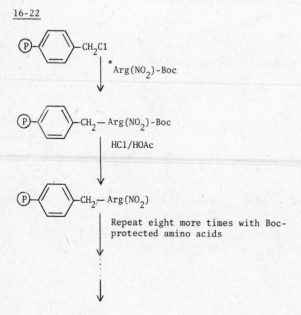

16-22 Contd....

(P)—⟨benzene⟩—CH$_2$—ArgNO$_2$—PHe—Pro—Ser—Phe—Gly—Pro—Pro—NO$_2$Arg

| HBr/CF$_3$CO$_2$H
↓

(P)—⟨benzene⟩—CH$_2$Br  +  HO$_2$C—ArgNO$_2$—PHe—Pro—Ser—Phe—Gly—Pro—Pro—ArgNO$_2$

| H$_2$/Pd
↓

HO$_2$CAr—Phe—Pro—Ser—Phe—Gly—Pro—Pro—ArgNH$_2$

(The C-terminal amino acid is connected to the polymer so that
the structure above is written opposite to the usual direction.)

*
Arginine was used as a nitro derivative, then reduced to the free amine at the last step.

16-23  At pH 6-7 the side chain amino group of each lysine segment is protonated.  Repulsions
between the cations disrupt the α-helix conformation.  At high pH each unit is electrically
neutral so that the favorable α-helix can form.

16-24  Two common mechanisms of enzyme inhibition are:
   i) the inhibitor complexes with the active site and blocks the enzymes ability to complex
      with substrate;
  ii) the inhibitor matches and complexes with the substrate and prevents approach of the
      enzyme.

16-25

a) The anion of the conjugate base is stabilized inductively by the adjacent ammonium nitrogen
atom and by d-orbital resonance with the adjacent sulfur atom.

b)

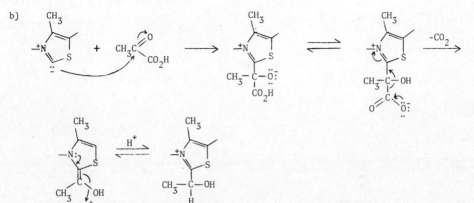

16-25 Contd...

c) The lipoic acid is reduced as it participates in the formation of acetyl CoA.

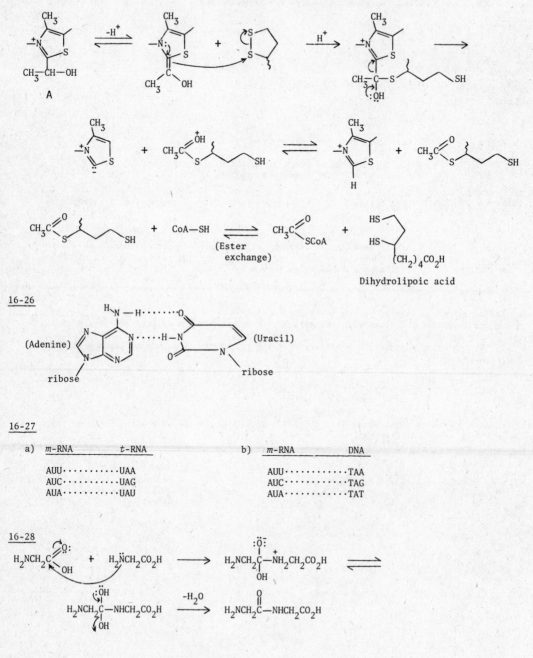

Dihydrolipoic acid

16-26

(Adenine)    (Uracil)

ribose    ribose

16-27

a) | *m*-RNA | *t*-RNA |
|---|---|
| AUU · · · · · · · · · · UAA | |
| AUC · · · · · · · · · UAG | |
| AUA · · · · · · · · · UAU | |

b) | *m*-RNA | DNA |
|---|---|
| AUU · · · · · · · · · · · TAA | |
| AUC · · · · · · · · · · · TAG | |
| AUA · · · · · · · · · · · TAT | |

16-28

$H_2NCH_2C \begin{smallmatrix} O: \\ OH \end{smallmatrix}$ + $H_2\ddot{N}CH_2CO_2H$ ⟶ $H_2NCH_2C-NH_2CH_2CO_2H$ ⇌

$H_2NCH_2C-NHCH_2CO_2H$  $\xrightarrow{-H_2O}$  $H_2NCH_2C-NHCH_2CO_2H$

16-28 Contd...

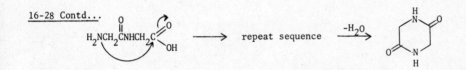

$\longrightarrow$ repeat sequence $\xrightarrow{-H_2O}$

16-29  Comparison of the proline and glutamic acid structures suggest that the skeleton of proline be attained by connection of the amino group of glutamic acid to its number 5 carbon atom. If that carbon, a carboxy group, were reduced to an aldehyde, cyclization could occur via imine formation.  That reduction is accomplished by NADH, probably on the phosphate derivative of glutamic acid.  Reduction of the cyclic imine is also carried out by NADH.

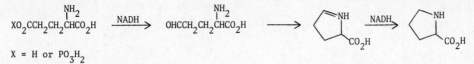

X = H or $PO_3H_2$

16-30  Racemization of $\alpha$-amino acyl halides is believed to be due to an enolization process.

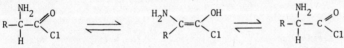

| Optically active | Optically inactive | Racemic |

16-31

a)  Moles of glycine  $= \dfrac{3.0g}{75g/mol} = 0.04$ mol

Moles of alanine  $= \dfrac{0.9g}{89g/mol} = 0.01$ mol

Moles of valine  $= \dfrac{3.7g}{117g/mol} = 0.03$ mol

Moles of proline  $= \dfrac{6.9g}{115g/mol} = 0.06$ mol

Moles of serine  $= \dfrac{7.3g}{105g/mol} = 0.07$ mol

Moles of arginine  $= \dfrac{86.0g}{174g/mol} = 0.5$ mol

The ratio of amino acid units is:

Gly:Ala:Val:Pro:Ser:Arg = 4:1:3:6:7:50

b)  The minimum molecular weight of the peptide is the sum of the molecular weights of all the amino acids less a mol of water for all the peptide bonds formed.

16-31 Contd.....
  b) Contd...

  MW = (4 x 75) + (1 x 89) + (3 x 117) + (6 x 115) + (7 x 105) + (50 x 174) - (70 x 18) = 9,605

16-32

a) The two resonance peaks in the nmr spectrum at 25° are the two methyl groups on nitrogen. They are not equivalent because the double bond character of the C—N bond does not allow free rotation. As the temperature is raised, thermal energy is sufficient to promote free rotation and the two methyl groups become equivalent.

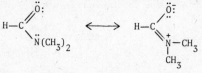

b) This experiment supports rigidity in peptide structures that has been attributed to the double bond character of peptide bonds.

16-33  The hydroxy group of a serine component in chymotrypsin is the active site. Reaction of that hydroxy group with the reactive phosphate derivative blocks the potential reactivity of the enzyme. Recall (prob. 8-53) that direct displacement occurs on the phosphorus atom.

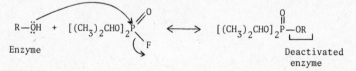

16-34

1) DNS—Gly shows that glycine is the N-terminal group.

2) DNS—Ser, Ser, Gly, Gly shows that two of the three glycine units are to the right (on the carboxy side) of a serine.

3) DNS—Gly, Ser, Gly, when combined with the information from (1) and (2) indicates an alteration of those three amino acids.

4) DNS—Ser, Gly, Ser, extends the alternation to a fourth amino acid and leads to the structure of the pentapeptide of Gly—Ser—Gly—Ser—Gly.

16-35

1) DNP—Val indicates that Val is the N-terminal amino acid and DNP—Val—Leu identifies the next unit.

16-35 Contd...

2) Carboxypeptidase cleaves the C-terminal amino acid so that the result shows that Ala is that end unit and Glu is next to it.

3) The fragments recovered from partial hydrolysis identify Leu—Ile and Ala—Phe—Glu or Ala—Glu—Phe.  The data from (2) support that Ala—Phe—Glu sequence.  All of the above data lead to a structure for the heptapeptide of:
Val—Leu—Ile—Ala—Phe—Glu—Ala

16-36  The conversion of ornithine to arginine by reaction with $H_2NCN$ is a key factor in establishing the ornithine structure.  Those two amino acids differ by only that $H_2NCN$ unit so that ornithine presumably has the structure:

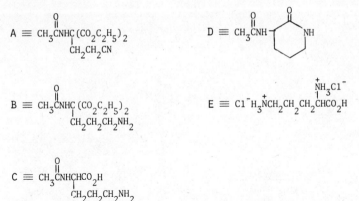

Ornithine                          Arginine

In the synthesis below note that the six-membered lactone readily forms on heating the δ-amino acid.

$$A \equiv CH_3\overset{O}{\overset{\|}{C}}NH\underset{CH_2CH_2CN}{\overset{|}{C}}(CO_2C_2H_5)_2 \qquad D \equiv CH_3\overset{O}{\overset{\|}{C}}NH-$$

$$B \equiv CH_3\overset{O}{\overset{\|}{C}}NH\underset{CH_2CH_2CH_2NH_2}{\overset{|}{C}}(CO_2C_2H_5)_2 \qquad E \equiv Cl^-\overset{+}{H_3N}CH_2CH_2CH_2\underset{\overset{|}{NH_3Cl^-}}{\overset{+}{C}}HCO_2H$$

$$C \equiv CH_3\overset{O}{\overset{\|}{C}}NH\underset{CH_2CH_2CH_2NH_2}{\overset{|}{C}}HCO_2H$$

16-37  The fit into the enzyme is best for an L configuration of the benzyl, acetamido, and hydrogen groups.  Methyl cannot replace benzyl or the hydrogen atom, nor can hydrogen replace the acetamido group.  The cyclic substrate reacts rapidly in the configuration opposite to that of the natural L-phenylalanine.  This suggests that tying back the benzyl and amido removes one restriction to a proper fit although the data do not indicate which group is more important. The position of the H-atom at the aymmetric carbon atom appears to be critical.

16-38  Fragments 4 and 5 indicate that the sequence in 5 must be Tyr—Ile—Glu.  The data provided by fragment 2 extends the sequence to $CySO_3H$—Tyr—Ile—Glu (7).  Similar reasoning using 3 and 6 leads to a tetrapeptide sequence of $HO_3SCys$—Pro—Leu—Gly (9).  The cysteic acid unit in fragment 6 must be different from that in 2.  The sequence of tetrapeptide 7 was established above and 8 can be deduced from 9 as being Asp—$CySO_3H$—Pro—Leu—Gly.  Since the two cysteine units are connected together we have -

16-38 Contd...

Glu—Ile—Tyr—Cys  
           |  
Asp—Cys—Pro—Leu—Gly

Knowing that glycine amide is the C-terminal group and that oxytocin is cyclic provides the final structure.

Ile—Tyr—Cys  
|           |  
Glu—Asp—Cys—Pro—Leu—Gly

16-39

a) $C_6H_6$ + $CH_3COCl$ $\xrightarrow{AlCl_3}$ $C_6H_5COCH_3$ $\xrightarrow[\text{2)HCl/}\Delta]{\text{1)NaCN/NH}_4\text{Cl}}$ $C_6H_5\underset{\underset{CH_3}{|}}{\overset{\overset{NH_2}{|}}{C}}-CO_2H$

b) $CH_3(CH_2)_3CO_2H$ $\xrightarrow{PBr_3}$ $CH_3CH_2CH_2\underset{\overset{|}{Br}}{C}HCO_2H$ $\xrightarrow{NH_3}$ $CH_3CH_2CH_2\underset{\overset{|}{NH_2}}{C}HCO_2H$

c) $CH_3CH_2MgBr$ + $^{14}CO_2$ $\xrightarrow[\text{2)H}_3O^+]{\text{1)Et}_2O}$ $CH_3CH_2^{14}CO_2H$ $\xrightarrow[\text{2)LiAlH[OC(CH}_3)_3]_3]{\text{1)SOCl}_2}$

$CH_3CH_2^{14}CHO$ $\xrightarrow[\text{2)HCl/}\Delta]{\text{1)NaCN/NH}_4\text{Cl}}$ $CH_3CH_2^{14}\underset{\overset{|}{NH_2}}{C}HCO_2H$

d) $CH_2(CO_2C_2H_5)_2$ + $Br_2$ $\xrightarrow{CCl_4}$ $BrCH(CO_2C_2H_5)_2$ $\xrightarrow[\text{DMF}]{}$

—CH(CO$_2$C$_2$H$_5$)$_2$ $\xrightarrow[\text{2)CH}_3\text{CH}_2\text{Br}]{\text{1)NaOEt/EtOH}}$ —$\underset{\overset{|}{CH_2CH_3}}{C}$(CO$_2$C$_2$H$_5$)$_2$ $\xrightarrow[\text{2)H}_2\text{NNH}_2]{\text{1)H}_3O^+}$

$CH_3CH_2\underset{\overset{|}{NH_2}}{C}HCO_2H$

e) =O + $H^{14}CN$ $\xrightarrow{NH_4Cl}$ $\xrightarrow[\Delta]{H_3O^+}$

16-39 Contd....

f)

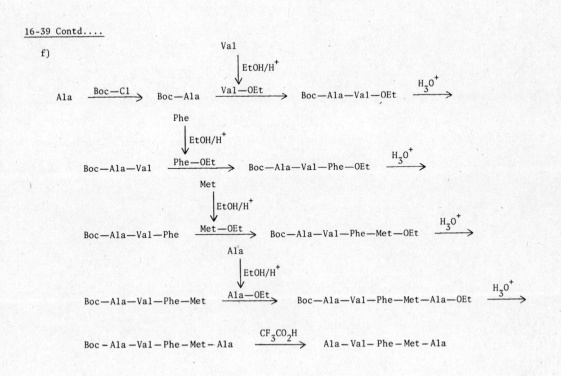

Val
↓ EtOH/H⁺

Ala  →[Boc—Cl]→  Boc—Ala  →[Val—OEt]→  Boc—Ala—Val—OEt  →[H₃O⁺]→

Phe
↓ EtOH/H⁺

Boc—Ala—Val  →[Phe—OEt]→  Boc—Ala—Val—Phe—OEt  →[H₃O⁺]→

Met
↓ EtOH/H⁺

Boc—Ala—Val—Phe  →[Met—OEt]→  Boc—Ala—Val—Phe—Met—OEt  →[H₃O⁺]→

Ala
↓ EtOH/H⁺

Boc—Ala—Val—Phe—Met  →[Ala—OEt]→  Boc—Ala—Val—Phe—Met—Ala—OEt  →[H₃O⁺]→

Boc—Ala—Val—Phe—Met—Ala  →[CF₃CO₂H]→  Ala—Val—Phe—Met—Ala

# 17 LIPIDS

17-1

P = Palmitoate; $CH_3(CH_2)_{14}CO_2-$

S = Stearate ; $CH_3(CH_2)_{16}CO_2-$

17-2  Elaidic acid is the thermodynamically more stable $E$-configurational isomer.

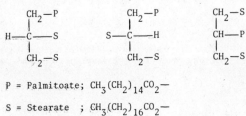

17-3  $CH_2O_2C(CH_2)_{12}CH_3$
      $CHO_2C(CH_2)_{12}CH_3$
      $CH_2O_2C(CH_2)_{12}CH_3$

17-4

$A \equiv$

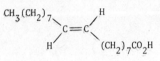

$B \equiv$

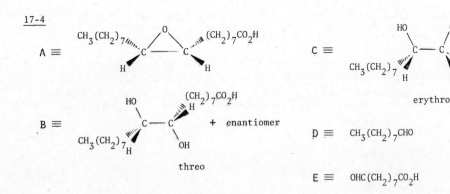

threo

$C \equiv$

erythro

$D \equiv$  $CH_3(CH_2)_7CHO$

$E \equiv$  $OHC(CH_2)_7CO_2H$

**17-5**  There are $2^9 = 512$ possible stereoisomers of cholestanol (coprostanol).

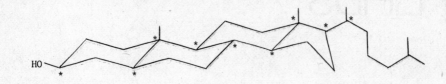

**17-6**  In each case the epimer with an equatorial hydroxy group is more favorable thermodynamically.

**17-7**

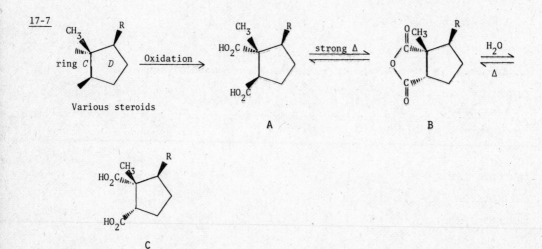

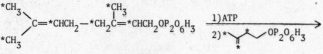

The *trans*-1,2-diacid A obtained from the trans C-D ring junction will not form an anhydride until it epimerizes to the *cis*-diacid C . The isomerization is a slow process and probably involves acid catalyzed enolization. The *cis*-diacid C readily interconverts with the anhydride B.

**17-8**  The sequence for the formation of labeled geranyl pyrophosphate from $^{14}CH_3CO_2H$ is depicted in fig. 11-2. A sequence to labeled farnesyl pyrophosphate and labeled squalene follows.

17-8 Contd...

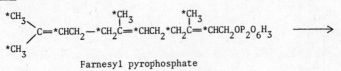

Farnesyl pyrophosphate

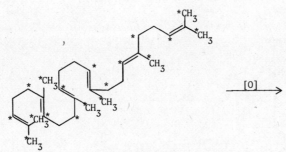

Squalene

[O] →

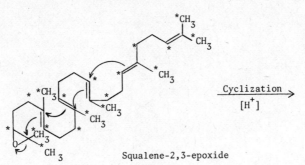

Squalene-2,3-epoxide

Cyclization →
[H$^+$]

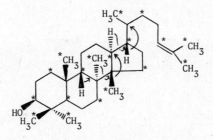

Rearrangement →

17-8 Contd...

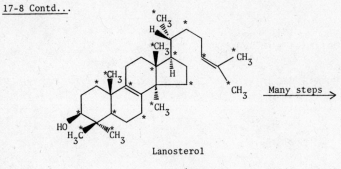

Lanosterol

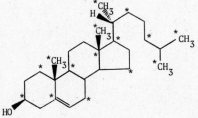

Cholesterol

$\xrightarrow{\text{Many steps}}$

17-9

A ≡ PBr₃

B ≡ HOCH₂CH₂OH/TsOH

C ≡ (C₆H₅)₃P

D ≡ CH₃C≡C(CH₂)₂MgBr

E ≡ HOCH₂(CH₂)₂$\overset{\overset{\displaystyle CH_3}{|}}{C}$=CH(CH₂)₂C≡CCH₃

F ≡

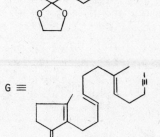

G ≡

H ≡ O₃

I ≡ KOH/H₂O

17-10

a) Cholic acid has *cis*-fused A-B rings and the epicoprostanol configuration (prob. 17-6) in which the 3-hydroxy group is α and thus equatorial. The 7- and 12-hydroxy groups are also both α- but are more hindered by other parts of the steroid structure.

b) Yes, because the two functional groups are cis to each other.

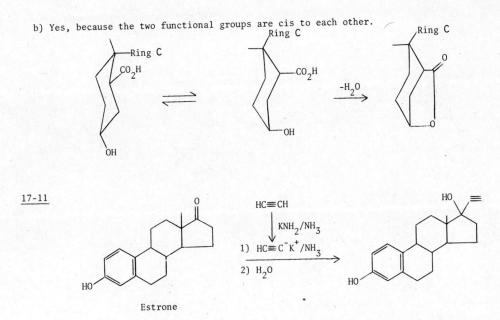

17-11

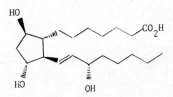

Estrone

17-12  PGF$_{1\beta}$  is the epimer of PGF$_{1\alpha}$ and differs in configuration at the position of the reduced carbonyl.

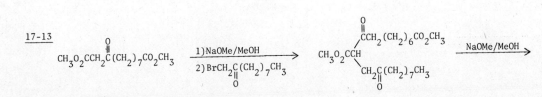

17-13

$CH_3O_2CCH_2\overset{O}{\overset{\|}{C}}(CH_2)_7CO_2CH_3$ $\xrightarrow[\text{2) BrCH}_2\overset{O}{\overset{\|}{C}}(CH_2)_7CH_3]{\text{1) NaOMe/MeOH}}$ $CH_3O_2C\overset{\overset{O}{\overset{\|}{C}CH_2(CH_2)_6CO_2CH_3}}{\underset{CH_2\overset{O}{\overset{\|}{C}}(CH_2)_7CH_3}{\overset{\|}{C}H}}$ $\xrightarrow{\text{NaOMe/MeOH}}$

17-13 Contd...

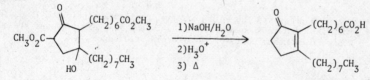

17-14

A ≡ ClCH₂OCH₂C₆H₅

B ≡

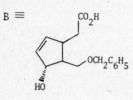

C ≡

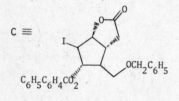

D ≡

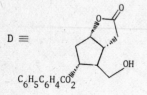

E ≡

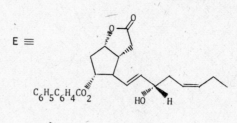

F ≡ 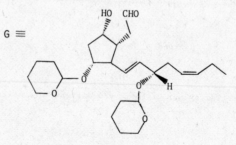 , TsOH

G ≡

H ≡ (C₆H₅)₃P=CH(CH₂)₃CO₂⁻/THF

17-15

A ≡ CH$_3$MgI/Et$_2$O

B ≡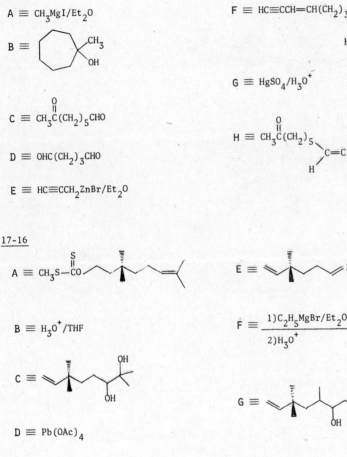

C ≡ CH$_3$C(CH$_2$)$_5$CHO

D ≡ OHC(CH$_2$)$_3$CHO

E ≡ HC≡CCH$_2$ZnBr/Et$_2$O

F ≡ HC≡CCH=CH(CH$_2$)$_3$

G ≡ HgSO$_4$/H$_3$O$^+$

H ≡ CH$_3$C(CH$_2$)$_5$

17-16

A ≡ CH$_3$S—CO

B ≡ H$_3$O$^+$/THF

C ≡

D ≡ Pb(OAc)$_4$

E ≡

F ≡ $\xrightarrow{\text{1)C}_2\text{H}_5\text{MgBr/Et}_2\text{O}}$ 2)H$_3$O$^+$

G ≡

H ≡ m-ClC$_6$H$_4$CO$_3$H

17-17 Under the basic conditions of the Robinson annelation, both A and B undergo elimination to produce methyl vinyl ketone *in situ*.

17-18 The two 6-bromocholestanone isomers differ in configuration at the 6-position. The more stable equatorial (β) isomer is favored thermodynamically but addition of bromine to the enol intermediate forms the 6-α epimer more rapidly (kinetics).

7-Cholestanone $\xrightarrow{Br_2/H_2O}$

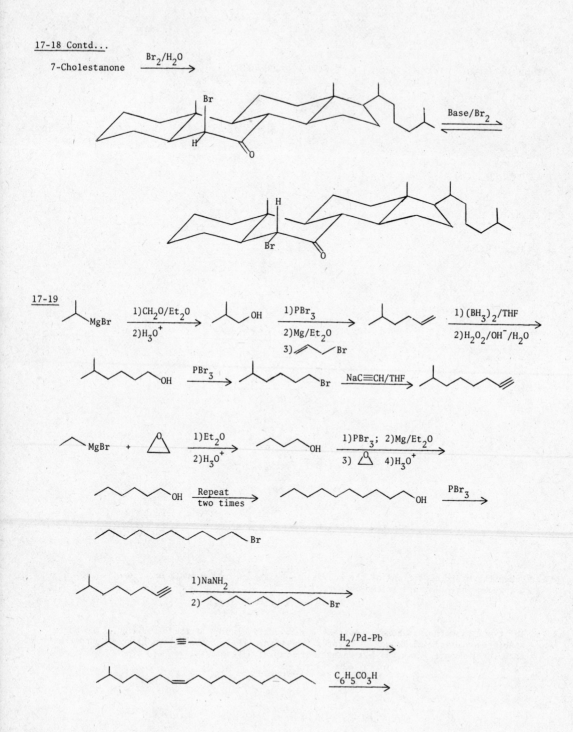

17-19

17-19 Contd....

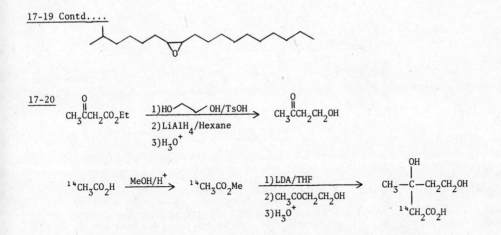

17-20

$$CH_3\overset{O}{\underset{}{C}}CH_2CO_2Et \quad \xrightarrow[\substack{2)LiAlH_4/Hexane \\ 3)H_3O^+}]{1)HO\diagdown\diagup OH/TsOH} \quad CH_3\overset{O}{\underset{}{C}}CH_2CH_2OH$$

$$^{14}CH_3CO_2H \xrightarrow{MeOH/H^+} {}^{14}CH_3CO_2Me \xrightarrow[\substack{2)CH_3COCH_2CH_2OH \\ 3)H_3O^+}]{1)LDA/THF} CH_3-\overset{OH}{\underset{{}^{14}CH_2CO_2H}{C}}-CH_2CH_2OH$$

17-21

a + b)  Epoxidation takes place from the side of the double bond further from the angular
        methyl group at C-10 (the back side in the drawing).  Addition of acid  opens the
        epoxide so as to give the more stable tertiary carbocation. The water adds to give the
        axial hydroxy at C-9 to maintain the chair conformation.

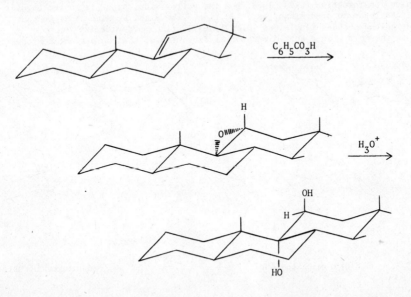

c)  The A-ring has little effect on reaction of the 9,10-double bond.  The bromonium ion
    intermediate follows  a stereochemical course similar to that of the epoxide reaction in
    part (b).

17-21 Contd...

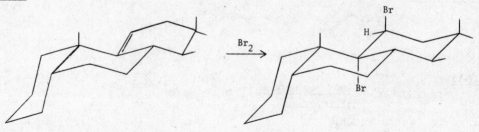

17-22  (See solution to prob. 17-8 for $^{14}$C-labeled structural formulas.)

a)  Six moles of acetic acid are formed per mole of squalene.  (The terminal *gem*-dimethyl groups of squalene each give only one mole acetic acid in the Kuhn-Roth oxidation.)  This accounts for 6/18 = 1/3 of the $^{14}$C in labeled squalene.

b)  Four moles of labeled acetic are recovered from cholesterol but one (that from the C-18 angular methyl group) will have both carbon atoms labeled.  The proportion of $^{14}$C recovered is thus 5/15 = 1/3.

17-23  Bromonium ion formation takes place from the bottom side, opposite to the angular methyl group, and leads to predominant anti addition.  The axial bromine atoms encounter considerable nonbonded repulsions. Slow isomerization and epimerization leads to the more stable anti-diequatorial dibromide of the coprostanol conformation.

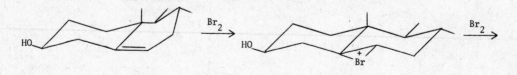

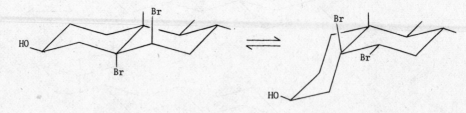

5,6-Dibromocholestanol                5,6-Dibromocoprostanol

17-24

A ≡ 2 C$_6$H$_5$MgBr/Et$_2$O

B ≡ H$_3$O$^+$/Δ

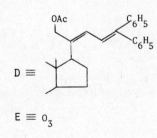

D ≡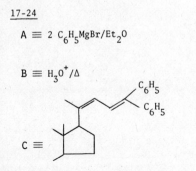

E ≡ O$_3$

C ≡ 

17-25  A double conjugate addition provides the product in one synthetic step.

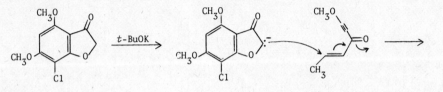

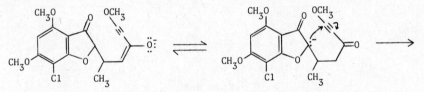

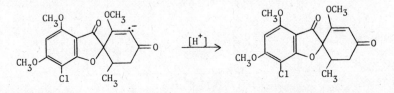

17-26

A ≡ 2 CH₃COCH₃/H⁺

C ≡ NaBH₄

B ≡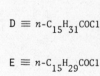

D ≡ $n$-C₁₅H₃₁COCl

E ≡ $n$-C₁₅H₂₉COCl

F ≡ H₂/Pd-C

17-27

A ≡ Ac₂O

B ≡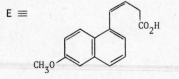

C ≡ NaNO₂/H₂SO₄

D ≡ KI

E ≡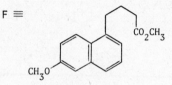

F ≡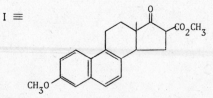

G ≡ BrZnCH₂CO₂CH₃/Et₂O

H ≡ NaOMe/MeOH

I ≡

J ≡ H₃O⁺/Δ

17-28 The mass spectrum shows a peak at 152 which seems reasonable for the molecular ion of a volatile compound.  The IR spectrum suggests that carbonyl and hydroxy groups are present. The nmr  indicates aromatic protons, probably para disubstituted.  We predict a molecular weight of 76 for such a fragment.  The nmr peak at 4.0 ppm suggest a deshielded methyl group and the broad, strong IR peak at 1280 cm⁻¹ is consistent with the C—O stretching vibration

17-28 Contd....

of an ester.  A methyl ester is reasonable and the large peak in the mass spectrum at 121 is consistent with loss of 31 (-OCH$_3$) from the compound.  A substituted methyl benzoate

accounts for a molecular weight of 135 plus the substituent.  The single proton deshielded to 10.5 ppm is consistent with a phenol so that the pheromone is identified as methyl $p$-hydroxybenzoate.

HO—⟨benzene ring⟩—CO$_2$CH$_3$

# 18 FREE RADICALS

18-1   Hexaphenylethane would be expected to show an approximate singlet in the aromatic region (six equivalent phenyl groups) and a UV spectrum characteristic of benzene ($\lambda_{max}$ 254 nm).

The actual "Gomberg dimer" shows only protons for five aromatic rings in the nmr spectrum and a UV absorption typical of a conjugated alkene. The nmr spectrum also shows 4 alkene protons. The dimer is now known to be a *para*-disubstituted benzene with the structure indicated below. Steric hindrance apparently inhibits dimerization at two benzylic carbon atoms.

18-2   Addition of X· involves formation of a C—X bond and conversion of a C=C bond to a C—C·. The energy for conversion of a double to a single bond is the same in all three cases.

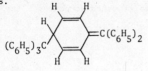      $\Delta H° = 146-83 = 63$ kcal/mol
            $(610-347 = 263$ kJ/mol)

∴   Cl· + >C=C< ⟶ Cl—C—C·      $\Delta H° = 63-81 = -18$ kcal/mol
                               $(263-339 = -76$ kJ/mol)

    Br· + >C=C< ⟶ Br—C—C·      $\Delta H° = 63-68 = -5$ kcal/mol
                               $(263-284 = -21$ kJ/mol)

    I· + >C=C< ⟶ I—C—C·        $\Delta H° = 63-51 = 12$ kcal/mol
                               $(263-213 = 50$ kJ/mol)

Abstraction of H· involves breaking an H—X bond and making a C—H bond. The energy of formation of the C—H bond is the same in all three cases.

C—C· + H· ⟶ C—C—H      $\Delta H° = -99$ kcal/mol
                       $(-414$ kJ/mol)

∴   Cl—C—C· + H—Cl ⟶ Cl—C—C—H + Cl·      $\Delta H° = 103-99 = 4$ kcal/mol
                                          $(431-414 = 17$ kJ/mol)

    Br—C—C· + H—Br ⟶ Br—C—C—H + Br·      $\Delta H° = 87-99 = -12$ kcal/mol
                                          $(365-414 = -49$ kJ/mol)

    I—C—C· + H—I ⟶ I—C—C—H + I·          $\Delta H° = 71-99 = -28$ kcal/mol
                                          $(299-414 = -115$ kJ/mol)

18-3    Only a low concentration of free radicals is required to keep the chain reaction going. There is a higher probability that a free radical species will react with the high concentration of nonradical reactants to propagate the chain rather than with another radical in a termination step.

18-4    The H—F bond energy is 136 kcal/mol (568 kJ/mol).  The bond is stronger than those of HCl and HBr.  A fluorine atom actually abstracts hydrogen atoms more rapidly than Cl· or Br·.

18-5

$$(CH_3)_2CHCH(CH_3)_2 \ + \ Cl_2 \ \xrightarrow[CCl_4]{h\nu} \ ClCH_2\overset{\overset{\displaystyle CH_3}{|}}{C}HCH(CH_3)_2 \ + \ (CH_3)_2\overset{\overset{\displaystyle Cl}{|}}{C}C(CH_3)_2$$

There are 12 primary hydrogen atoms and 2 tertiary hydrogen atoms to account for the reactivity at each position:

$$\frac{0.60}{12} = 0.05 \qquad\qquad \frac{0.40}{2} = 0.20$$

∴ *prim* : *tert* reactivity = 0.05 : 0.20 = 1 : 4.

18-6

a)

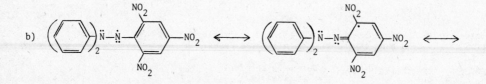

b)

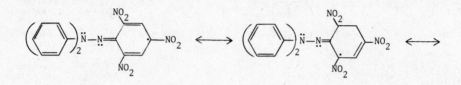

18-6 Contd....

b) Contd.....

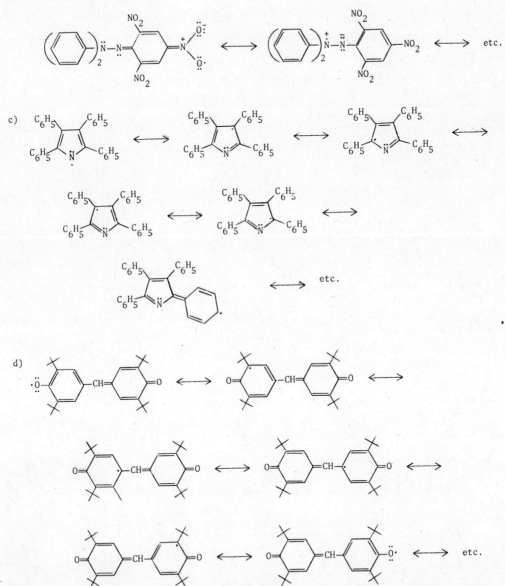

18-7

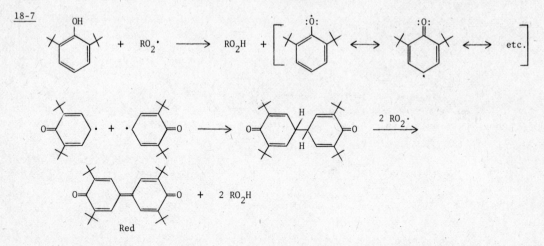

Red

Dimerization takes place at the unhindered para position to give a highly conjugated product.

18-8

a) The isotope effect for various free radicals should be approximately the same for transition state A since cleavage of the C—H (or C—D) bond is relatively independent of Z.

b) The less reactive - more selective bromine atom is expected and found to have a larger kinetic isotope effect

18-9

a) A doublet. The H nucleus splits the electron signal.

b) A singlet since no adjacent magnetic nuclei are encountered, even in the important resonance-delocalized structures.

c) Because the single electron is delocalized over six carbon atoms, only one-sixth of an electron (on the average) actually experiences splitting by a hydrogen atom.

d) The electron is actually on the atom which accounts for the splitting in the hydrogen atom. The magnitude of the coupling constant is therefore quite large.

18-10 These reagents are found to be very similar to NBS since they all can provide a low concentration of $Br_2$.

18-11  
| Bonds broken | kcal/mol | kJ/mol |
|---|---|---|
| Sn—H | 80 | 334 |
| C—Cl | $\underline{81}$ | $\underline{339}$ |
| | 161 kcal/mol | 673 kJ/mol |

| Bonds formed | | |
|---|---|---|
| Sn—Cl | 120 | 502 |
| C—H | $\underline{99}$ | $\underline{414}$ |
| | 219 kcal/mol | 916 kJ/mol |

$\therefore \Delta H° = 161-219 = -58$ kcal/mol  
$(673-916 = -243$ kJ/mol)

$\therefore$ Reaction is exothermic

18-12  The absence of a hydrogen-deuterium kinetic isotope effect indicates that hydrogen abstraction is not the rate controlling step. The addition step in the mechanism proposed is believed to be rate controlling.

18-13  Copper acts as the electron transfer agent. In the first step Cu(I) gives up an electron to the aromatic ring to form the phenyl radical and Cu(II). Abstraction of a bromine atom from $CuBr_2$ reduces the copper back to Cu(I) and the sequence repeats.

18-14  Both reactions proceed with complete loss of optical activity as is typical of most radical reactions. The deuterated tin hydride produces deuterated product as is consistent with the chain mechanism.

18-15

a)  $CH_3\overset{O}{\overset{\|}{C}}-O-O-\overset{O}{\overset{\|}{C}}CH_3 \xrightarrow{\Delta} CH_3CH_3 + CH_3CO_2CH_3 + CO_2$

b)  $C_6H_5\overset{O}{\overset{\|}{C}}-O-O-\overset{O}{\overset{\|}{C}}CH_2CH_3 \xrightarrow{\Delta} C_6H_5CH_2CH_3 + C_6H_5CO_2CH_2CH_3 + CH_3CH_2CO_2C_6H_5 +$

$C_6H_5-C_6H_5 + CH_3CH_2CH_2CH_3 + CO_2$

18-16  The more viscous the medium, the lower the tendency for components of the radical pair to diffuse out of the cage.

18-17  The results show that, in isooctane, each molecule decomposes within a solvent cage. Methyl radicals do not escape from the cage in which they form nor do trideuteriomethyl radicals escape and dimerize since this would lead to some 1,1,1-trideuterioethane. In

18-17 Contd...

the gas phase the methyl and trideuteriomethyl scramble and dimerize since no solvent cage exists.

18-18   Addition proceeds to form the more stable benzylic free radical.

18-19   At low HBr concentration, hydrogen atom abstraction is slow.  The bridged bromine intermediate has a sufficient lifetime to equilibrate between stereoisomers.

18-20   The bromine atom of the reactant acts as a neighboring group to aide hydrogen abstraction and protect the back side of the chiral carbon atom at which reaction occurs. The new Br substitutes regiospecifically at the carbon atom expected to form the more stable radical.

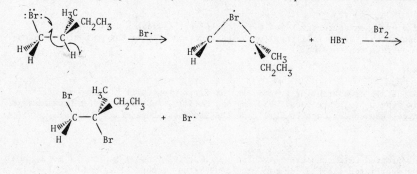

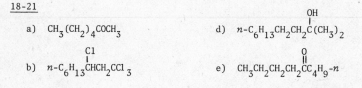

18-21

a)   $CH_3(CH_2)_4COCH_3$

b)   $n\text{-}C_6H_{13}\overset{\underset{\textstyle |}{Cl}}{C}HCH_2CCl_3$

d)   $n\text{-}C_6H_{13}CH_2CH_2\overset{\underset{\textstyle |}{OH}}{C}(CH_3)_2$

e)   $CH_3CH_2CH_2CH_2\overset{\underset{\textstyle \|}{O}}{C}C_4H_9\text{-}n$

c)   $ICH_2CH_2CF_3$

18-22   An initial free radical and subsequent hydroperoxide can form at the number 1,2,or 3 carbon atom.  Carbon-carbon bond cleavage then leads to formic, acetic, or propionic acids respectively.  (Interestingly, butyric acid is not an important product from this process.)

18-23

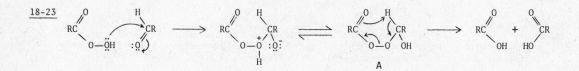

18-24  The three double bonds of tung oil are conjugated, thus more readily lead to the stabilized radical intermediates which form dimers and polymers.

$$CH_3(CH_2)_3CH=CHCH=CHCH=CH(CH_2)_7CO_2H$$

9,11,13-Octadecatrienoic acid

18-25

$$CH_3CH_2CH=CHCH_2CH=CHCH_2CH=CH(CH_2)_7CO_2-R \xrightarrow{\text{Initiator}}$$

Linolenic acid

$$\left[\begin{array}{l} CH_3CH_2CH=CHCH_2CH=CH\overset{\cdot}{C}HCH=CH(CH_2)_7CO_2-R \\[2mm] \updownarrow \\[2mm] CH_3CH_2CH=CHCH_2\overset{\cdot}{C}H-CH=CHCH=CH(CH_2)_7CO_2-R \\[2mm] \updownarrow \\[2mm] \text{etc.} \end{array}\right] \xrightarrow{O_2}$$

$$\overset{\displaystyle O-O\cdot}{\underset{\displaystyle |}{CH_3CH_2CH=CHCH_2CHCH=CHCH=CH(CH_2)_7CO_2-R}} \xrightarrow{R'H}$$

$$\overset{\displaystyle O-OH}{\underset{\displaystyle |}{CH_3\overset{\cdot}{C}H_2CH=CHCH_2CHCH=CHCH=CH(CH_2)_7CO_2-R}} + R'\cdot \longrightarrow$$

$$\overset{\displaystyle O\cdot}{\underset{\displaystyle |}{CH_3CH_2CH=CHCH_2CH-CH=CHCH=CH(CH_2)_7CO_2-R}} + HO\cdot \longrightarrow$$

$$CH_3CH_2CH=CHCH_2\overset{O}{\underset{H}{C}} + \cdot CH=CHCH=CH(CH_2)_7CO_2-R$$

$$CH_3CH_2CH=CHCH_2\overset{O}{\underset{H}{C}} \xrightarrow{\text{Further oxidation}} CH_3CH_2CH=CHCH_2CO_2H$$

18-26

a)  $R \equiv CH_3(CH_2)_7CH=CH(CH_2)_7$

$$R-\overset{:\overset{..}{O}:}{\underset{\underset{\cdot Na}{|}}{C}}OEt \longrightarrow R-\overset{:\overset{..}{O}:^- Na^+}{\underset{\cdot}{C}}-OEt \xrightarrow{EtOH} R-\overset{OH}{\underset{\cdot}{C}}-OEt$$

18-26 Contd...

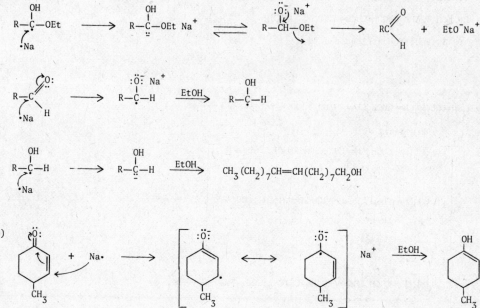

b)

c)

A magnesium ketyl

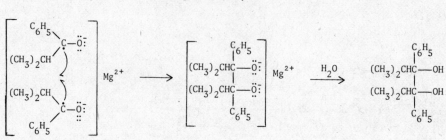

18-27

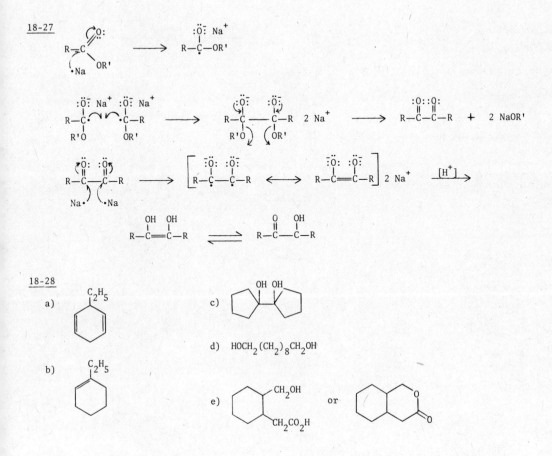

18-28

a)

c)

d)    $HOCH_2(CH_2)_8CH_2OH$

b)

e)

or

18-29  The order of reactivity reflects the relative stabilities of the intermediate free radicals formed on initial addition of a bromine atom. The tertiary free radical formed from 2-methylpropene is expected to be considerably more stable than the primary free radical formed from ethylene. The kinetic data indicate that transition state stabilities are in the same order as stabilities of the intermediates.

18-30

a)  The benzoyloxy radical pair could recombine without change (a), recombine at the opposite oxygen atoms from which cleavage occurred (b), or rotate relative to each other, then combine (c).

18-30 Contd...

a) Contd....

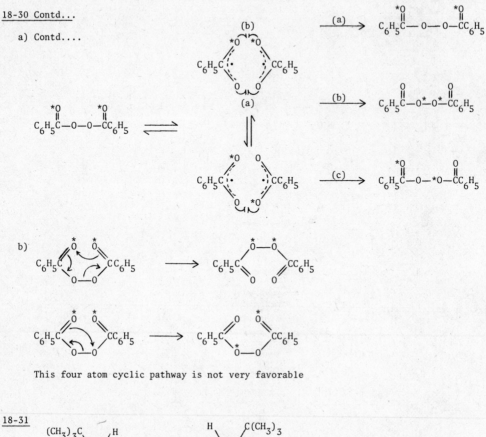

b)

This four atom cyclic pathway is not very favorable

18-31

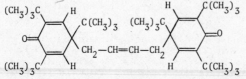

Dimerization of the phenoxyl radical is sterically inhibited, but 1,4-addition to butadiene can take place through the electron-delocalized intermediate. If addition had occurred at either ortho position of the aromatic rings more than two *tert*-butyl peaks would have shown in the nmr spectrum.

18-32

a) $R-N=N-R \longrightarrow 2 R\cdot + N_2$

18-32 Contd....

a) Contd...

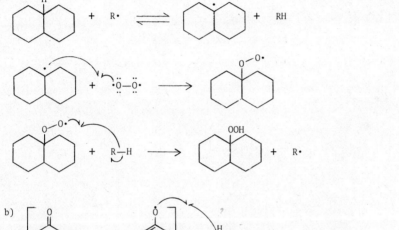

b)

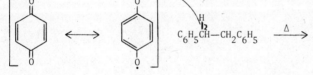

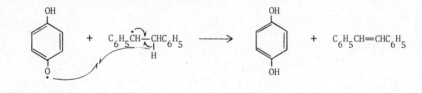

c)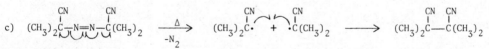

d) HBr $\xrightarrow{\text{Peroxide}}$ •Br

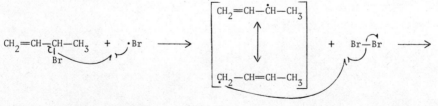

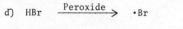

BrCH$_2$—CH=CH—CH$_3$

18-32 Contd...

e)  (Only bridgehead position shown.)

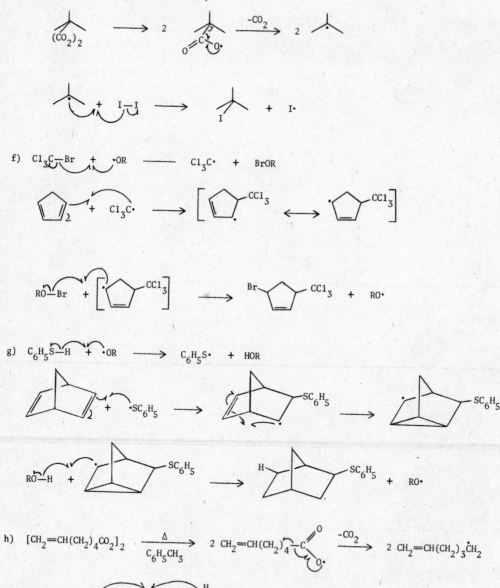

f)  $Cl_3C-Br$  +  $\cdot OR$  ———  $Cl_3C\cdot$  +  BrOR

g)  $C_6H_5S-H$  +  $\cdot OR$  ⟶  $C_6H_5S\cdot$  +  HOR

h)  $[CH_2=CH(CH_2)_4CO_2]_2$  $\xrightarrow[C_6H_5CH_3]{\Delta}$  2 $CH_2=CH(CH_2)_4-C\overset{O}{\underset{O\cdot}{}}$  $\xrightarrow{-CO_2}$  2 $CH_2=CH(CH_2)_3\dot{C}H_2$

$CH_2=CH(CH_2)_3\dot{C}H_2$  +  $CH_2=CH(CH_2)_2\overset{H}{\underset{}{C}H-\dot{C}H_2}$  ⟶  $\underline{CH_2=CH(CH_2)_3CH_3}$  +  $\underline{CH_2=CHCH_2CH_2CH=CH_2}$

18-32 Contd...

h) Contd...

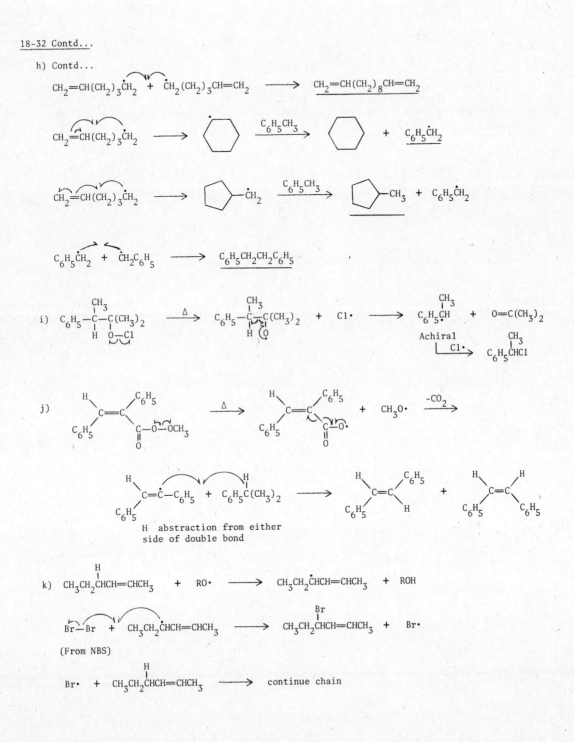

H  abstraction from either
side of double bond

(From NBS)

continue chain

18-32 Contd...

1)

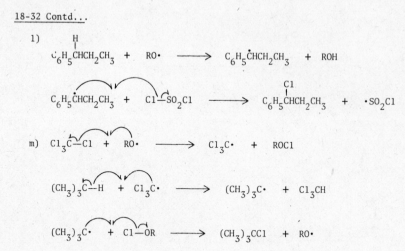

m)  $Cl_3C-Cl$  +  RO·  $\longrightarrow$  $Cl_3C·$  +  ROCl

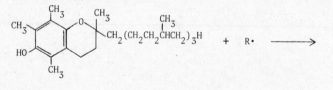

$(CH_3)_3C-H$  +  $Cl_3C·$  $\longrightarrow$  $(CH_3)_3C·$  +  $Cl_3CH$

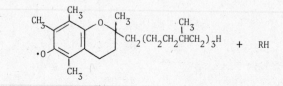

$(CH_3)_3C·$  +  $Cl-OR$  $\longrightarrow$  $(CH_3)_3CCl$  +  RO·

18-33  Reaction of a free radical (R·) with vitamin E can form a persistent phenoxyl radical similar to those of synthetic antioxidants.  A radical chain is terminated.

b)  Reduction of coenzyme Q, presumably by NADH, produces a phenol which can function as an antioxidant as does vitamin E.

18-34

a)   $CH_3COCH_2CH_2CH_2O_2CCH_3$

b)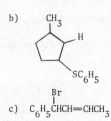

Br
|
c)   $C_6H_5CHCH=CHCH_3$

d)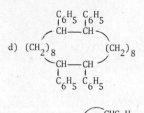

or   2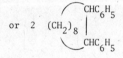

e)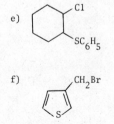

f)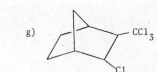

g)

# 19 MOLECULAR REARRANGEMENTS

19-1 In each case the same carbocation is formed which then reacts with water to form pinacol or rearranges to pinacolone.

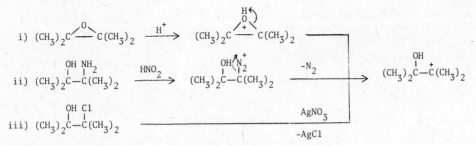

19-2

a) $C_6H_5CH_2CHO$

The phenyl group stabilizes the intermediate cation and $H^-$ migrates.

b) $(C_6H_5)_3\overset{O}{\overset{\|}{C}}CCH_3$

Two phenyl groups stabilize the intermediate cation, then phenyl migrates better than methyl.

c) $CH_3CH_2CHO$

Methyl stabilizes the cation and $H^-$ migrates.

d) $p\text{-}NO_2C_6H_4\overset{O}{\overset{\|}{C}}\underset{\underset{C_6H_5}{|}}{C}(C_6H_4OCH_3\text{-}p)_2$

$p$-Anisyl stabilizes the cation; phenyl migrates better than $p\text{-}NO_2C_6H_4\text{-}$.

e)

Migration of a ring methylene (an alkyl group) leads to ring expansion.

<u>19-3</u> The suggestion is based on the assumption that a concerted process would lead to 100%
inversion as only the labeled phenyl group migrates.  A front-sided concerted rearrangement
is not normally considered to be a reasonable pathway for a nucleophilic displacement.  Thus
the resutlts are

<u>19-4</u> In each case the most stable rotamers (the rotamers in which H is between the two aromatic
groups) account for back sided migration.  Migratory aptitudes have little effect on which
group migrates in these deaminative-rearrangement sequences.

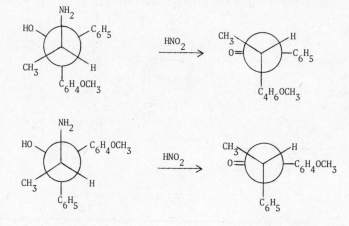

<u>19-5</u> In this example deamination produces a phenyl stabilized carbocation which is sufficiently
long-lived to rotate partially before migration takes place.  The transition state leading
to retention is less crowded than that leading to inverted product and therefore accounts
for the predominent reaction pathway.

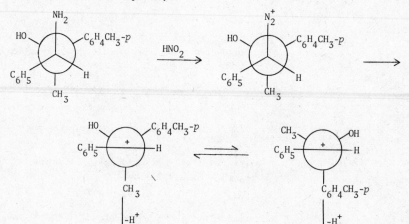

19-5 Contd...

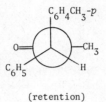 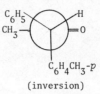

          (retention)                    (inversion)

19-6   The electron donating *p*-methoxy group enhances formation of and stabilizes the intermediate phenonium ion.

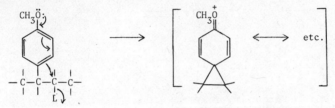

19-7   The intermediate phenonium ion forms by a stereospecific back sided displacement of tosylate then reverts to starting material.  Since formation of the ion is stereospecific, the intermediate from *erythro* reactant retains chirality and returns to optically active starting material.  In the case of *threo*, the phenonium ion is symmetrical and leads back to racemic starting material.

*threo*-3-Phenyl-2-butyl tosylate   ⟶

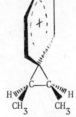

Symmetrical

*erythro*-3-Phenyl-2-butyl tosylate   ⟶

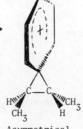

Asymmetrical

19-8

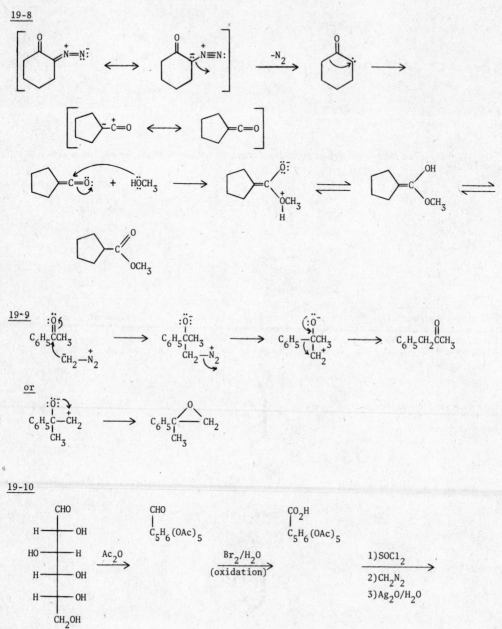

19-9

or

19-10

19-10 Contd...

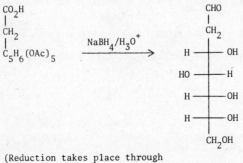

(Reduction takes place through
the cyclic lactone sec. 15-2.)

19-11

$$n\text{-}C_3H_7CONH_2 \xrightarrow{NaOBr} \longrightarrow n\text{-}C_3H_7\text{---}N{=}C{=}0$$

$$n\text{-}C_3H_7\text{---}N{=}C{=}0 \xrightarrow{H_2O} n\text{-}C_3H_7NH_2$$

$$n\text{-}C_3H_7N{=}C{=}0 \ + \ n\text{-}C_3H_7NH_2 \longrightarrow n\text{-}C_3H_7NH\overset{\overset{\text{O}}{\|}}{C}NHC_3H_7\text{-}n$$

19-12   The $N$-haloamide which is formed from an $N$-substituted amide has no hydrogen atom on
nitrogen.  The anion required for rearrangement cannot form.

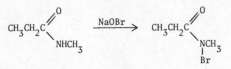

19-13   Migration is enhanced by increasing electron density at the migrating group as is expected
if reaction is a nucleophilic substitution on the nitrogen atom.  A phenonium ion-like
intermediate has also been proposed for the aryl migration.

19-14  Neopentyl cation readily undergoes Wagner-Meerwein rearrangement to the 2-methylbutyl
       cation.  The predominent pathway would therefore be expected to be:

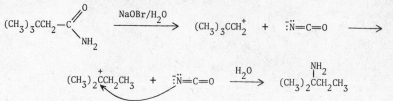

19-15

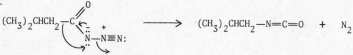

(The potential nitrene intermediate which would be formed if $N_2$ departed before rearrangement
has never been detected.)

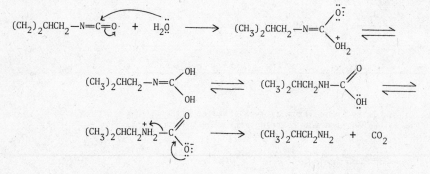

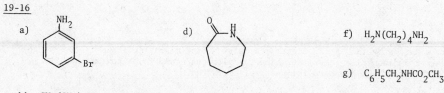

19-16

a)

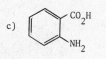

b)  $CH_3(CH_2)_4NH_2$

c)

d)

e)

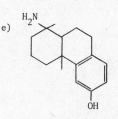

f)  $H_2N(CH_2)_4NH_2$

g)  $C_6H_5CH_2NHCO_2CH_3$

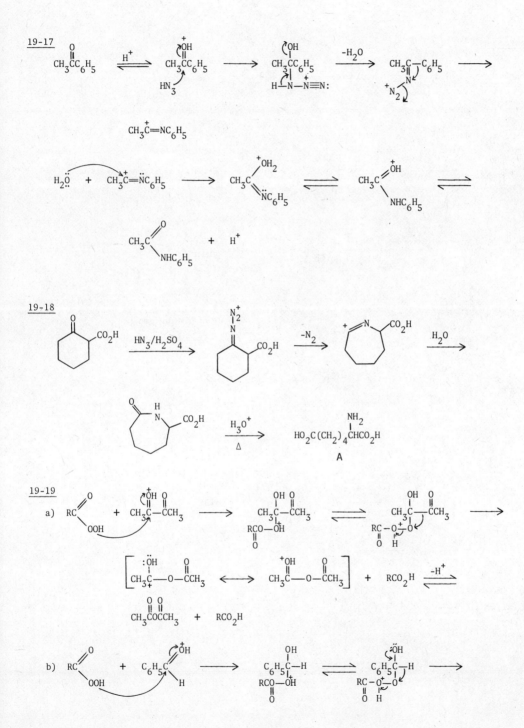

19-17

19-18

19-19

a)

b)

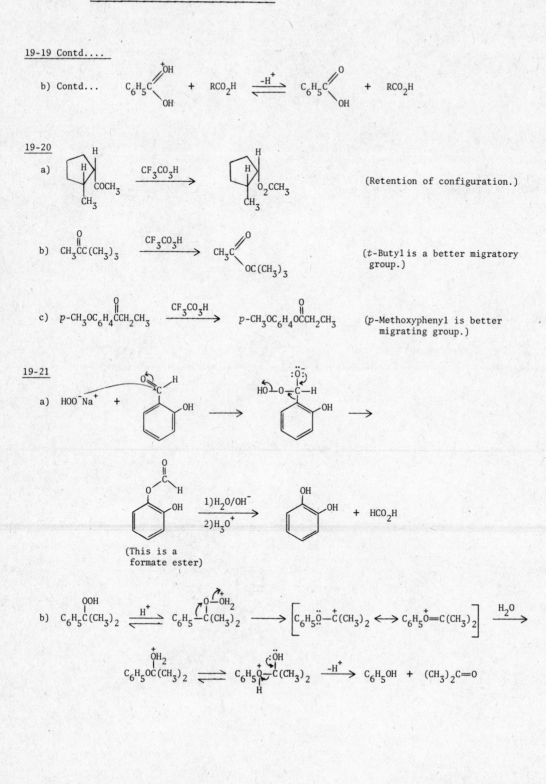

19-19 Contd....

b) Contd...     $C_6H_5C\overset{+OH}{\underset{OH}{}}$  +  $RCO_2H$   $\underset{}{\overset{-H^+}{\rightleftharpoons}}$   $C_6H_5C\overset{O}{\underset{OH}{}}$  +  $RCO_2H$

19-20

a)   [cyclopentane structure with H, COCH₃, CH₃]   $\xrightarrow{CF_3CO_3H}$   [cyclopentane structure with H, O₂CCH₃, CH₃]     (Retention of configuration.)

b)   $CH_3\overset{O}{\overset{\|}{C}}C(CH_3)_3$   $\xrightarrow{CF_3CO_3H}$   $CH_3C\overset{O}{\underset{OC(CH_3)_3}{}}$     ($t$-Butyl is a better migratory group.)

c)   $p\text{-}CH_3OC_6H_4\overset{O}{\overset{\|}{C}}CH_2CH_3$   $\xrightarrow{CF_3CO_3H}$   $p\text{-}CH_3OC_6H_4\overset{O}{\underset{}{O}}CCH_2CH_3$     ($p$-Methoxyphenyl is better migrating group.)

19-21

a)   $HOO^-Na^+$  +  [benzaldehyde with ortho OH structure]   $\rightarrow$   [$HO-O-C-H$ structure with OH]   $\rightarrow$

   [formate ester structure with OH]   $\xrightarrow[\text{2)}H_3O^+]{\text{1)}H_2O/OH^-}$   [catechol structure, OH, OH]  +  $HCO_2H$

   (This is a
   formate ester)

b)   $C_6H_5\overset{OOH}{\overset{|}{C}}(CH_3)_2$   $\underset{}{\overset{H^+}{\rightleftharpoons}}$   $C_6H_5-\overset{O-OH_2}{\overset{|}{C}}(CH_3)_2$   $\longrightarrow$   $\left[ C_6H_5\ddot{O}-\overset{+}{C}(CH_3)_2 \longleftrightarrow C_6H_5\overset{+}{O}=C(CH_3)_2 \right]$   $\xrightarrow{H_2O}$

   $C_6H_5O\overset{+OH_2}{\underset{}{C}}(CH_3)_2$   $\rightleftharpoons$   $C_6H_5\overset{+}{\underset{H}{O}}-\overset{\ddot{O}H}{\underset{}{C}}(CH_3)_2$   $\xrightarrow{-H^+}$   $C_6H_5OH$  +  $(CH_3)_2C{=}O$

19-21 Contd...

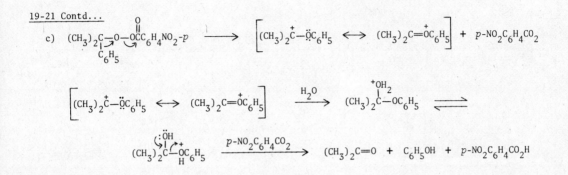

c) $(CH_3)_2C-O-OCC_6H_4NO_2-p \longrightarrow \left[ (CH_3)_2\overset{+}{C}-\overset{\cdot\cdot}{O}C_6H_5 \longleftrightarrow (CH_3)_2C=\overset{+}{O}C_6H_5 \right] + p\text{-}NO_2C_6H_4CO_2$

$\left[ (CH_3)_2\overset{+}{C}-\overset{\cdot\cdot}{O}C_6H_5 \longleftrightarrow (CH_3)_2C=\overset{+}{O}C_6H_5 \right] \xrightarrow{H_2O} (CH_3)_2\overset{\overset{+}{O}H_2}{\underset{}{C}}-OC_6H_5 \rightleftharpoons$

$(CH_3)_2\overset{\overset{\cdot\cdot}{O}H}{\underset{H}{C}}-\overset{+}{O}C_6H_5 \xrightarrow{p\text{-}NO_2C_6H_4CO_2} (CH_3)_2C=O + C_6H_5OH + p\text{-}NO_2C_6H_4CO_2H$

19-22   The observation that there is no scrambling of ethyl and butyl groups supports the proposed intramolecular nature of the rearrangement.

19-23

$RB\underset{O}{-}CR_2 \xrightarrow{H_2O} RB\underset{OH}{-}\underset{OH}{CR_2}$

A 1,2-diol is presumed to be formed. That diol, by analogy with carbon analogs, would only be expected to rearrange under strongly acidic conditions.  By contrast epoxides readily open to provide a driving force for the third rearrangement that occurs under anhydrous conditions.

19-24

a)  3 $CH_3CH=CHCH_3$   $\xrightarrow[\substack{2)CO/H_2O \\ 3)NaOH/H_2O_2}]{1)(BH_3)_2/Diglyme}$   $[CH_3CH_2CH(CH_3)]_2C=O$

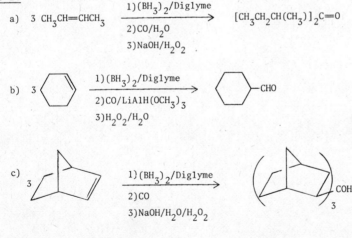

b)  3 [cyclohexene]   $\xrightarrow[\substack{2)CO/LiAlH(OCH_3)_3 \\ 3)H_2O_2/H_2O}]{1)(BH_3)_2/Diglyme}$   [cyclohexyl]—CHO

c)  3 [norbornene]   $\xrightarrow[\substack{2)CO \\ 3)NaOH/H_2O/H_2O_2}]{1)(BH_3)_2/Diglyme}$   ([norbornyl])$_3$COH

19-25

a) The result supports formation of the symmetrical nonclassical norbornyl cation intermediate. When departing brosylate adds back to the intermediate, chemically unchanged, but racemic, starting material is formed.

b)

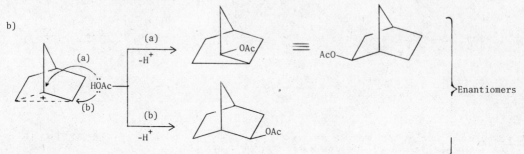

19-26 Thiols (mercaptans) are excellent hydrogen atom donors. The initially formed radical abstracts H· from the thiol more rapidly than rearrangement takes place.

19-27

a) $Br· + CH_2=CHCCl_3 \longrightarrow BrCH_2\overset{\cdot}{CH}-CCl_2 \longrightarrow BrCH_2\overset{Cl}{\underset{|}{CH}}\overset{\cdot}{C}Cl_2 \xrightarrow{HBr}$

$\qquad\qquad BrCH_2\overset{Cl}{\underset{|}{CH}}CHCl_2 + Br·$

b) $CH_3\overset{Br}{\underset{|}{CH}}CH_2-H + Cl· \longrightarrow CH_3\overset{Br}{\underset{|}{CH}}\overset{\cdot}{C}H_2 + HCl$

$CH_3\overset{Br}{\underset{|}{CH}}-\overset{\cdot}{C}H_2 \longrightarrow CH_3\overset{\cdot}{C}HCH_2Br \xrightarrow{t\text{-BuOCl}} CH_3\overset{Cl}{\underset{|}{CH}}CH_2Br + t\text{-BuO·}$

c)

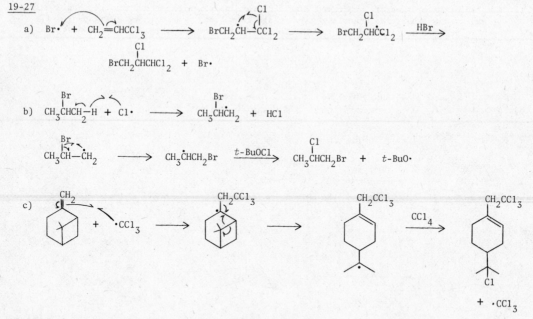

19-28 Both reactants form the same intermediate cyclopropanone.

19-28 Contd....

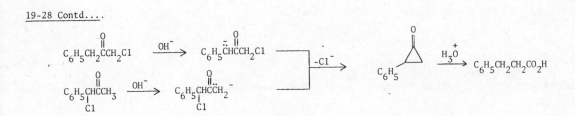

19-29  Back sided attack by the α-carbanion inverts configuration at the cyclohexane number one
carbon atom as Cl⁻ is displaced.

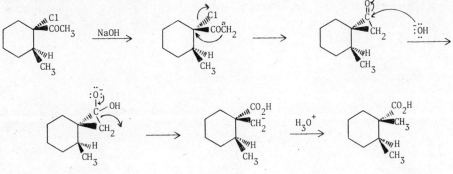

19-30

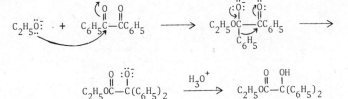

19-31

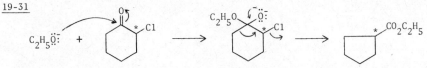

All labeled carbon would be at the C—1 position of the cyclopentane ring if this mechanism
were operating.

19-32  No atoms change positions; only an electron moves.

19-33

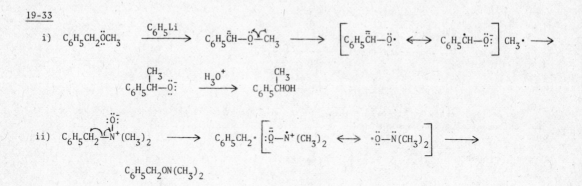

i) $C_6H_5CH_2\ddot{O}CH_3 \xrightarrow{C_6H_5Li} C_6H_5\bar{C}H-\ddot{O}\overset{\curvearrowright}{} CH_3 \longrightarrow \left[ C_6H_5\bar{C}H-\ddot{O}\cdot \longleftrightarrow C_6H_5\overset{\cdot}{C}H-\ddot{O}\ddot{:} \right] CH_3\cdot \longrightarrow$

$\underset{C_6H_5CH-\ddot{O}\ddot{:}}{\overset{CH_3}{|}} \xrightarrow{H_3O^+} \underset{C_6H_5CHOH}{\overset{CH_3}{|}}$

ii)  $C_6H_5CH_2\overset{:\ddot{O}:}{\overset{|}{\overset{\curvearrowright}{N}}^+(CH_3)_2} \longrightarrow C_6H_5CH_2\cdot \left[ :\overset{..}{\ddot{O}}-\overset{\cdot}{N}^+(CH_3)_2 \longleftrightarrow \cdot\overset{..}{O}-\overset{..}{N}(CH_3)_2 \right] \longrightarrow$

$C_6H_5CH_2ON(CH_3)_2$

19-34

a) The rearrangement is a [1,5] hydrogen shift and is an allowed suprafacial process. Note that although the migrating hydrogen atom actually moves to an adjacent carbon atom, a formal [1,2] shift would not involve migration across an unsaturated system.

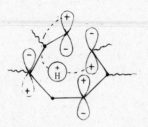

b) The rearrangement is a [1,7] hydrogen shift and is an allowed antarafacial process. A [1,7] antarafacial shift is geometrically possible in this open chain system. The signs for this $\psi_4$ orbital of a 7-atom system can be derived by continuing the alternation of orbital lobes observed in fig. 12-1.

c) Migration of either deuterium atom involves a suprafacial [1,5] shift. Continual [1,5] shifts give only the two labeled materials. The orbital picture is the same pentadienyl $\psi_3$ used in part (a).

19-35  The reaction is a stereospecific [1,5] suprafacial shift of hydrogen.  If we consider the
       *cis*-diene as rigid but the chiral atom freely rotating, then orbital symmetry analysis
       enables the hydrogen atom to move across the top or the bottom face of the pentadienyl
       system in an allowed suprafacial process.  (Note that we can treat the hydrogen atom as
       it were in a symmetrical 1*s* orbital of either + or - sign.)

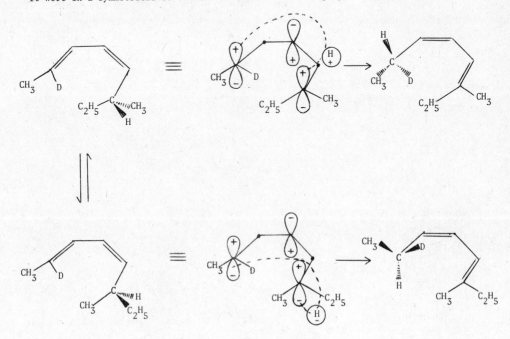

19-36  Each portion of the hexadiene system is considered as an allyl system with three electrons,
       two from the double bond and one from cleavage of the sigma bond.  The HOMO's are $\psi_2$ of the
       allyl system.

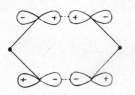

19-37  Two successive [3,3] shifts occur.  The first is an *ortho*-Claisen rearrangement and the
       second a Cope rearrangement.

19-37 Contd...

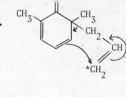 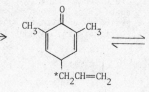

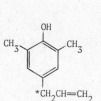

19-38

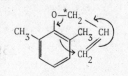

Meso

19-39 The initial rearrangement product is an enol.  Tautomerism produces the aldehyde which cannot undergo a reverse Cope rearrangement.

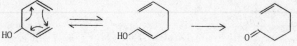

19-40

a)

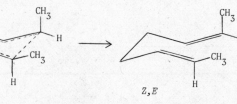

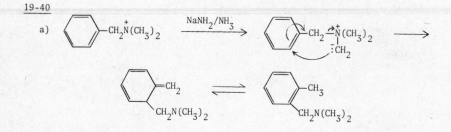

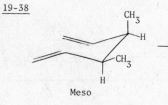

19-40 Contd....

b)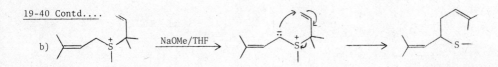

In each case formation of the ylid provides the precursor for an allowed, suprafacial [2,3] sigmatropic rearrangement. The HOMO of the $C_3$ fragment is $\psi_2$ and the LUMO for the $C_2$ fragment is $\psi_2'$.

(Use of the $C_3$ LUMO and $C_2$ HOMO gives identical results.)

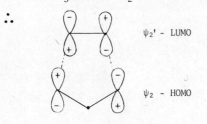

$\psi_2'$ - LUMO

$\psi_2$ - HOMO

19-41  Symmetry properties of 1,3-cyclohexadiene relative to a plane and an axis of symmetry are:

| Orbital | Representation | Symmetry element | |
|---------|----------------|-------|------|
| | | Plane | Axis |
| $\sigma^*$ | | A | A |
| $\pi_4^*$ | | A | S |
| $\pi_3^*$ | | S | A |
| $\pi_2$ | | A | S |

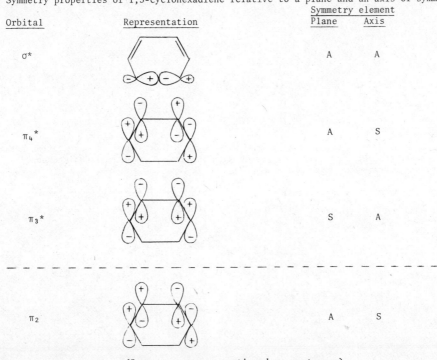

(Symmetry summary continued on next page)

19-41 Contd...

| Orbital | Representation | Symmetry element |  |
|---------|----------------|------------------|--|
|         |                | Plane | Axis |

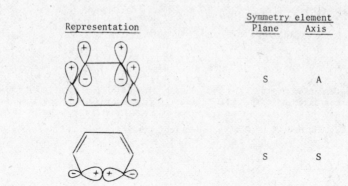

| | | Plane | Axis |
|--|--|--|--|
| $\pi_1$ | | S | A |
| $\sigma$ | | S | S |

Symmetry properties for 1,3,5-hexatriene can be obtained from figure 12-1.  The results are compiled below.

### 1,3,5-Hexadiene

| Orbital | Symmetry element |  |
|---------|-------|------|
|         | Plane | Axis |
| $\psi_6$ | A | S |
| $\psi_5$ | S | A |
| $\psi_4$ | A | S |
| $\psi_3$ | S | A |
| $\psi_2$ | A | S |
| $\psi_1$ | S | A |

Correlation diagrams are constructed from these data.  They show that correlation between ground state molecular orbitals is present when a plane of symmetry is maintained.  A disrotatory reaction is therefore allowed.

a) Plane of symmetry (disrotatory)

| (A) | $\psi_6$ | — | — | $\sigma^*$ | (A) |
| (S) | $\psi_5$ | — | — | $\pi_4^*$ | (A) |
| (A) | $\psi_4$ | — | — | $\pi_3^*$ | (S) |
| (S) | $\psi_3$ | ↑↓ | ↑↓ | $\pi_2$ | (A) |
| (A) | $\psi_2$ | ↑↓ | ↑↓ | $\pi_1$ | (S) |
| (S) | $\psi_1$ | ↑↓ ——— ↑↓ | | $\sigma$ | (S) |

b) Axis of symmetry (conrotatory)

| (S) | $\psi_6$ | — | — | $\sigma^*$ | (A) |
| (A) | $\psi_5$ | — | — | $\pi_4^*$ | (S) |
| (S) | $\psi_4$ | — | — | $\pi_3^*$ | (A) |
| (A) | $\psi_3$ | — | — | $\pi_2$ | (S) |
| (S) | $\psi_2$ | — | — | $\pi_1$ | (A) |
| (A) | $\psi_1$ | — | — | $\sigma$ | (S) |

19-42

a)

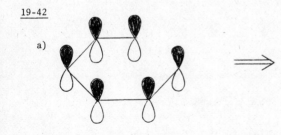
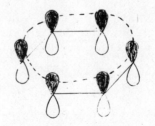

Zero phase changes; the pathway is Hückel.
Since there are $4n + 2 = 6$ electrons, it
is an allowed process.

b)

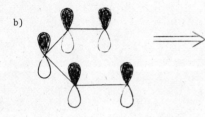
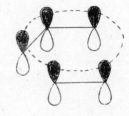

Zero phase changes; the pathway is
Hückel.  Since there are $4n + 2 = 6$
electrons (including the anion electron)
the reaction is allowed.

c)

One phase change; the pathway is
Möbius.  Since there are $4n$ electrons
(including the anion) the process is allowed.

d)

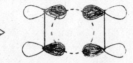

Zero phase change; the pathway is Hückel.
Since there are $4n = 4$ electrons, the
reaction is forbidden.

19-42 Contd...

e)

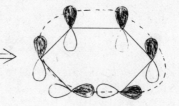

One phase change; the pathway is Möbius.
Since there are $4n + 2 = 6$ electrons
the process is forbidden.

19-43  Alkyl-oxygen cleavage would lead to the neopentyl carbocation.  That would surely lead to alcohol with a rearranged skeleton.

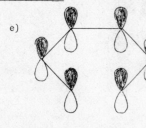

$(CH_3)_2\overset{\overset{OH}{|}}{C}CH_2CH_3$

19-44

a)  $C_6H_5CH_2CH_2CO_2H$

b)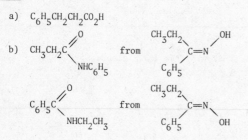

The first reaction which involves migration of phenyl is expected to be the faster of the two rearrangements.

e)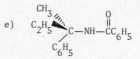

Optically active

f)

g)  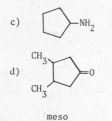 via a free radical mechanism and ring expansion

c)  —NH₂ cyclopentane with NH₂

d)  dimethyl cyclopentanone

meso

<u>19-45</u>

$CH_2=CH_2$ + $\cdot CD_3$ $\longrightarrow$ $CD_3CH_2CH_2\cdot$ $\xrightarrow{CH_2=CH_2}$ $CD_3CH_2CH_2CH_2CH_2\cdot$

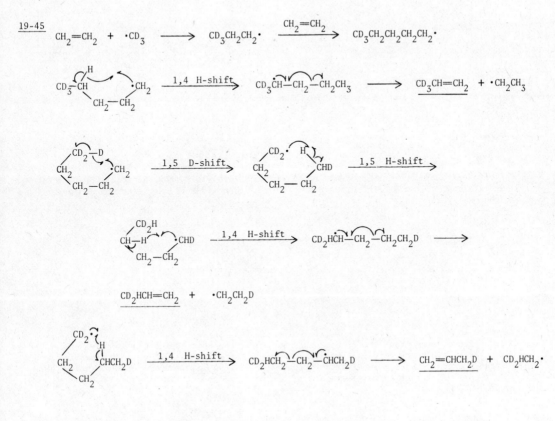

$CD_3\!-\!CH \qquad \cdot CH_2$  $\xrightarrow{\text{1,4 H-shift}}$  $CD_3\dot{C}H\!-\!CH_2\!-\!CH_2CH_3$ $\longrightarrow$ $\underline{CD_3CH=CH_2}$ + $\cdot CH_2CH_3$
$\quad\; CH_2\!-\!CH_2$

$\xrightarrow{\text{1,5 D-shift}}$         $\xrightarrow{\text{1,5 H-shift}}$

$\xrightarrow{\text{1,4 H-shift}}$  $CD_2H\dot{C}H\!-\!CH_2\!-\!CH_2CH_2D$ $\longrightarrow$

$\underline{CD_2HCH=CH_2}$ + $\cdot CH_2CH_2D$

$\xrightarrow{\text{1,4 H-shift}}$  $CD_2HCH_2\!-\!CH_2\!-\!CHCH_2D$ $\longrightarrow$ $\underline{CH_2=CHCH_2D}$ + $CD_2HCH_2\cdot$

<u>19-46</u>  The cis isomer has methyl anti to the adjacent hydroxy group and leads to pinacol rearrangement with methyl migration.

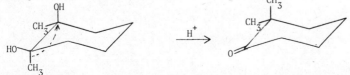

The more favorable conformation of the trans isomer has no easily accessible group for back-sided migration to a carbinol carbon atom.  Ring flip provides a conformation in which a ring carbon atom can migrate.

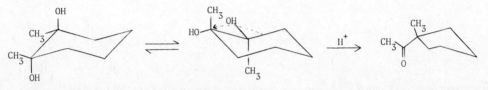

<u>19-47</u>

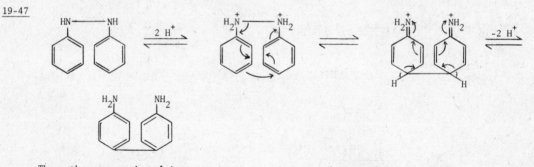

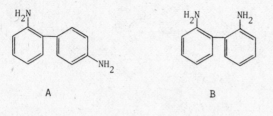

The ortho-para product A is commonly recovered in 20-30% yield from the reaction along with a small amount of the diortho product B . Both of these isomers can be accounted for by mechanisms similar to the above.

              A                                    B

<u>19-48</u>  Most of the endo reactant looses brosylate and forms the nonclassical 2-norbornyl cation which leads only to racemic exo product. However, there is no backside participation in loss of the brosylate. A small amount of the acetate can approach the initial carbocation from the exo direction before formation of the nonclassical ion and thus form inverted product.

<u>19-49</u>

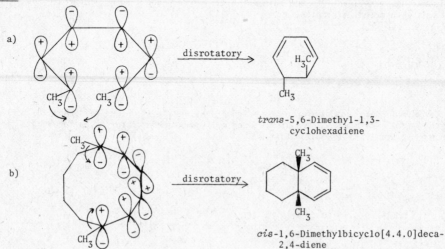

a)          $\xrightarrow{\text{disrotatory}}$

*trans*-5,6-Dimethyl-1,3-cyclohexadiene

b)          $\xrightarrow{\text{disrotatory}}$

*cis*-1,6-Dimethylbicyclo[4.4.0]deca-2,4-diene

19-49 Contd...

c)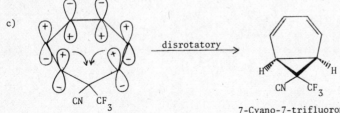

7-Cyano-7-trifluoromethylnorcaradiene

d)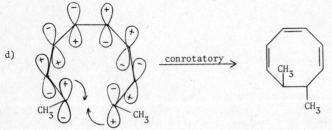

*trans*-7,8-Dimethyl-1,3,5-cyclooctatriene

19-50

a)  The dehalogenation is accompanied by rearrangement.

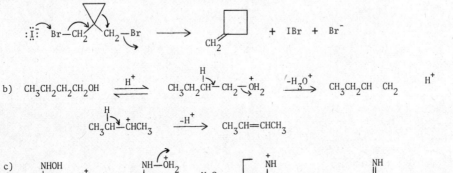

b)  $CH_3CH_2CH_2CH_2OH \rightleftharpoons \xrightarrow{H^+} CH_3CH_2\overset{H}{C}H - CH_2 - \overset{+}{O}H_2 \xrightarrow{-H_3O^+} CH_3CH_2CH\ CH_2 \quad H^+$

$CH_3\overset{H}{C}H - \overset{+}{C}HCH_3 \xrightarrow{-H^+} CH_3CH=CHCH_3$

c)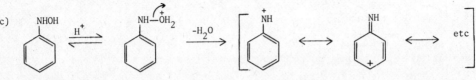

19-50 Contd...

c) Contd....

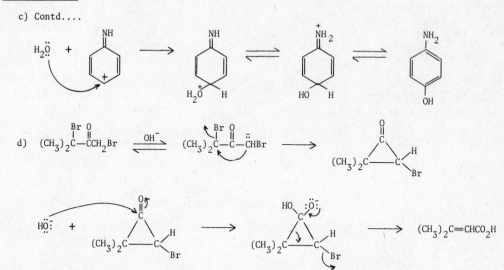

d)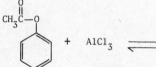

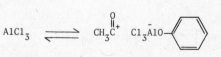

e) Acyl-oxygen cleavage of the two esters gives acyl and phenacyl fragments and the corresponding phenoxy anions.  Scrambling and recombination of all groups gives the product mixture.

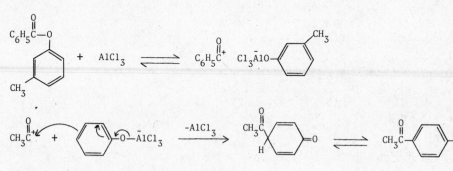

Same kind of sequences lead to the other products.

19-50 Contd...

f)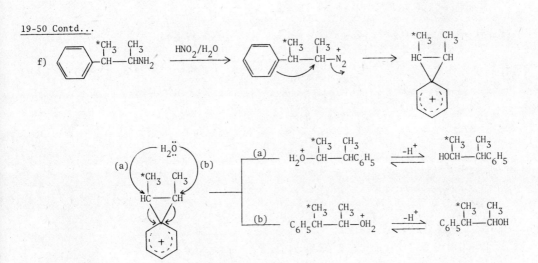

19-51 Orbital symmetry predicts inversion for such [1,2] sigmatropic processes which must, due to geometrical constraints proceed in a suprafacial manner. The orbital picture utilizes an ethylene orbital (the ylid bond) with three electrons thus the HOMO is $\psi_2$.

19-52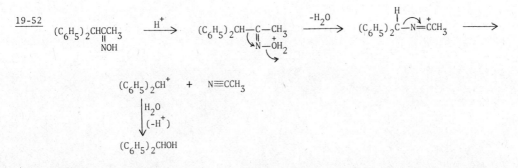

Fragmentation is favored when the migrating group can form a stabilized carbocation.

19-52 Contd....
 following rearrangement.  In either case fragmentation is favored when the migrating group can form a stabilized carbocation.

19-53

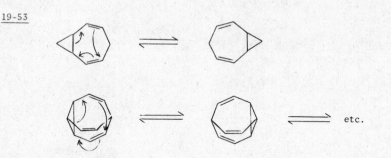

19-54

a)

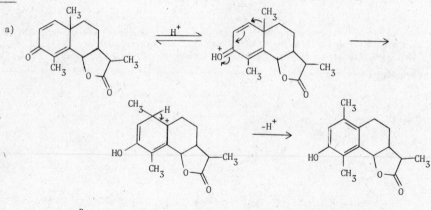

b)

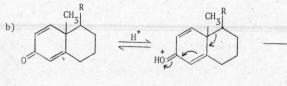

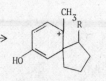

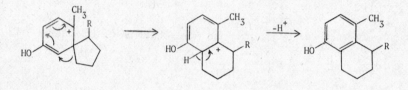

19-54 Contd....

b) Contd....

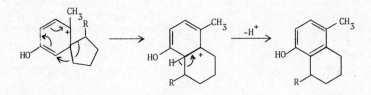

c)

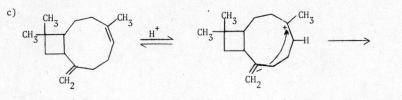

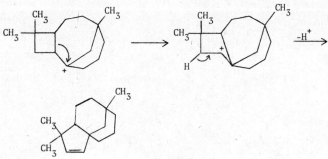

d)

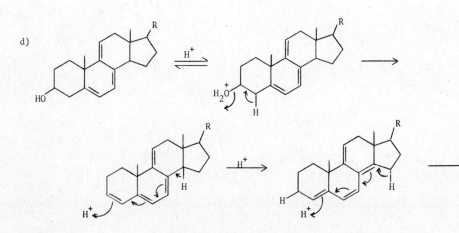

19-54 Contd...

d) Contd...

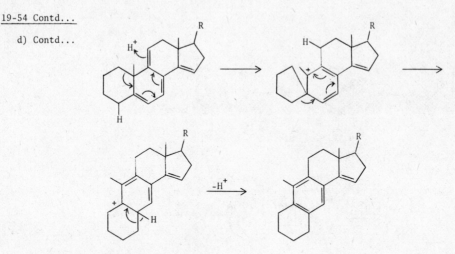

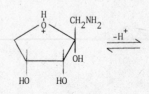

e)

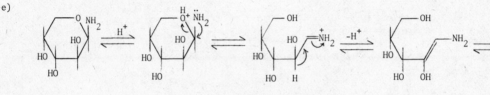

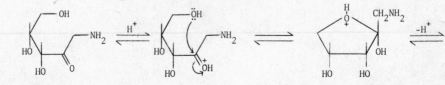

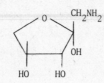

19-55

a)  $(C_6H_5)_2CO$  $\xrightarrow{NH_2OH}$  $C_6H_5-\overset{\overset{\displaystyle NOH}{\|}}{C}-C_6H_5$  $\xrightarrow[H_2O]{H_2SO_4}$  $C_6H_5CONHC_6H_5$

19-55 Contd...

b)

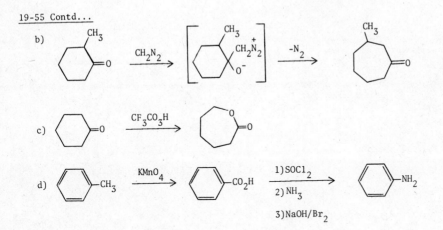

c)

d)

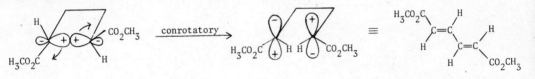

19-56

a)  The product butadiene HOMO($\psi_2$) has identical end lobe signs on the opposite sides of the
    molecular plane.  Conrotatory opening of the sigma bond is necessary to attain that
    configuration.

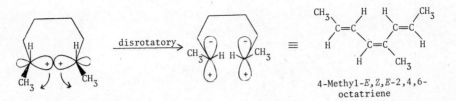

E,E-1,4-Dicarbomethoxybutadiene

b)  The hexatriene HOMO ($\psi_3$) has end orbital lobes of identical sign on the same side of the
    molecular plane; a disrotatory ring opening is required.

4-Methyl-E,Z,E-2,4,6-
octatriene

19-56 Contd...

c)  Same orbital analysis as in part (b).

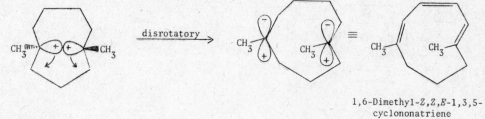

1,6-Dimethyl-Z,Z,E-1,3,5-
cyclononatriene

<u>19-57</u>  The product is formed by a Cope rearrangement followed by tautomerization to the aldehyde.

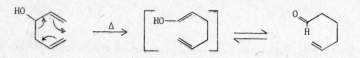

# 20 NATURAL AND SYNTHETIC POLYMERS

<u>20-1</u>

a) $\sim\!\!\lnot CH_2\!-\!O\!\lnot\! CH_2\!-\!O\!\lnot\! CH_2\!-\!O\!\lnot\! CH_2\!-\!O\!\lnot\!\sim$

Homopolymer; no cross links.

b) $\sim\!\!\lnot O\!-\!CH_2\!-\!CH_2\!-\!O\!\lnot\!\overset{\overset{O}{\parallel}}{C}\!-\!CH_2\!-\!CH_2\!-\!CH_2\!-\!CH_2\!-\!\overset{\overset{O}{\parallel}}{C}\!\lnot\! O\!-\!CH_2\!-\!CH_2\!-\!O\!\lnot\!\overset{\overset{O}{\parallel}}{C}\!-\!CH_2\!-\!CH_2\!-\!CH_2\!-\!CH_2\!-\!\overset{\overset{O}{\parallel}}{C}\!\lnot\!\sim$

Copolymer; no cross links.

c) $\sim\!\!\lnot\overset{\overset{Cl}{|}}{CH}\!-\!CH_2\!\lnot\!\overset{\overset{Cl}{|}}{CH}\!-\!CH_2\!\lnot\!\overset{\overset{Cl}{|}}{CH}\!-\!CH_2\!\lnot\!\sim$

Homopolymer; no cross links

d) $\sim\!\!\lnot CH_2\!-\!\overset{\overset{Cl}{|}}{C}\!=\!CH\!-\!CH_2\!\lnot\! CH_2\!-\!\overset{\overset{Cl}{|}}{C}\!=\!CH\!-\!CH_2\!\lnot\! CH_2\!-\!\overset{\overset{Cl}{|}}{C}\!=\!CH\!-\!CH_2\!\lnot\!\sim$

Homopolymer; no cross links.

e)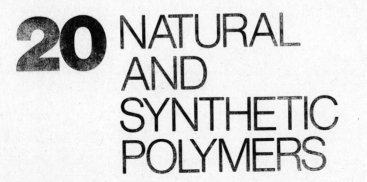

Copolymer (Cl—$\overset{\overset{O}{\parallel}}{C}$—Cl is one reactant)

f)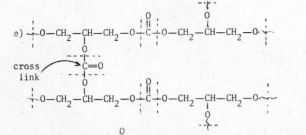

Copolymer; no cross links

20-2  Initiation probably involves abstraction of a hydrogen atom at the allylic carbon atoms of polyisoprene monomer units.

20-3

a) $\sim CH_2-CH=\overset{\overset{\displaystyle CH_3}{|}}{C}-CH_2-CH_2-CH=\overset{\overset{\displaystyle CH_3}{|}}{C}-CH_2\sim \xrightarrow[\text{Zn/HOAc/H}_2\text{O}_2]{\text{O}_3} O=\overset{\overset{\displaystyle CH_3}{|}}{C}-CH_2CH_2CO_2H$

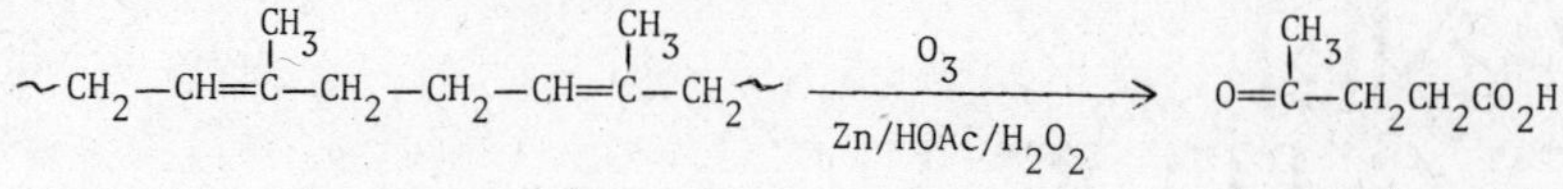

Levulinic acid

b)  If the polymer were head to head:

$\sim CH_2CH=\overset{\overset{\displaystyle CH_3}{|}}{C}-CH_2-CH_2-\overset{\overset{\displaystyle CH_3}{|}}{C}=CHCH_2 \xrightarrow[\text{Zn/HOAc/H}_2\text{O}]{\text{O}_3} O=\overset{\overset{\displaystyle CH_3}{|}}{C}-CH_2CH_2\overset{\overset{\displaystyle CH_3}{|}}{C}=O$

If it were tail to tail:

$\sim CH_2-\overset{\overset{\displaystyle CH_3}{|}}{C}=CH-CH_2-CH_2-CH=\overset{\overset{\displaystyle CH_3}{|}}{C}-CH_2 \xrightarrow[\text{Zn/HOAc/H}_2\text{O}]{\text{O}_3} HO_2CCH_2CH_2CO_2H$

20-4

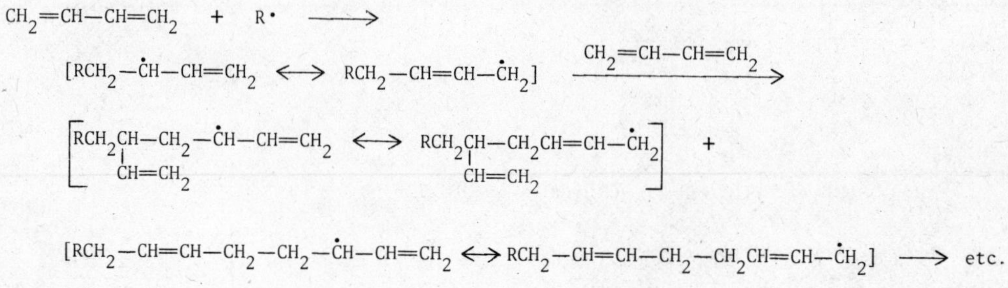

$CH_2=CH-CH=CH_2 \quad + \quad R\cdot \quad \longrightarrow$

$[RCH_2-\overset{\displaystyle\cdot}{C}H-CH=CH_2 \longleftrightarrow RCH_2-CH=CH-\overset{\displaystyle\cdot}{C}H_2] \xrightarrow{CH_2=CH-CH=CH_2}$

$\left[\begin{matrix} RCH_2CH-CH_2-\overset{\displaystyle\cdot}{C}H-CH=CH_2 \\ \quad | \\ \quad CH=CH_2 \end{matrix} \longleftrightarrow \begin{matrix} RCH_2CH-CH_2CH=CH-\overset{\displaystyle\cdot}{C}H_2 \\ \quad | \\ \quad CH=CH_2 \end{matrix}\right] \quad +$

$[RCH_2-CH=CH-CH_2-CH_2-\overset{\displaystyle\cdot}{C}H-CH=CH_2 \longleftrightarrow RCH_2-CH=CH-CH_2-CH_2CH=CH-\overset{\displaystyle\cdot}{C}H_2] \longrightarrow$ etc.

20-5

$(CH_3)_3C-\left[-CH_2\overset{\overset{\displaystyle CH_3}{|}}{\underset{\underset{\displaystyle CH_3}{|}}{C}}-\right]_{n-1} -CH_2\overset{\overset{\displaystyle CH}{|}}{\underset{\displaystyle +}{C}}-CH_2-H \quad \bar{B}F_3OH \longrightarrow$

$CH_2=C(CH_3)_2$

$(CH_3)_3C-\left[-CH_2\overset{\overset{\displaystyle CH_3}{|}}{\underset{\underset{\displaystyle CH_3}{|}}{C}}-\right]_{n-1} -CH_2\overset{\overset{\displaystyle CH_3}{|}}{C}=CH_2 \quad + \quad (CH_3)_3\overset{+}{C} \quad \bar{B}F_3OH$

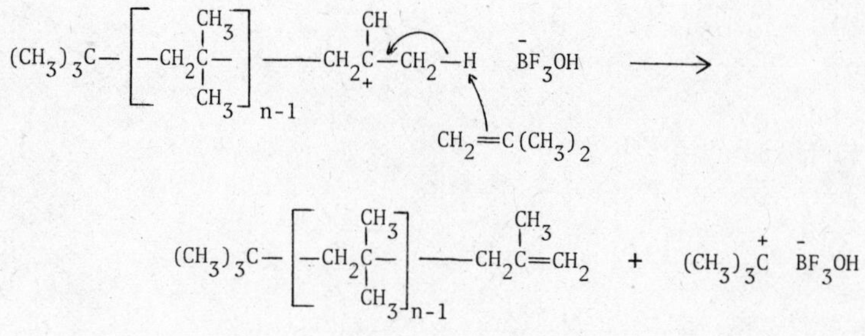

20-6

a)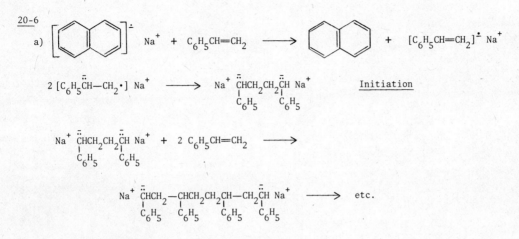

$$2 [C_6H_5\ddot{C}H{-}CH_2\cdot] \; Na^+ \longrightarrow Na^+ \; \ddot{C}HCH_2CH_2\ddot{C}H \; Na^+ \qquad \underline{Initiation}$$
$$\qquad\qquad\qquad\qquad\qquad\qquad\qquad\qquad C_6H_5 \qquad C_6H_5$$

$$Na^+ \; \ddot{C}HCH_2CH_2\ddot{C}H \; Na^+ \; + \; 2 \; C_6H_5CH{=}CH_2 \longrightarrow$$
$$\qquad C_6H_5 \qquad C_6H_5$$

$$Na^+ \; \ddot{C}HCH_2{-}CHCH_2CH_2CH{-}CH_2\ddot{C}H \; Na^+ \longrightarrow \quad etc.$$
$$\qquad\quad C_6H_5 \quad\;\; C_6H_5 \qquad\; C_6H_5 \quad\;\; C_6H_5$$

b) Anything that adds to an anion can be used to terminate the chain, i.e., $H^+$, $CO_2 + H^+$, etc.

20-7

a) $CH_2{=}CHCl + R\cdot \longrightarrow RCH_2{-}\dot{C}HCl$

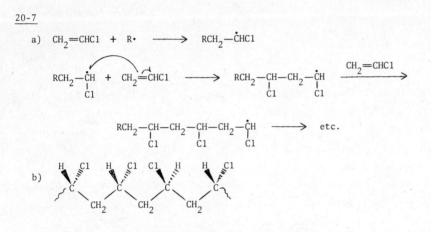

$$RCH_2{-}CH{-}CH_2{-}CH{-}CH_2{-}\dot{C}H \longrightarrow \quad etc.$$
$$\qquad\quad Cl \qquad\quad Cl \qquad\quad Cl$$

b)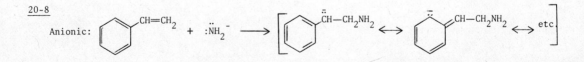

c) Elimination of HCl produces an alkene that can decompose further.

$$\overset{Cl\;\; H}{\underset{\sim CH{-}CH\sim}{|\quad\;|}} \xrightarrow{\; -HCl \;} \sim CH{=}CH\sim$$

20-8

Anionic:  $\displaystyle \bigcirc\!\!-CH{=}CH_2 \; + \; :\ddot{N}H_2^- \longrightarrow \Big[ \bigcirc\!\!-\ddot{C}H{-}CH_2NH_2 \longleftrightarrow \bigcirc\!\!-CH{-}CH_2NH_2 \longleftrightarrow etc. \Big]$

20-8 Contd...

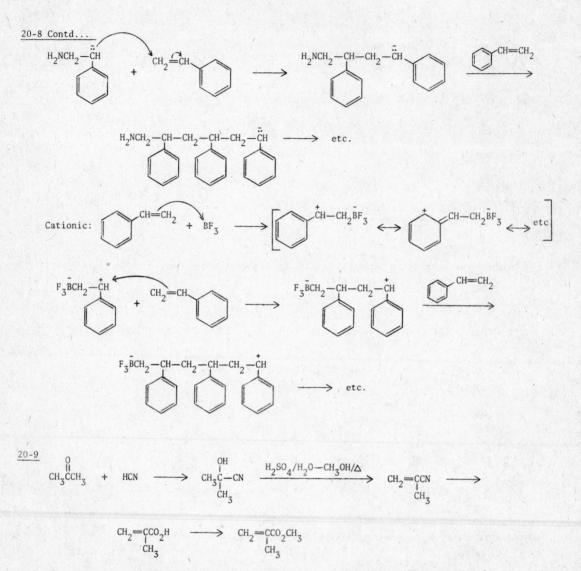

The raw materials are readily available.  Elimination, hydrolysis, and esterification all take place in one synthetic step.

<u>20-10</u>

a)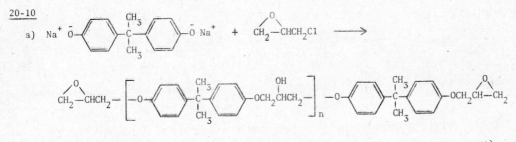

(The use of excess epichlorohydrin insures that terminal epoxide groups are present.)

b) Cross link with triamine B form at the terminal epoxide groups.

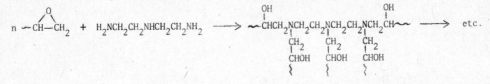

Cross link with maleic anhydride form at the free hydroxy and epoxide groups.

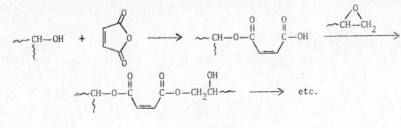

<u>20-11</u>

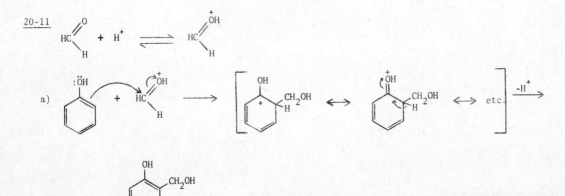

20-11 Contd....

b)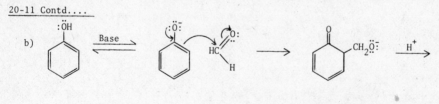

c)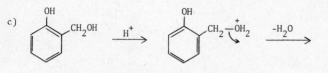

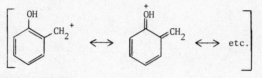

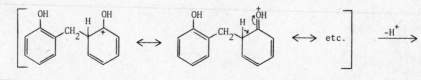

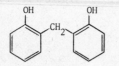

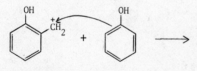

20-12

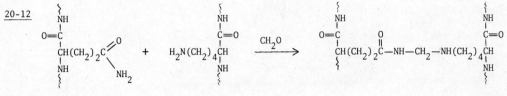

A glutamine unit        A lysine unit

20-13

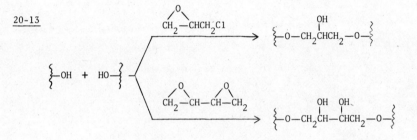

20-14    ROH   +   NaOH   $\longrightarrow$   RO$^-$Na$^+$   +   H$_2$O

"Cellulose"

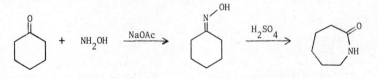

Viscose

20-15   A Beckmann rearrangement of cyclohexanone oxime provides a reasonable industrial route.

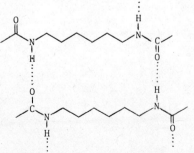

20-16

20-17

a) Fatty acids and their degradation products.

b)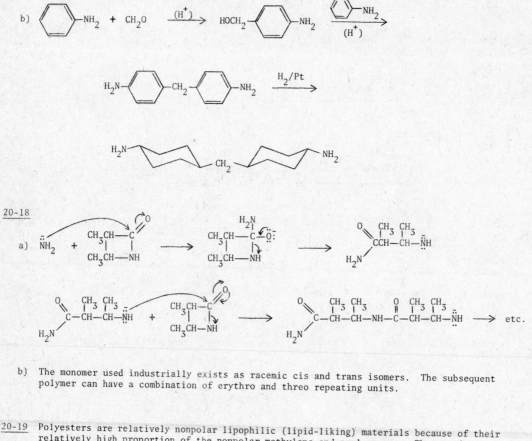

20-18

a)

b) The monomer used industrially exists as racemic cis and trans isomers.  The subsequent polymer can have a combination of erythro and threo repeating units.

20-19 Polyesters are relatively nonpolar lipophilic (lipid-liking) materials because of their relatively high proportion of the nonpolar methylene and aryl groups.  They tend to dissolve greases and resist penetration by the usual aqueous laundering agents.

20-20 At the high temperature of the melt-spin process, the presence of water would result in ester hydrolysis and consequent shortening of the polymer chains.

20-21

a)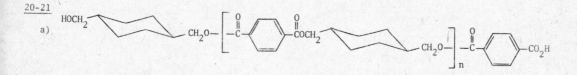

20-21 Contd...

b) The large, nonplanar cyclohexane groups prohibit the polymer chains from packing as close together as is found in polyethylene terephthalate. Kodel fibers tend to be somewhat more labile thermally than the polyethylene terephthalates.

20-22 The low density (high pressure) polyethylene is formed by a relatively random free radical sequence. The polymer structure is more random so that chains do not pack together well. The material is less dense and amorphorous.
The high density polyethylene is prepared by a stereoselective Ziegler-Natta catalyzed process. The polymer is more crystalline and forms a more dense structural array.

20-23

a) Teflon is a linear perfluorinated polyethylene.

$$-(-CF_2-)_n-$$

b) Free radical chain polymerization catalyzed by peroxides or oxygen.

c) Thermal decomposition of the chlorodifluoromethane is believed to produce a carbene by α-elimination of HCl. Dimerization of the carbene gives the monomer.

$$HCClF_2 \xrightarrow{\Delta} :CF_2 + HCl$$

$$2 \ :CF_2 \longrightarrow F_2C{=}CF_2$$

20-24

$$-(-CH_2\underset{\underset{\underset{O={CCH_3}}{O}}{|}}{CH}-)_n \xrightarrow{CH_3OH/H^+} -(-CH_2\underset{\underset{OH}{|}}{CH}-)_n + n \ CH_3CO_2CH_3$$

Polyvinyl acetate

The reaction is a transesterification.

20-25
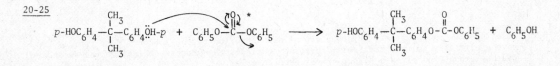

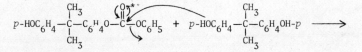

* A shorthand notation to show the two step addition-elimination.

20-25 Contd...

$$p\text{-HOC}_6\text{H}_4-\overset{\overset{\text{CH}_3}{|}}{\underset{\underset{\text{CH}_3}{|}}{\text{C}}}-\text{C}_6\text{H}_4\text{O}-\overset{\overset{\text{O}}{\|}}{\text{C}}-\text{OC}_6\text{H}_4-\overset{\overset{\text{CH}_3}{|}}{\underset{\underset{\text{CH}_3}{|}}{\text{C}}}-\text{C}_6\text{H}_4\text{OH-}p \quad + \quad \text{C}_6\text{H}_5\text{OH} \quad \longrightarrow \quad \text{etc.}$$

20-26   The polymer end is a labile hemiacetal which readily begins the unzipping sequence. End-capping gives a more stable acetal structure.

$$\sim\text{CH}_2\text{OCH}_2\text{OCH}_2-\text{OH} \quad \xrightarrow[\text{or}]{\text{RX}} \quad \sim\text{CH}_2\text{OCH}_2\text{OCH}_2-\text{OR}$$

$$\text{R'CO}_2\text{X} \qquad\qquad \text{or } -\text{O}_2\text{CR'}$$

The "unzipping" mechanism is:    $\sim\text{CH}_2\overset{\curvearrowleft}{}\text{O}\overset{\curvearrowright}{}\text{CH}_2\overset{\curvearrowleft}{}\text{O}\overset{\curvearrowright}{}\text{CH}_2\overset{\curvearrowleft}{}\ddot{\text{O}}\text{H}$

20-27   The polymer is a polyester formed in a chain process.

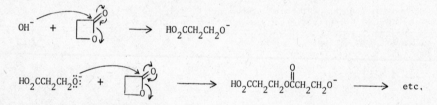

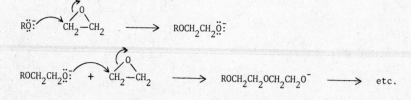

20-28   Polyethylene glycol is prepared commercially from ethylene oxide (formed from ethylene) by anionic chain polymerization. (Acid catalysis might also be used.)

$$\text{R}\ddot{\text{O}}{:}^- \quad \overset{\curvearrowright}{}\quad \underset{\text{CH}_2-\text{CH}_2}{\overset{\text{O}}{\triangle}} \quad \longrightarrow \quad \text{ROCH}_2\text{CH}_2\ddot{\text{O}}{:}^-$$

$$\text{ROCH}_2\text{CH}_2\ddot{\text{O}}{:}^- \quad + \quad \overset{\curvearrowright}{}\quad \underset{\text{CH}_2-\text{CH}_2}{\overset{\text{O}}{\triangle}} \quad \longrightarrow \quad \text{ROCH}_2\text{CH}_2\text{OCH}_2\text{CH}_2\text{O}^- \quad \longrightarrow \quad \text{etc.}$$

20-29   Reaction between the primary hydroxy groups and anhydride carbonyl occurs most rapidly to give a partially polymerized rsein. Heating continues the process to include the secondary hydroxy groups and gives a highly crosslinked material.

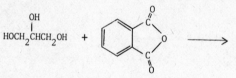

20-29 Contd...

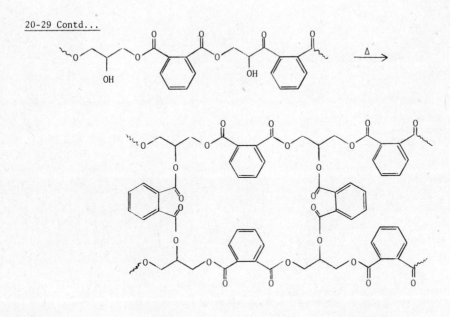

20-30

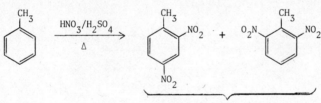

Separate isomers

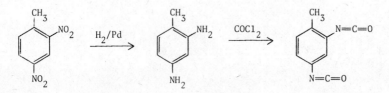

20-31

<u>20-31 Contd...</u>

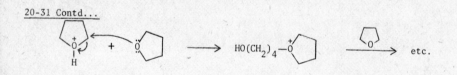

$$\text{etc.}$$

<u>20-32</u>  We expect this coordination vinyl type of polymerization to give a linear polymer.  The
high ethylene content suggests that the polymer is a random array of monomer units, thus
is highly amorphous.  Linear, amorphous polymers are characteristic elastomers.

<u>20-33</u>

a)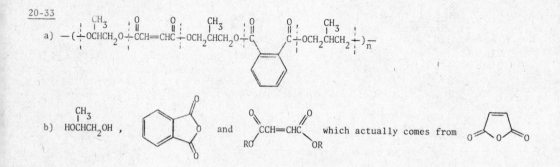

b) HOCHCH$_2$OH ,        and        which actually comes from

c)  The radical initiator forms a styryl free radical which reacts at the polymer double bonds
to form a highly cross linked polymer.

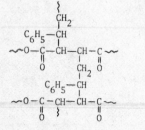

# 21 PHOTOCHEMISTRY AND ELECTROCHEMISTRY

<u>21-1</u>

219 nm is a $\pi \longrightarrow \pi^*$ transition

324 nm is an $n \longrightarrow \pi^*$ transition.

The conjugated compound has two ground state and two excited state $\pi$-molecular orbitals. Conjugation results in lowering the energies of the lowest occupied and unoccupied $\pi$ orbitals relative to the nonconjugated $\pi$ system of acetone. Little, if any change, takes place in the energy of the $n$-electrons. Electron transitions take place from the $n$-orbital and the highest occupied $\pi$-orbital ($\pi_2$) to the lowest excited state orbital ($\pi^*$ or $\pi_3^*$).

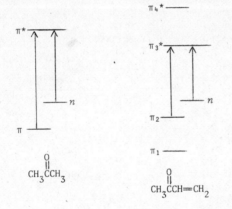

<u>21-2</u> Some energy is lost from the excited state by vibrational relaxation. The emission transition is thus of lower energy (longer wavelength) than the original absorption.

<u>21-3</u> An increase in temperature as energy is converted to molecular vibrations and rotations.

<u>21-4</u> When the 2-hydroxy-2-propyl radical gives up a hydrogen atom to benzophenone, a stable molecule (acetone) is formed. Furthermore, the new radical (benzophenone ketyl) is more stabilized than is the 2-hydroxy-2-propyl radical. Similar favorable reaction energetics are not possible when the free radical is benzyl.

21-5

$(C_6H_5)_2C=O \xrightarrow{h\nu} \longrightarrow (C_6H_5)_2C=O*^{(3)}$

$(C_6H_5)_2C=O*^{(3)} + (C_6H_5)_2CHOH \longrightarrow 2 (C_6H_5)_2\dot{C}-OH$

$2 (C_6H_5)_2\dot{C}-OH \longrightarrow (C_6H_5)_2\overset{OH}{\underset{}{C}}-\overset{OH}{\underset{}{C}}(C_6H_5)_2$

The maximum quantum yield for the disappearance of benzophenone is expected to be 1 because only one required benzophenone ketyl is formed by absorption of one photon.   Since formation of one excited benzophenone molecule produces one molecule of benzpinacol, the maximum quantum yield for formation of benzpinacol is 1.

21-6

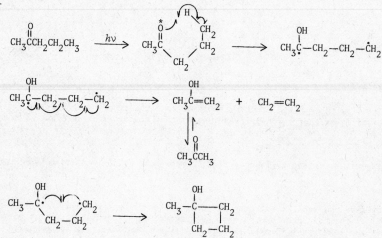

21-7

21-8

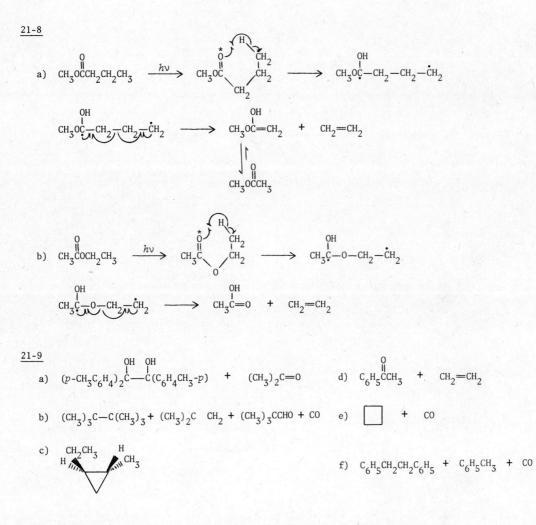

a) $CH_3OCCH_2CH_2CH_3$ $\xrightarrow{h\nu}$ ...

21-9

a) $(p\text{-}CH_3C_6H_4)_2C\text{---}C(C_6H_4CH_3\text{-}p)$  +  $(CH_3)_2C{=}O$     d) $C_6H_5CCH_3$  +  $CH_2{=}CH_2$

b) $(CH_3)_3C\text{---}C(CH_3)_3 + (CH_3)_2C\ \ CH_2 + (CH_3)_3CCHO + CO$     e) ☐  +  CO

c) ...                                     f) $C_6H_5CH_2CH_2C_6H_5$  +  $C_6H_5CH_3$  +  CO

21-10  The first synthesis of grandisol was carried out in the following way.

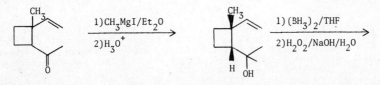

A mixture of
stereoisomers

The isomeric mixture was separated by gas
chromatography at this point.

21-10 Contd..

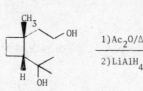 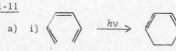

1) $Ac_2O/\Delta$

2) $LiAlH_4$

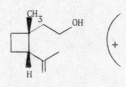 

21-11

a)  i)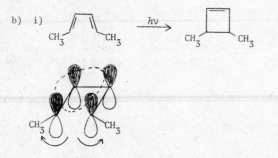

A conrotatory pathway for ring closure has one phase change and is a Möbius system.  Since there are $4n + 2$ electrons ($n = 1$) in the interacting orbitals, the process is photochemically allowed

ii)  The solution to problem 19-41 shows that an axis of symmetry correlates the first excited states of reactant and product.  The photochemical process is thus predicted to be conrotatory.

b)  i)  $CH_3$ $\xrightarrow{h\nu}$ $CH_3$ $CH_3$ $CH_3$

The disrotatory pathway has zero phase changes, thus is a Hückel system.  Since there are $4n$ electrons ($n = 1$) in the interacting orbitals, the process is photochemically allowed.

ii)  The correlation diagram is the same as that for butadiene-cyclobutene depicted in figure 19-6.  Diagram 19-6B correlates a plane of symmetry between reactant and product using the first excited states of each.  That is an allowed photochemical process and is seen to be disrotatory.

21-12

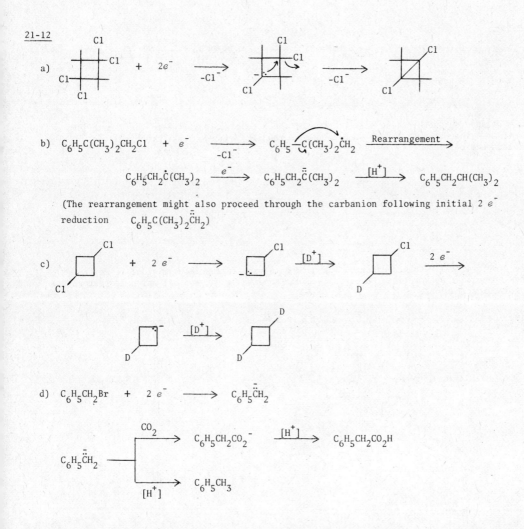

(The rearrangement might also proceed through the carbanion following initial 2 $e^-$ reduction     $C_6H_5C(CH_3)_2\overset{\cdot\cdot}{C}H_2$)

21-13  The initial prediction about the structure of $\Delta^{1,4}$-bicyclo[2.2.0]hexane is that the molecule is held in a planar shape by the double bond and experiences considerable angle strain (possibly like cyclopropane).  The $^1H$ nmr spectrum confirms this in exhibiting one sharp singlet peak (3.24 ppm) for the eight equivalent hydrogen atoms.

21-14  This sequence differs from that in aprotic media in that protonation can readily occur at each step.

$$C_6H_5NO_2 + e^- \longrightarrow C_6H_5NO_2^{\cdot -} \overset{H^+}{\longrightarrow} C_6H_5\overset{+}{\underset{OH}{N}}-\overset{\cdot\cdot}{\underset{\cdot\cdot}{O}}: \overset{e^-}{\longrightarrow} C_6H_5\underset{OH}{\overset{\cdot\cdot}{N}}-\overset{\cdot\cdot}{\underset{\cdot\cdot}{O}}: \overset{-OH^-}{\longrightarrow}$$

21-14 Contd...

$$C_6H_5\ddot{N}\!\!=\!\!\ddot{Q} \xrightarrow{\ e^- \ } C_6H_5\ddot{N}\!\!=\!\!\dot{\ddot{O}}^- \xrightarrow{\ H^+ \ } C_6H_5\dot{\ddot{N}}\!\!-\!\!OH \xrightarrow{\ e^- \ }$$

$$C_6H_5\ddot{\bar{N}}\!\!-\!\!OH \xrightarrow{\ H^+ \ } C_6H_5NHOH$$

21-15  In the anhydrous methylamine solvent much of the ketone is converted to the *N*-methylimine derivate.  The carbon-nitrogen double bond is readily reduced.  That process is an electrochemical reductive amination.

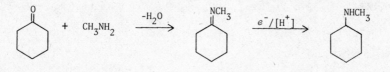

21-16  The dimer initially formed undergoes an acid catalyzed intramolecular aldol reaction and  subsequent dehydration.  Under the acidic conditions the radical anion is protonated before dimerization.

$$(CH_3)_2C\!\!=\!\!CHCOCH_3 \xrightarrow{\ e^- \ } (CH_3)_2\dot{C}\!\!-\!\!\ddot{\bar{C}}HCOCH_3 \xrightarrow{\ H^+ \ } (CH_3)_2\dot{C}CH_2COCH_3$$

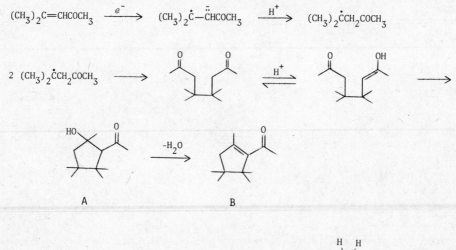

A                              B

21-17

a)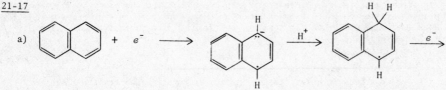

21-17 Contd...

a) Contd....

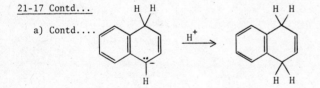

b)  In aprotic media the abstraction of H$^+$ from solvent is slow.  The second wave in the
voltammogram indicates that a second, more cathodic process takes  place.  This is probably
formation of the naphthalene dianion.

21-18

a)  EtO$_2$CCH$_2$CH—CHCH$_2$CO$_2$Et

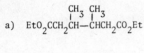

b)

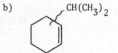

c)

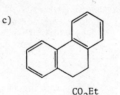

d)  EtO$_2$CCH$_2$CHCHCH$_2$CO$_2$Et   +   EtO$_2$CCH$_2$CHCO$_2$Et

(Only maleate forms a radical anion at -1.4V.)

21-19

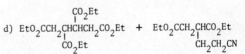

21-20

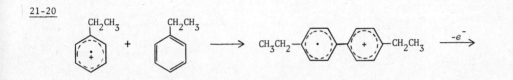

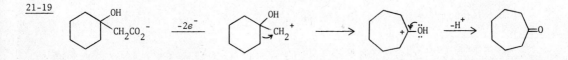

21-20

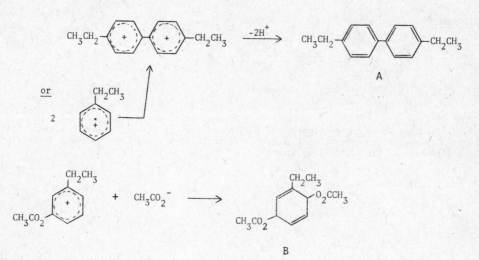

21-21 Only the carbonyl compounds absorb radiation above 200 nm. Excited acetophenone can transfer sufficient triplet energy to norbornene to promote cycloaddition. This is not possible with benzophenone so that excited benzophenone itself undergoes cycloaddition to norbornene.

21-22 Iodine is an excellent free radical trapping reagent.

$$CH_3COCH_3 \longrightarrow CH_3CO\cdot + CH_3\cdot \xrightarrow{I_2} CH_3COI + CH_3I$$

21-23

a) The major UV absorption of 1,3-butadiene comes at 217 nm so that visible light is not absorbed.

b) Direct absorption of UV light promotes butadiene to an excited singlet state from which a photochemically allowed disrotatory 4π-electron electrocyclic ring closure occurs.

c) Benzophenone absorbs the light due to its broad end absorption, then transfers triplet energy to butadiene. Triplet butadiene functions as a diradical (spins unpaired) and reacts stepwise with a molecule of ground state butadiene to give dimers which then cyclize.

$$CH_2{=}CH{-}CH{=}CH_2 \xrightarrow{(C_6H_5)_2CO^{*3}} \left[ \overset{\uparrow}{C}H_2{-}\overset{\uparrow}{C}H{-}CH{=}CH_2 \longleftrightarrow \text{etc.} \right] \xrightarrow{CH_2{=}CH{-}CH{=}CH_2}$$

21-23 Contd....

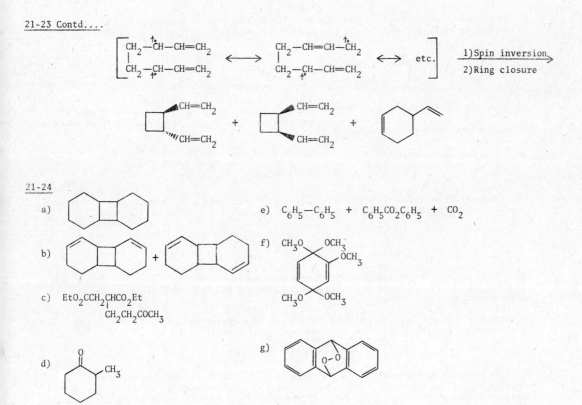

21-24

a)

e) $C_6H_5 — C_6H_5$ + $C_6H_5CO_2C_6H_5$ + $CO_2$

b)   +

f)

c) $EtO_2CCH_2CHCO_2Et$
     $CH_2CH_2COCH_3$

d)

g)

21-25   We saw (sec. 21-2D) that this stereoisomer is sterically inhibited from undergoing an allowed electrocyclic ring opening. However photochemical formation of a 4-membered ring can proceed by a symmetry and geometrically allowed cycloaddition. Orbital symmetry analysis by the HOMO method utilizes the $\psi_3$ M.O. of butadiene and predicts a disrotatory ring closure.

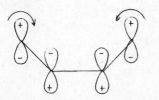

(The Mobius-Huckel and correlation diagram analysis of a related butadiene photo-induced cycloaddition is presented in the solution to problem 21-11b.)

21-26   Reaction with ground state oxygen (a triplet) in a free radical process would be expected
to proceed by abstraction of H to give the allylic radical

and thus racemic product. (Note that the chiral center at C-4 becomes symmetric when the
radical is formed.) This has been experimentally demonstrated. The singlet oxygen reaction
is believed to proceed by a concerted process.

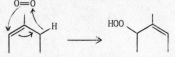

That pathway can be shown to be symmetry allowed by combining a $C_2$ M.O. having 2 electrons
(the $O_2$) with a $C_3$ M.O. having three electrons (the allylic portion of limonene).


21-27

i)   One photon is required for each benzyl free radical which is formed. Thus two photons are
required for the two radicals which combine to give one molecule of bibenzyl. The
maximum quantum yield is 0.5.

ii)  In the formation of  benzyldiphenyl carbinol only one photon is required for the generation
of the the two precursor radicals. The maximum quantum yield is 1.


21-28   Reaction involves disproportionation of one-half of the ketyls to give acetone and
dimerization of the other one-half to give pinacol. In the disproportionation step, H· is
abstracted from a methyl group to give acetone enol which rapidly tautomerizes to acetone.

$$(CH_3)_2C{=}O \xrightarrow{h\nu} \longrightarrow (CH_3)_2C{=}O^{*3}$$

$$(CH_3)_2C{=}O^{*3} + (CH_3)_2CHOH \longrightarrow 2\ (CH_3)_2\overset{\cdot}{C}OH$$

$$2\ (CH_3)_2\overset{\cdot}{C}OH \quad
\begin{array}{l}
\xrightarrow{50\%}\ (CH_3)_2\overset{\overset{OH}{|}}{C}{-}\overset{\overset{OH}{|}}{C}(CH_3)_2 \\[2em]
\xrightarrow{50\%}\ (CH_3)_2CHOH + \left[\ \cdot CH_2{-}\underset{\underset{CH_3}{|}}{\overset{\cdot}{C}}OH \ \equiv\ CH_2{=}\underset{\underset{CH_3}{|}}{C}OH\ \right]
\end{array}$$

$$(CH_3)_2C{=}O$$

21-29

a)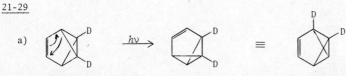

A photochemically allowed [1,3] sigmatropic rearrangement.

b)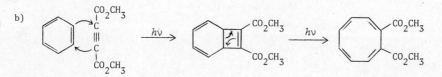

A photochemically allowed [2 + 2] cycloaddition followed by an allowed electrocyclic ring opening.

c)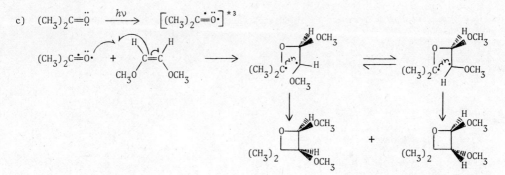

$(CH_3)_2C=\ddot{O}$  $\xrightarrow{h\nu}$  $[(CH_3)_2C=\ddot{O}\cdot]^{*3}$

The triplet adds stepwise to the alkene allowing time for the intermediate diradical to rotate before spin inversion and cyclization.

d)  $(C_6H_5)_2C=O$  $\underset{}{\overset{h\nu}{\rightleftharpoons}}$  $(C_6H_5)_2C=\ddot{O}\cdot$

21-29 Contd...

e)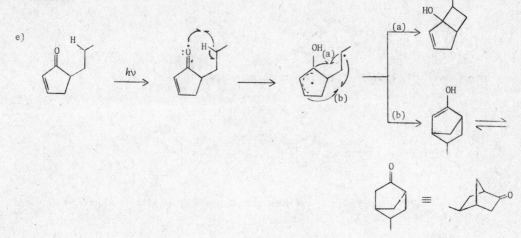

f) Both reactants produce common intermediates which then lead to common products.

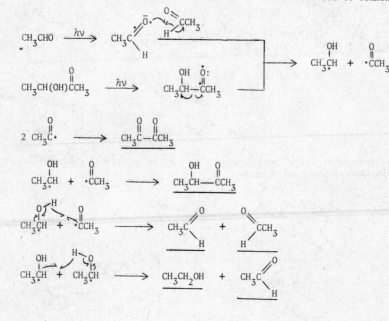

21-29 Contd...

g)

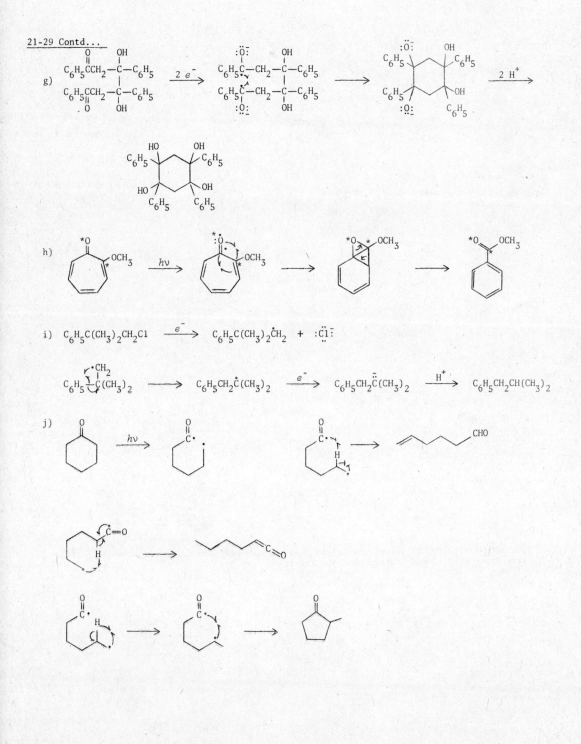

h)

i)

j)

21-29 Contd...

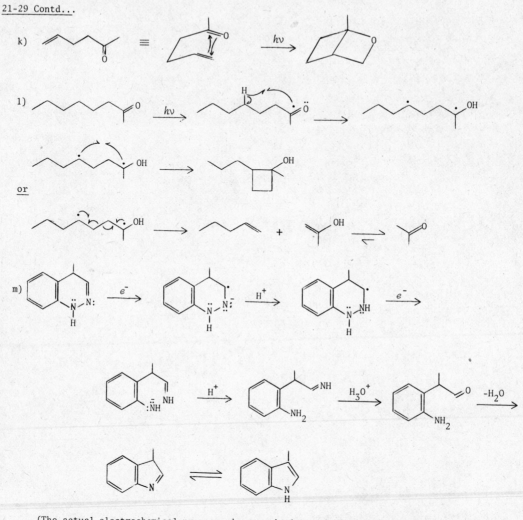

(The actual electrochemical process gives a single two-electron voltammogram showing that
the second step is much faster than the first.)

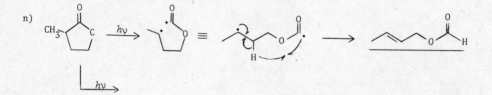

21-29 Contd...

n) Contd...

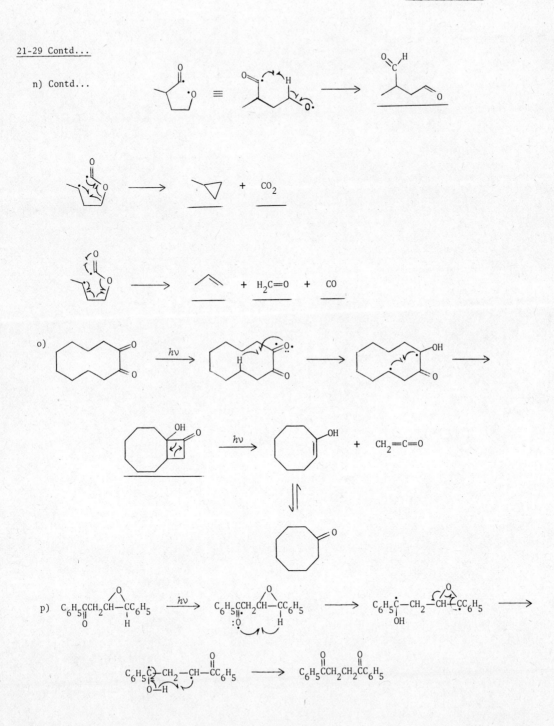

NOTES

NOTES